Welcome to

HOW IT WORKS

BOOK OF

SPACE

Space has fascinated mankind from the earliest days of
civilization, and as we keep scratching the surface of the
vast universe in which we live, our sense of awe and wonder
continues to grow unabated. Now, with the technological
advancements being made by the world's space agencies,
we understand more than ever about the things that are
happening beyond our own planet. This fifth revised edition
of the How It Works Book of Space has been updated with
more of latest astronomical advancements, stunning space
photography from the most advanced telescopes on the
planet, and glimpses at what the future of space exploration
holds, such as the planned mission to Mars. Taking you from
the heart of our Solar System and out into deep space, we
show you incredible solar tornadoes, supernovae, zombie
stars, black holes and much more. Get ready for lift off.

SPACE

Imagine Publishing Ltd
Richmond House
33 Richmond Hill
Bournemouth
Dorset BH2 6EZ
☎ +44 (0) 1202 586200
Website: www.imagine-publishing.co.uk
Twitter: @Books_Imagine
Facebook: www.facebook.com/ImagineBookazines

Publishing Director
Aaron Asadi

Head of Design
Ross Andrews

Production Editor
Sanne de Boer

Senior Art Editor
Greg Whitaker

Assistant Designer
Alexander Phoenix

Photographer
James Sheppard

Printed by
William Gibbons, 26 Planetary Road, Willenhall, West Midlands, WV13 3XT

Distributed in the UK, Eire & the Rest of the World by
Marketforce, Blue Fin Building, 110 Southwark Street, London, SE1 0SU
Tel 0203 148 3300 www.marketforce.co.uk

Distributed in Australia by
Network Services (a division of Bauer Media Group), Level 21 Civic Tower, 66-68 Goulburn Street,
Sydney, New South Wales 2000, Australia Tel +61 2 8667 5288

How It Works Book of Space Volume 1 Fifth Revised Edition © 2015 Imagine Publishing Ltd

ISBN 978-1785461095

Part of the

HOW IT WORKS

bookazine series

IMAGINE
PUBLISHING

HOW IT WORKS BOOK OF SPACE
CONTENTS

"The Sun's most intense sight is a solar tornado"

021 Solar eclipse

Earth from space 014

Life in space 072

158 Evolution of telescopes

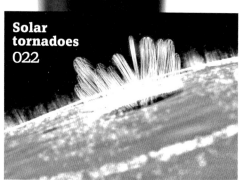
Solar tornadoes 022

058 Dwarf planets

044
Saturn

036
Venus

Mystery of dark matter
130

170
Wild space weather

© SPL

SOLAR SYSTEM

024
Exploring the Moon

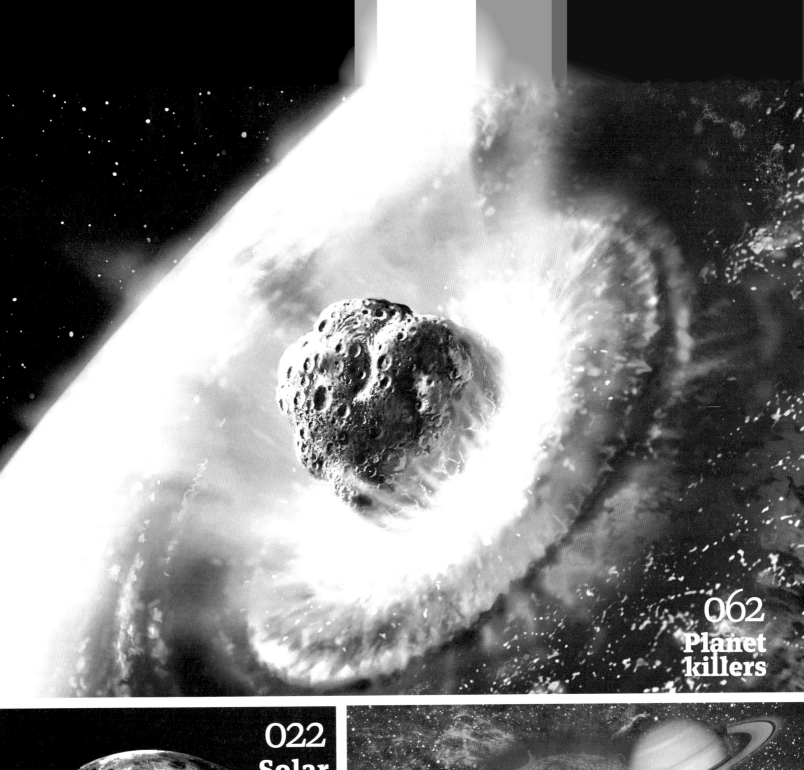

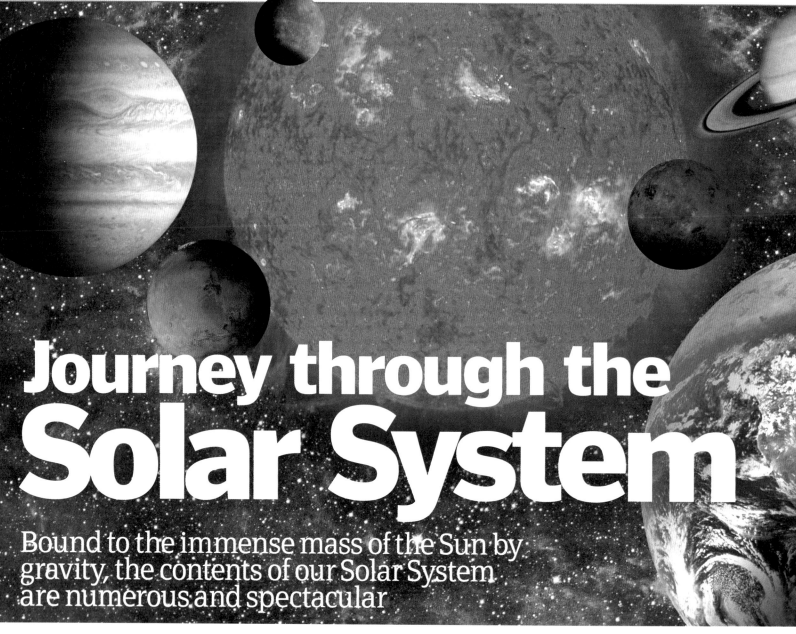

Journey through the Solar System

Bound to the immense mass of the Sun by gravity, the contents of our Solar System are numerous and spectacular

The Solar System formed about 4.6 billion years ago, when part of a giant molecular cloud had a gravitational collapse. The centre became the Sun, which comprises more than 99 per cent of the Solar System's total mass. The rest became a dense, flat rotating disk of gas from which planets formed, called a protoplanetary disk. In our Solar System, most of that disk became the eight planets, each of which orbits the Sun.

There are two different categories of planets: gas giants and terrestrials. The gas giants are the four outer planets: Jupiter, Saturn, Uranus and Neptune. They are much bigger than the terrestrial planets and are mostly made of helium and hydrogen, although Uranus and Neptune also contain ice. All of the outer planets have ring systems made of cosmic dust. These planets comprise more than 90 per cent of the rest of the solar system's mass.

The four inner planets are very close to the Sun. To grant perspective, for example, the distance between Jupiter and Saturn is larger than the radius of all the inner planets put together. These terrestrials are made up from rocks and metals, have no ring systems and have a low number of satellites (moons). They include Mercury, Venus, Earth and Mars. Except for Mercury, the inner planets also have recognisable weather systems operating in their atmospheres.

In addition to the eight main planets, there are also dwarf planets such as Pluto. The five dwarf planets are Ceres, Pluto, Haumea, Makemake and Eris. In addition, the Solar System is home to numerous small solar system bodies, which include all minor planets, asteroids and comets.

Earth to Saturn in a Mini Metro!
How long would it take to reach the planets in a moderately priced car?

Can't afford that ticket on the next spaceship out of town? Well, fear not, for if you are the patient type and hold an interplanetary driving licence then you can drive to that Earth colony orbiting Saturn in next to no time... well, relatively speaking. In our souped-up Mini Metro, travelling at an average speed of 120mph, any traveller can reach Saturn in only 842 years. Better stock up on travel sweets then...

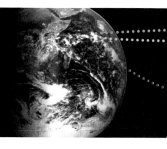

1. Uranus
Diameter at equator: 25,559km
Average distance from Sun:
2.88 billion km (19 AU)
Orbital period: 84.02 years
Mass (Earth=1): 14.37
Earth masses

BIG

2. Saturn
Diameter at equator:
60,260km
Average distance from Sun:
1.4 billion km (9.4 AU)
Orbital period: 29.5 years
Mass (Earth=1): 95 Earth masses

BIGGER

3. Jupiter
Diameter at equator: 142,985km
Average distance from Sun:
778 million km (5.2 AU)
Orbital period: 11.86 years
Mass (Earth=1): 318 Earth masses

BIGGEST

DID YOU KNOW? Astronomers estimate there may be billions of solar systems in our galaxy. About 70 have been discovered

What and where are the asteroid belts?

There are a few asteroid belts in our Solar System, but none can compare to the main belt, a massive ring between the orbits of Mars and Jupiter. Here the dwarf planet Ceres, the large asteroids 2 Pallas, 10 Hygiea and 4 Vesta, and millions of small asteroids and dust particles orbit the Sun. Most of the larger asteroids have elliptical orbits and an orbital period of a few years. Some astronomers believe that the main belt's contents are left over from a planetary collision or from a planet that never formed due to the strong gravitational pull of Jupiter.

Image courtesy of NASA

Below shows the placement of inner Solar System objects on 20 July 2002. Light blue lines are planet orbits. Green dots show asteroids. Red dots are asteroids that come within 1.3AU of the Sun. Comets are dark blue squares, and dark blue points are Jupiter Trojans

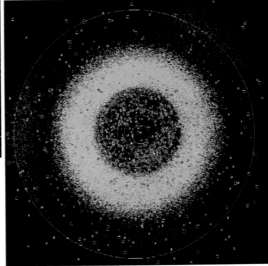

Bound together by gravity

When the International Astronomical Union (IAU) defined planets in 2006, part of that definition included the requirement that a planet has enough mass that its self-gravity causes it to reach hydrostatic equilibrium. The planet is able to resist compressive forces in space to hold together and stay rounded in shape.

Planets also "clear the neighbourhood" around their orbits. This means that there are no other bodies of the same size in its orbit. The Sun has a strong enough pull to keep the planets and other bodies orbiting around it.

A map of Earth's gravitational strength

Measuring our Solar System

Understanding the size of planets and where they are

Before the development of radar, astronomers measured the distance between planets through trigonometry, a process where distance to an object is derived from the measurements of angles and distances taken between two known positions. Today, radar is the predominant method of measuring distance and allows for more accurate measurements to be attained. This process works by astronomers timing how long it takes the radar beam, which is travelling at the speed of light, to travel the distance to an object and back. By multiplying the speed of light by time taken, then dividing that in two, scientists can derive the distance to the object.

Once distance has been derived, the mass of the object can be ascertained by monitoring the orbital periods of circling satellites. To do this astronomers measure the angular separation between the satellite and the object and then use trigonometry to convert that angular separation into distance. Astronomers can then use Kepler's third law to determine total mass.

1 AU (astronomical unit) = 92,960,000 miles, the mean distance between the Sun and the Earth

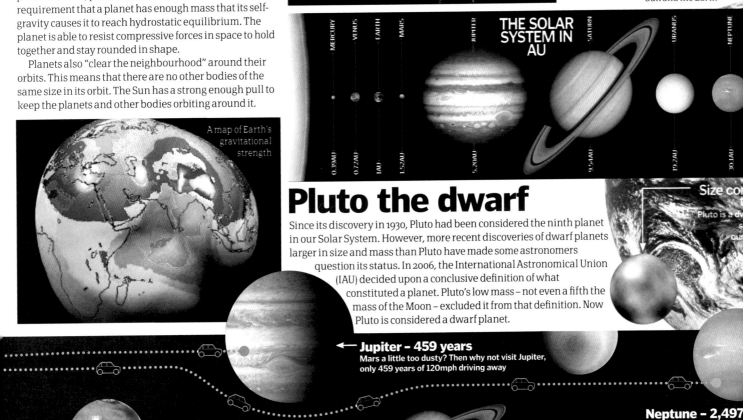

THE SOLAR SYSTEM IN AU

MERCURY · VENUS · EARTH · MARS · JUPITER · SATURN · URANUS · NEPTUNE · PLUTO

0.39AU · 0.72AU · 1AU · 1.52AU · 5.20AU · 9.54AU · 19.2AU · 30.1AU · 39.5AU

Pluto the dwarf

Since its discovery in 1930, Pluto had been considered the ninth planet in our Solar System. However, more recent discoveries of dwarf planets larger in size and mass than Pluto have made some astronomers question its status. In 2006, the International Astronomical Union (IAU) decided upon a conclusive definition of what constituted a planet. Pluto's low mass – not even a fifth the mass of the Moon – excluded it from that definition. Now Pluto is considered a dwarf planet.

Size compared to Earth
Pluto is a dwarf-planet, smaller than our own moon

Jupiter – 459 years
Mars a little too dusty? Then why not visit Jupiter, only 459 years of 120mph driving away

Mars – 134 years
At 120mph you could drive to the planet named after the Roman god of war in only 134 years

Neptune – 2,497 years
One for colder climates? Then Neptune should be top of your list. At 2,497 years distance, though, it is a long drive, so make sure you take regular breaks and keep at 120mph!

8. Neptune

Neptune was imaged for the first time in 1989, discovering an encircling set of rings and six of its 13 moons. Neptune's structure is very similar to that of Uranus, with no solid surface and central layers of water, methane and ammonia ices as well as a possible rock/ice-based core.

The Statistics
Neptune

Type: Gas giant
Rotation (Equatorial): 60,179 days
Rotation (Polar): 16.11 hours
Volume: (Earth = 1) 57.74
Average distance from Sun: 2.8 billion miles
Number of moons: 13
Speed: 5.43km/s
Surface temp: -220°C

Comets

Comets are small, fragile, irregularly shaped bodies composed of a mixture of non-volatile grains and frozen gases

9. Pluto

Often mistaken as the last planet in our Solar System, Pluto is actually not one but instead a dwarf planet. Dwarf planets are bodies that orbit the Sun and have enough mass and gravity to be spherical, but ones that have not cleared the region around its orbit. Pluto is such a dwarf planet and is one of the furthest circling bodies of our solar system. Pluto's atmosphere is 99.97 per cent nitrogen and it is astronomically cold, with an average temperature of -230 degrees Celsius.

The Statistics
Pluto

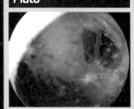

Type: Dwarf
Rotation (Equatorial): 90,613 days
Rotation (Polar): N/A
Volume: (Earth = 1) 0.0059
Average distance from Sun: 3.7 billion miles
Number of moons: 3
Speed: 4.666km/s
Surface temp: -230°C

7. Uranus

The first planet to be discovered by telescope, Uranus appears to the eye as a pale blue, characterless disk, encircled by a thin system of 11 rings and 27 tiny moons. Its blue colour is a result of the absorption of the sunlight's red wavelengths by methane-ice clouds within the planet's cold atmosphere – a process which also renders its atmosphere calm and inert thanks to the creation of haze particles. In reality, however, Uranus's atmosphere is active and consistently changing with huge winds driving systems of ammonia and water over its surface.

The Statistics
Uranus

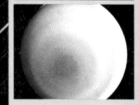

Type: Gas giant
Rotation (Equatorial): 30,799 days
Rotation (Polar): 17.24 hours
Volume: (Earth = 1) 63.1
Average distance from Sun: 1.78 billion miles
Number of moons: 27
Speed: 6.81km/s
Surface temp: -214°C

6. Saturn

A massive ball of gas and liquid, Saturn is the least dense of all the planets in the Solar System. Circled by a spectacular system of rings, which are composed of stellar dust, boulders and gases, Saturn has a hazy appearance and due to its rapid spin is a massive ten per cent larger at its equator than at its pole. Interestingly, Saturn is so light – thanks to its composition from the lightest elements – that if it could be hypothetically placed in a galactic-sized ocean of water it would float. As with Jupiter, Saturn is a gas giant with a tiny solid core composed of rock and ice.

The Statistics
Saturn

Type: Gas giant
Rotation (Equatorial): 10,759 days
Rotation (Polar): 10.66 hours
Volume: (Earth = 1) 763.59
Average distance from Sun: 888 million miles
Number of moons: 34
Speed: 9.69km/s
Surface temp: -140°C

5. Jupiter

The largest and most massive of all planets in the Solar System, Jupiter has almost 2.5 times the mass of the other eight planets combined and over 1,300 Earths could fit inside it. Jupiter is also the first of the gas giants and is largely not solid in composition, consisting of an outer layer of gaseous hydrogen and helium, an outer layer of liquid hydrogen and helium and an inner layer of metallic hydrogen. However, deep in its body (roughly 37,000 miles in) there is a solid core made up of rock, metal and hydrogen compounds.

The Sun

4.6 billions years old and currently in its main-sequence stage, our Sun is a huge sphere of exceedingly hot plasma containing 750 times the mass of all the solar system's planets put together. Deep in its core nuclear fusion of hydrogen produces massive energy that is gradually carried outwards through convection before escaping into space.

The Statistics
The Sun

Type: Star
Rotation (Equatorial): 25 days
Rotation (Polar): 34 days
Mass: (Earth = 1) 333,000
Surface temperature: 5,500°C
Core temperature: 15 million °C
Diameter (Equatorial): 864,900 miles

Main belt

Often referred to as the asteroid belt, the Main belt is an encircling ring of meteors, asteroids, dwarf planets and dust particles that sits between the terrestrial planets and the gas giants

5 TOP FACTS
SOLAR SYSTEM

Lightweight
1 Hypothetically speaking, Saturn is so light that if it were placed in a galactic sized swimming pool it would float. Hard experiment to carry out though!

Binary
2 Due to the size and short orbital distance between Pluto and its largest moon Charon, it is often treated as a binary system as its centre of mass lies with neither.

Dust bowl
3 Mars, often referred to by people as the 'red planet', is actually red thanks to its coating of iron dust, which prevails in its carbon dioxide-rich atmosphere.

Big boy
4 Jupiter is so large that over 1,300 Earths could fit inside it and it has a mass which is 2.5 times larger than the total of all other eight planets in the solar system combined.

Tantastic
5 During the day on Mercury, the closest planet to our Sun in the solar system, the temperature reaches up to a positively scorching 430 degrees Celsius.

DID YOU KNOW? Our solar system is nearly five billion years old and is made up of eight planets and 170 moons

The Statistics
Jupiter

Type: Gas giant
Rotation (Equatorial): 4,331 days
Rotation (Polar): 9.93 hours
Volume: (Earth = 1) 1,321
Average distance from Sun: 483.6 million miles
Number of moons: 63
Speed: 13.07km/s
Surface temp: -110°C

The Statistics
Earth

Type: Terrestrial
Rotation (Equatorial): 365.26 days
Rotation (Polar): 23.93 hours
Mass: (Earth = 1) 1
Average distance from Sun: 93 million miles
Number of moons: 1
Speed: 29.783km/s
Surface temp: 15°C

3. Earth
While similar in internal composition to its neighbouring planets – composed of three distinct layers made up mainly of iron, magnesium and silicates respectively – Earth differs on its surface thanks to an abundance of liquid water and an oxygen-rich atmosphere. Due to Earth's rotation the planet bulges at its equator by 13 miles when compared to both its poles and its spin axis is tilted at an angle of 23.5 degrees, one of the factors that gives rise to its seasons.

4. Mars
Known as the red planet thanks to its rust-red colouring, and named after the Roman god of war, Mars is home to the highest volcanoes (albeit dry and inactive) of any planet in the Solar System. Current research and evidence suggests that while Mars is an inert planet now, in the past it was very much active, with volcanic activity and water existing over large parts of it. Mars is the outermost of the four terrestrial 'rocky' planets and its internal structure is rich in sulphur, iron sulphide and silicate rock.

The Statistics
Mars

Type: Terrestrial
Rotation (Equatorial): 687 days
Rotation (Polar): 24.63 days
Mass: (Earth = 1) 0.15
Average distance from Sun: 141.6 million miles
Number of moons: 2
Speed: 24.007km/s
Surface temp: -125°C – 25°C

Map of the Solar System
Discover the star, planets and space phenomena that make up our Solar System

The Statistics
Mercury

Type: Terrestrial
Rotation (Equatorial): 88 days
Rotation (Polar): 59 days
Mass: (Earth = 1) 0.056
Average distance from Sun: 36 million miles
Number of moons: 0
Speed: 47.87km/s
Surface temp: -187°C – 427°C

1. Mercury
Iron-rich Mercury is the smallest of the main planets in the Solar System and the closest to the Sun. There is almost no protective atmosphere surrounding Mercury and, because of this, temperatures on the planet fluctuate massively from 427 degrees Celsius during the day to -187 degrees Celsius during the night. Worryingly, if an observer were able to stand on the planet they would experience a period of 176 Earth days between one sunrise and the next. Better stock up on suntan lotion and woolly socks then.

2. Venus
The hottest of all planets, Venus – thanks to its permanent atmospheric blanket of dense gaseous clouds – has an average temperature of 464 degrees Celsius. The surface is dry, lifeless, scorching hot and littered with volcanoes and dust storms. Named after the Roman goddess of love and beauty due to its beautiful, sun-reflecting, cloud-based atmosphere, in reality Venus holds one of the most hostile environments of any planet. Interestingly, Venus spins in the opposite direction from most other planets

The Statistics
Venus

Type: Terrestrial
Rotation (Equatorial): 224.7 days
Rotation (Polar): 243 days
Mass: (Earth = 1) 0.86
Average distance from Sun: 67.2 million miles
Number of moons: 0
Speed: 35.02km/s
Surface temp: 464°C

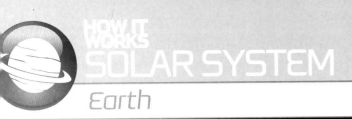
Earth

From astronaut snaps taken with handheld cameras to advanced satellite imagery that enables us to predict natural disasters, discover the planet as you've never seen it before

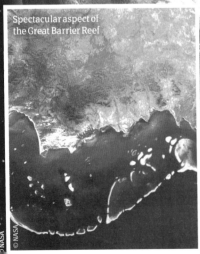

Spectacular aspect of the Great Barrier Reef

© NASA

© NASA

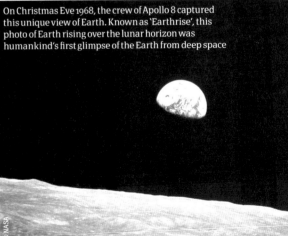

On Christmas Eve 1968, the crew of Apollo 8 captured this unique view of Earth. Known as 'Earthrise', this photo of Earth rising over the lunar horizon was humankind's first glimpse of the Earth from deep space

© NASA

5 TOP FACTS
EARTH OBSERVATION

First
1 Explorer VII was the first Earth observation satellite. It was launched on 13 October 1959 and measured thermal energy that was reflected by the Earth.

Largest
2 The ESA's environmental satellite Envisat is the world's largest operational non-military Earth observation satellite. It is the size of a double-decker bus.

Worldwide terrain map
3 1.3 million images from the Terra satellite's telescopes, covering 99% of the Earth's surface, have created the most complete terrain map of our planet.

Accuracy
4 The Landsat satellites discovered that maps of small islands in the Pacific Ocean were indicated as much as 16km (10 miles) from their true position.

Polar
5 Most Earth observation satellites travel in polar orbits that go over the North and South Poles, and are able to view the whole of the globe as it turns beneath it.

DID YOU KNOW? ISS astronauts spend ten mins each day taking photos of Earth with digital and 35mm and 70mm film cameras

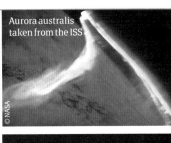
Aurora australis taken from the ISS
© NASA

ESA's Envisat

The European Space Agency's environmental satellite (Envisat) was launched into a polar orbit on 1 March 2002. Its instruments are used to study the ocean, agriculture, ice formations and atmospheric conditions of Earth.

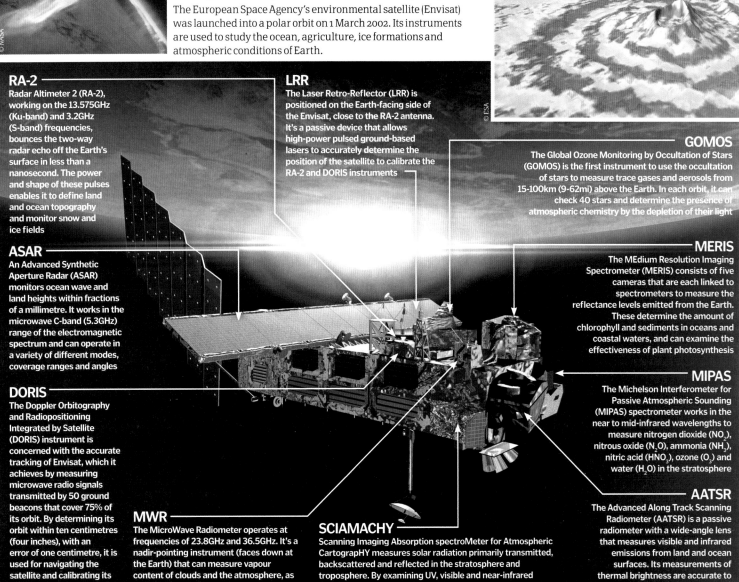
© ESA

RA-2
Radar Altimeter 2 (RA-2), working on the 13.575GHz (Ku-band) and 3.2GHz (S-band) frequencies, bounces the two-way radar echo off the Earth's surface in less than a nanosecond. The power and shape of these pulses enables it to define land and ocean topography and monitor snow and ice fields

LRR
The Laser Retro-Reflector (LRR) is positioned on the Earth-facing side of the Envisat, close to the RA-2 antenna. It's a passive device that allows high-power pulsed ground-based lasers to accurately determine the position of the satellite to calibrate the RA-2 and DORIS instruments

GOMOS
The Global Ozone Monitoring by Occultation of Stars (GOMOS) is the first instrument to use the occultation of stars to measure trace gases and aerosols from 15-100km (9-62mi) above the Earth. In each orbit, it can check 40 stars and determine the presence of atmospheric chemistry by the depletion of their light

ASAR
An Advanced Synthetic Aperture Radar (ASAR) monitors ocean wave and land heights within fractions of a millimetre. It works in the microwave C-band (5.3GHz) range of the electromagnetic spectrum and can operate in a variety of different modes, coverage ranges and angles

MERIS
The MEdium Resolution Imaging Spectrometer (MERIS) consists of five cameras that are each linked to spectrometers to measure the reflectance levels emitted from the Earth. These determine the amount of chlorophyll and sediments in oceans and coastal waters, and can examine the effectiveness of plant photosynthesis

DORIS
The Doppler Orbitography and Radiopositioning Integrated by Satellite (DORIS) instrument is concerned with the accurate tracking of Envisat, which it achieves by measuring microwave radio signals transmitted by 50 ground beacons that cover 75% of its orbit. By determining its orbit within ten centimetres (four inches), with an error of one centimetre, it is used for navigating the satellite and calibrating its on-board instruments

MIPAS
The Michelson Interferometer for Passive Atmospheric Sounding (MIPAS) spectrometer works in the near to mid-infrared wavelengths to measure nitrogen dioxide (NO_2), nitrous oxide (N_2O), ammonia (NH_3), nitric acid (HNO_3), ozone (O_3) and water (H_2O) in the stratosphere

MWR
The MicroWave Radiometer operates at frequencies of 23.8GHz and 36.5GHz. It's a nadir-pointing instrument (faces down at the Earth) that can measure vapour content of clouds and the atmosphere, as well as moisture levels of landscapes

SCIAMACHY
Scanning Imaging Absorption spectroMeter for Atmospheric CartograpHY measures solar radiation primarily transmitted, backscattered and reflected in the stratosphere and troposphere. By examining UV, visible and near-infrared wavelengths, it detects low concentrations of gases and aerosols

AATSR
The Advanced Along Track Scanning Radiometer (AATSR) is a passive radiometer with a wide-angle lens that measures visible and infrared emissions from land and ocean surfaces. Its measurements of thermal brightness are accurate to at least 0.05°C

The crew of Apollo 8 were the first people to see and photograph our planet as a globe in its entirety. During the fourth orbit around the Moon, Lunar module commander William Anders took a series of photographs of the Earth that became known as 'Earthrise'. They revealed the true splendour of our planet suspended in stark contrast with the barren lunar surface, and became an icon for showing that our home is a fertile and fragile dot of life in an immense and deadly universe.

From the Sixties onwards an enormous number of Earth observation satellites have been launched to look at the hard facts about the state of our global environment, as it is assaulted by extremes of natural events and the impact of human activities.

Observations from space can study large patterns of change throughout the Earth's surface and in the atmosphere, and can be used to supplement information gained by ground or ocean-going instruments. The additional benefit of satellites is they can transmit data continuously, and cover areas of the Earth that are inaccessible or too hostile for any other methods of gaining information.

At first, Earth observation satellites simply used visible light and infrared sensors to monitor the position of clouds for weather forecasting. Later, microwave sensors were introduced to improve these forecasts by obtaining measurements of the temperature, pressure and humidity in different layers of the atmosphere.

The success of such satellites led NASA to launch the Landsat series of observation satellites in July 1972. Using multi-spectral scanner instrumentation, Landsats were able to produce images of the Earth's surface gained from up to eight different wavelengths, showing the distribution of snow and ice cover, vegetation, landscapes, coastal regions and human settlements, which proved to be a rich source of new data for cartography, geology, regional planning, forestry, agriculture, climate studies and educational purposes.

In the Seventies, Landsat data about the worldwide state of wheat crop growth was used to forecast yield rates and stabilise the market for this crop, which led to more stable prices for consumers. Using data from Landsat images, researchers recently discovered 650 previously unknown barrier islands, including a chain of 54 islands that stretch 563km (350mi) from the mouth of the Amazon River.

Satellites save lives and reduce property damage by tracking and warning of the arrival of hurricanes, tornadoes, floods and other extremes of weather or natural disaster. For example, in August 2005 satellites provided an accurate early warning of the approach of Hurricane Katrina and, a month later, Hurricane Rita. Unfortunately, responses to these warnings were slow, resulting in extensive damage and loss of life. Afterwards, satellites (NASA's TRMM and NOAA's GOES and POES) provided imagery of the damaged areas to help in the reconstruction of the areas affected. This helped bring about the pledge by nations that operate satellites to provide imagery to any nation affected by a major disaster under the terms of the International Disaster Charter.

The sensing technologies used by satellites consist of optical sensors that can detect the strength of reflections from the Earth in the visible/near infrared spectrum and thermal infrared rays that are radiated from the surface. Microwave sensors can detect radiation in this longer wavelength of the spectrum coming from the Earth's surface, or active microwave sensors can send microwaves to the Earth and observe their reflections.

Civilian Earth observation satellite surveillance is co-ordinated by the committee on Earth observation satellites (CEOS), which is currently affiliated to agencies that are operating 116 active satellites. These broadly study the long-term and changing global environment from the atmosphere, land, ice and snow, oceans, gravity and magnetic fields to the oceans. In the next 15 years, CEOS agencies are planning 260 satellites, which will carry 400 instruments to develop better weather forecasting and knowledge of climate changes.

Since the Nineties, NASA has run the Earth observing system (EOS) program that co-ordinates the activities of its polar-orbiting satellites to study "radiation, clouds, water vapour and precipitation; the oceans; greenhouse gases; land-surface hydrology and ecosystem processes; glaciers, sea ice and ice sheets; ozone and stratospheric chemistry and natural and anthropogenic aerosols." To further this research, it plans to launch 15 Earth observation satellites by 2020. The European Space Agency also plans several 'Earth explorer' missions, which includes the launch of three satellites in 2013 to study the Earth's magnetic field ('Swarm') and one to profile global winds (ADM-Aeolus).

NASA Earth Observatories

NASA's range of satellites in their Earth observing system (EOS) program includes Terra and a planned launch of Aquarius in June 2011, to measure the salt levels of our oceans. Overall, they cover every aspect of surface and atmospheric environmental conditions

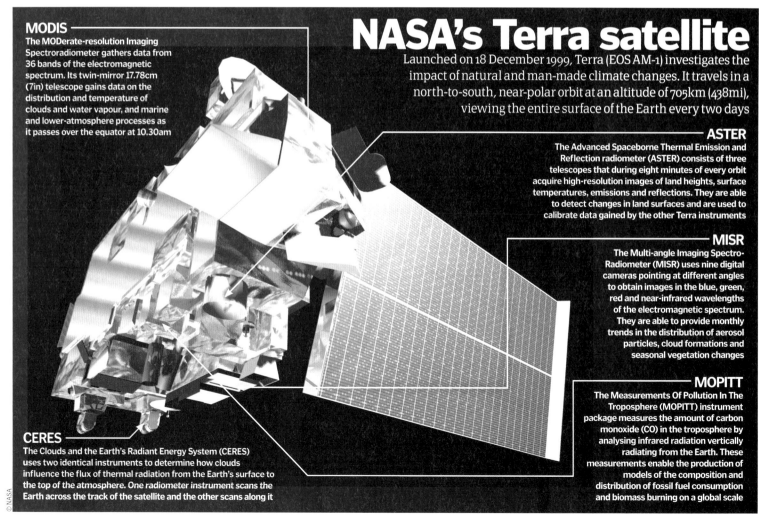

NASA's Terra satellite

Launched on 18 December 1999, Terra (EOS AM-1) investigates the impact of natural and man-made climate changes. It travels in a north-to-south, near-polar orbit at an altitude of 705km (438mi), viewing the entire surface of the Earth every two days

MODIS
The MODerate-resolution Imaging Spectroradiometer gathers data from 36 bands of the electromagnetic spectrum. Its twin-mirror 17.78cm (7in) telescope gains data on the distribution and temperature of clouds and water vapour, and marine and lower-atmosphere processes as it passes over the equator at 10.30am

ASTER
The Advanced Spaceborne Thermal Emission and Reflection radiometer (ASTER) consists of three telescopes that during eight minutes of every orbit acquire high-resolution images of land heights, surface temperatures, emissions and reflections. They are able to detect changes in land surfaces and are used to calibrate data gained by the other Terra instruments

MISR
The Multi-angle Imaging Spectro-Radiometer (MISR) uses nine digital cameras pointing at different angles to obtain images in the blue, green, red and near-infrared wavelengths of the electromagnetic spectrum. They are able to provide monthly trends in the distribution of aerosol particles, cloud formations and seasonal vegetation changes

MOPITT
The Measurements Of Pollution In The Troposphere (MOPITT) instrument package measures the amount of carbon monoxide (CO) in the troposphere by analysing infrared radiation vertically radiating from the Earth. These measurements enable the production of models of the composition and distribution of fossil fuel consumption and biomass burning on a global scale

CERES
The Clouds and the Earth's Radiant Energy System (CERES) uses two identical instruments to determine how clouds influence the flux of thermal radiation from the Earth's surface to the top of the atmosphere. One radiometer instrument scans the Earth across the track of the satellite and the other scans along it

HEAD 2 HEAD
images captured

NATURAL DISASTER

1. Japanese earthquake
Within hours of the Japanese earthquake and tsunami on 11 March 2011, Terra and Aqua satellites transmitted images.

STARTLING IMAGES

2. Natural and man-made
AATSR instruments recorded images of the Buncefield oil depot fire in 2005 and the decline of Arctic sea ice during 2007.

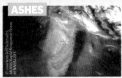

ASHES

3. Icelandic volcanic eruption
When Iceland's Eyjafjallajokull volcano erupted in April 2010, MERIS on Envisat recorded composition and distribution of the volcanic ash.

DID YOU KNOW? Only 24 astronauts have seen the entire Earth from space while on their Apollo missions to the Moon

Gulf oil spill creeps towards the Mississippi Delta

Which aspects of Earth are the satellites observing?

Atmosphere

NASA launched eight Nimbus Earth observation satellites between 1964 and 1978. They pioneered the use of 'sounders' that measure the humidity and temperature of the atmosphere. They obtain temperature measurements by analysing infrared radiation (IR) on wavelengths linked with oxygen or carbon dioxide. IR or microwave sounders identify water vapour in the atmosphere to measure humidity. Microwave sounders have a lower resolution, but can be used in all weather conditions as they can sound through clouds.

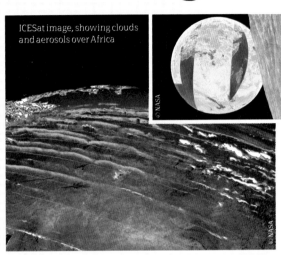
ICESat image, showing clouds and aerosols over Africa

Oceans

In the Seventies the USA and USSR ran ocean observation satellite programmes, which carried synthetic aperture radar (SAR) equipment. A number of radar images are taken by SARs and combined to produce a single detailed image. This is able to determine the height of sea levels, waves, currents and their distribution and can detect oil slicks and shipping movements. The Jason 1 and 2 spacecraft currently use these techniques to study the topography and characteristics of the oceans, to give a better warning of floods or climate changes.

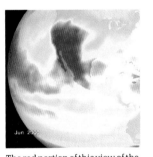
The red portion of this view of the US reveals the highest ground levels of ultraviolet radiation

Land

The Shuttle Radar Topography Mission (SRTM) by the Endeavour space shuttle in February 2000 used two radar antennas to produce the most comprehensive hi-res digital topographical map of the Earth's terrain. The data is used by Google Earth to create maps that can be viewed in 2D or 3D.

Earth observation satellites are important in monitoring the seasonal variation of vegetation. Besides studying long-term changes, they are also used to observe and issue warnings of natural disasters such as volcanic eruptions, forest fires and earthquakes.

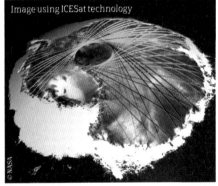
Image using ICESat technology

Ice

Carrying on from the work of Envisat, which discovered that every decade since 1978 the Arctic ice fields have shrunk by 2.7%, the European Space Agency launched CryoSat-2 on 8 April 2010. It uses radar altimeters with SAR technology, specifically designed for its mission to study the thickness and distribution of ice in the polar oceans. NASA's ICESat (2004) carried a Geoscience Laser Altimeter System (GLAS), which used pulses of laser light to measure the height and characteristics of Greenland and Antarctic ice fields. These satellites have indicated the role of greenhouse gases in the polar atmosphere and that the ozone layer has shown signs of recovery.

Radiation

Visible blue, green and red light only provides a limited amount of information about the Earth's surface, so satellites use spectrometers to study the invisible near-infrared and infrared parts of the electromagnetic spectrum.

They can identify and track the growth of plant species, as they all reflect infrared light. The infrared 'fingerprint' of plants can also indicate the amount of water present and can warn of potential droughts. Likewise, exposed rocks radiate their own infrared fingerprint that allows geologists to identify valuable mineral/oil deposits.

Infrared data from satellites is 'false coloured', so invisible light from up to three wavelengths is rendered into a combination of visible red, green and blue.

Perspective view of Santa Barbara, generated using data from the shuttle radar topography mission

View of Antarctica, showing ice sheet elevation and cloud data

Gravity

The European gravity field and steady-state ocean circulation explorer (GOCE), launched in March 2009, carries an Electrostatic Gravity Gradiometer (EGG) to measure the gravity field of Earth. By measuring the minute variations in the tug of gravity, it enables the production of Geoid maps of the globe that can indicate ocean circulation and changes, the movement and composition of polar ice sheets and the physics of the Earth's interior.

In March 2002, NASA launched two Gravity Recovery And Climate Experiment (GRACE) spacecraft. They use a microwave system that accurately measures any minute changes between their speed and distance, indicating the influence of the Earth's gravitational pull.

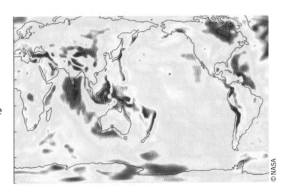

Inside the Sun
The giant star that keeps us all alive...

A celestial wonder, the Sun is a huge star formed from a massive gravitational collapse when space dust and gas from a nebula collided, It became an orb 100 times bigger and weighing over 300,000 times that of Earth. Made up of 70 per cent hydrogen and about 28 per cent helium (plus other gases), the Sun is the centre of our solar system and the largest celestial body anywhere near us.

"The surface of the Sun is a dense layer of plasma at a temperature of 5,800 degrees kelvin that is continually moving due to the action of convective motions driven by heating from below," says David Alexander, a professor of physics and astronomy at Rice University. "These convective motions show up as a distribution of what are called granulation cells about 1,000 kilometers across and which appear across the whole solar surface."

At its core, the Sun's temperature and pressure are so high and the hydrogen atoms are moving so fast that it causes fusion, turning hydrogen atoms into helium. Electromagetic radiation travels out from the Sun's core to its surface, escaping into space as electromagnetic radiation, a blinding light, and incredible levels of solar heat. In fact, the core of the Sun is actually hotter than the surface, but when heat escapes from the surface, the temperature rises to over 1-2 million degrees. Alexander explained that astronomers do not fully understand why the Sun's atmosphere is so hot, but think it has something to do with magnetic fields. ✿

Radiative zone
The first 500,000k of the Sun is a radioactive layer that transfers energy from the core, mostly toward the outer layers, passed from atom to atom

Sun's core
The core of a Sun is a dense, extremely hot region – about 15 million degrees – that produces a nuclear fusion and emits heat through the layers of the Sun to the surface

Beneath the surface of the Sun
What is the Sun made of?

Convective zone
The top 30 per cent of the Sun is a layer of hot plasma that is constantly in motion, heated from below

Right conditions
The core of the Sun, which acts like a nuclear reactor, is just the right size and temperature to product light

Engine room
The centre of a star is like an engine room that produces the nuclear fusion required for radiation and light

The Statistics
The Sun

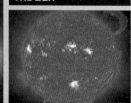

Diameter: 100 times Earth
Mass: 300,000 times Earth
Average surface temp: 1-2 million degrees
Core temp: 15 million degrees

All images courtesy of NASA

Magnetic influence
How the Sun affects the Earth's magnetic field

Solar wind
Solar wind shapes the Earth's magnetosphere and magnetic storms are illustrated here as approaching Earth

Plasma release
The Sun's magnetic field and plasma releases directly affect Earth and the rest of the solar system

Bow shock line
The purple line is the bow shock line and the blue lines surrounding the Earth represent its protective magnetosphere

What is a solar flare?

A massive explosion, but one that happens to be several million degrees in temperature...

"A solar flare is a rapid release of energy in the solar atmosphere (mostly the chromosphere and corona) resulting in localised heating of plasma to tens of millions of degrees, acceleration of electrons and protons to high energies, some to near the speed of light, and expulsion of material into space," says Alexander. "These electromagnetic disturbances here on Earth pose potential dangers for Earth-orbiting satellites, space-walking astronauts, crews on high-altitude spacecraft, and power grids on Earth."

Solar flares can cause geomagnetic storms on the Sun, including shock waves and plasma expulsions

Solar eclipses
When the Moon blocks out the Sun

A solar eclipse is a unique phenomena where the Moon passes directly into a line between the Earth and the Sun, partially or completely blocking our view of the Sun. The Sun is blocked according to the relative orbits of each celestial body. There are two kinds of eclipses: one where the Moon orbit shows the outer edge of the Sun, or where the Moon lines up perfectly and the Sun is blocked completely from view.

Sometimes, the orbits of the Earth and Sun line up perfectly so that the Sun is blocked (eclipsed) by the Moon, shown here with a shadow cast from the eclipse, taken from the ISS

How big is the Sun?
Our Sun has a diameter of 1.4 million km and Earth a diameter of almost 13,000km

What is a sunspot?

Signifying cooler areas, sunspots show up as dark dots on the photosphere (the visible layer of plasma across the Sun's surface). These 'cool' regions – about 1,000 degrees cooler than the surface temperature – are associated with strong magnetic fields. Criss-crossing magnetic-field lines can disturb the flow of heat from the core, creating pockets of intense activity. The build up of heat around a sunspot can be released as a solar flare or coronal mass ejection, which is separate to but often accompanies larger flares. Plasma from a CME ejects from the Sun at over 1 million miles per hour.

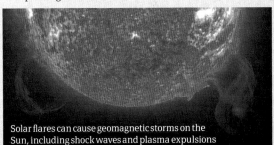

If the Sun were the size of a basketball, Earth would be a little dot no more than 2.2mm

It's the Sun, but not as we know it

■ These amazing images of the Sun are the first taken by NASA's Solar Dynamics Observatory (SDO). Taken on 30 March 2010, this false colour image traces the different gas temperatures with reds relatively cool (about 60,000 Kelvin or 107,540 F), while blues and greens are hotter (1 million Kelvin or 1,799,540 F). The SDO provides images with clarity ten times better than high-definition TV.

Image © NASA

Larger than it appears
1 In a total eclipse the Sun and the Moon appear to be the same size, due to their respective diameters and distances. The size difference is actually monumental.

Don't stare directly
2 Our retinas cannot sense any pain, so permanent vision loss caused by staring at an eclipse may not become evident until hours later, so be sensible when viewing.

'Tis the season
3 Eclipse season happens twice a year (approximately every 173 days), when the Moon crosses the orbital plane of the Earth. Each season lasts between 24 and 37 days.

A brief observation
4 Total eclipses generally take a couple of hours from start to finish, with the period of totality lasting for a few minutes and plunging an area into complete darkness.

An indirect view
5 The best and safest way to view any kind of eclipse is through a special solar filter (such as eclipse sunglasses) or possibly a pinhole camera.

DID YOU KNOW? Ancient cultures were often frightened by solar eclipses and attributed them to supernatural beings

This is an image of the Moon's transit across the Sun, taken from NASA's STEREO-B spacecraft

© NASA

The solar eclipse is a truly breathtaking sight

© NASA

The view of the shadow cast by the Moon during a solar eclipse in 1999, taken by the Mir space station

Solar eclipse

Solar eclipses occur when the Moon passes between the Earth and the Sun

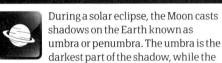

During a solar eclipse, the Moon casts shadows on the Earth known as umbra or penumbra. The umbra is the darkest part of the shadow, while the penumbra is the area where part of the Moon is blocking the Sun. Partial eclipses happen when the Sun and Moon are not in perfect alignment – only the penumbra of the Moon's shadow passes over the surface of the Earth. In a total eclipse, the umbra touches the Earth's surface.

There are also annular eclipses, in which both the Sun and the Moon are in alignment but the Moon appears to be slightly smaller than the Sun. The Sun appears as a bright ring, or annulus, around the Moon's profile. The umbra is still in line with a region on the Earth's surface, but the distance is too great to actually touch the surface of the Earth.

Depending on your location, an eclipse may appear to be any of the three possible types. For example, if your region lies in the path of totality, you will experience a total eclipse, while people in other regions may only see a partial eclipse. Solar eclipses occur between two and five times per year, with most of these being partial or annual eclipses.

Total eclipses have four phases. First contact occurs when you first notice the shadow of the Moon on the Sun's surface. During second contact, you will observe a phenomenon called Baily's beads, when sunlight shines jaggedly through the rugged peaks and valleys of the Moon's surface. When one bead of light is left, it appears as a single dot in the ring, known as the diamond ring effect. Next, the Moon completely covers the Sun's surface with only a corona of light showing. The final stage is third contact, when the Moon's shadow moves away from the Sun.

When the Moon blocks out the Sun

The relationship between the Sun, Moon and Earth during an eclipse is geometric

1. Sun
The Sun and the Moon often appear to be the same size, because the ratio between their diameters is about the same as the ratio between their respective distances from Earth

2. Moon
The magnitude of an eclipse is the ratio between the angular diameters of the Moon and Sun. During a total eclipse this ratio is one or greater

3. Umbra
The umbra is the central area of the shadow of the Moon. If this area passes over you, you'll see a total eclipse. The sky will be completely dark

4. Penumbra
The penumbra is the outer part of the Moon's shadow. You will see a partial eclipse if this part passes over you and the sky will only be partially dark

5. Earth
In an annular solar eclipse, the umbra never touches the Earth because the Moon is too far away in its orbit. The Sun appears as a bright ring around the Moon's profile

Solar tornadoes

The story behind twisters on the Sun, a thousand times larger than their Earthling counterparts

A gigantic sphere of hydrogen plasma (ionised gas), our Sun is by far the most dominant body in the Solar System and one of its most visually intense events is the solar tornado. These twisting magnetic fields are between 100 to 1,000 times larger than their equivalents on Earth and have been observed at a gigantic 70,000 kilometres (43,496 miles) tall. Over 11,000 of these phenomena are on the Sun's surface at any time and they are believed to potentially be the source of heating for the outer reaches of the Sun and could contribute to auroras on our planet.

Solar tornadoes differ from Earth-based twisters because they are comprised of a magnetic field of plasma. They are more frequently spotted around the Sun's equator and poles, as this is where magnetism is most prominent. They exist on other stars as well as the Sun, burn at over a million degrees Celsius (1.8 million degrees Fahrenheit) and have swirling speeds of 10,000 kilometres (6,213 miles) per hour.

They appear in clusters and their main function is to heat the star's outer atmosphere by moving energy from the surface to the uppermost layer, the corona. They generate 100 to 300 watts per square metre (10.8 square feet) and are believed to be the reason for the corona's heat production, which has puzzled scientists and astronomers for generations. Observations from the Swedish 1m Solar Telescope in 2008 have increased our understanding of how nature heats magnetised plasma and how the 'chromospheric swirls' we can see are the result of the tornadoes. ✿

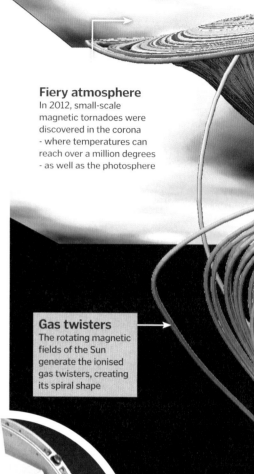

Fiery atmosphere
In 2012, small-scale magnetic tornadoes were discovered in the corona - where temperatures can reach over a million degrees - as well as the photosphere

Gas twisters
The rotating magnetic fields of the Sun generate the ionised gas twisters, creating its spiral shape

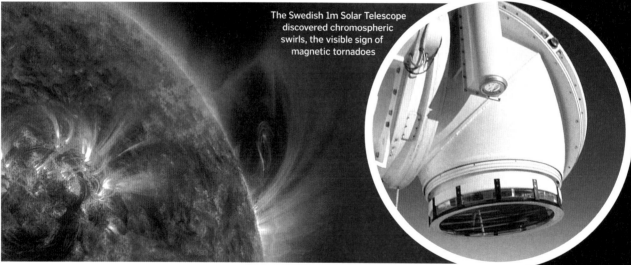

The Swedish 1m Solar Telescope discovered chromospheric swirls, the visible sign of magnetic tornadoes

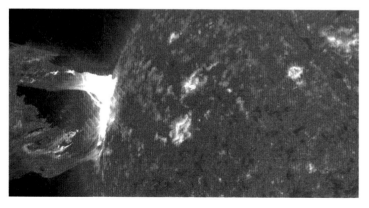

Why is the corona so hot?

A curious anomaly of our nearest star is the fact that the corona, an aura of plasma surrounding the star, is hotter than many other areas of the Sun closer to its core. The corona can get up to two million degrees Celsius (3.6 million degrees Fahrenheit) while on the surface it is a measly 5,500 degrees Celsius (9,932 degrees Fahrenheit). Scientists and astronomers have long been perplexed by this but some new theories might explain why. Recent notions reason that heat is injected into the corona by wave heating from the core. As the corona is dominated by magnetic fields that are constantly connecting and engaging with each other, a convection zone is created, which releases high amounts of energy and heat. Solar tornadoes are linked to the plasma's astonishing heat levels as they contribute to coronal mass ejections (CME) and the solar winds in the Sun's atmosphere. To discover more, NASA has planned a mission known as the Solar Probe Plus, which is pencilled in for 2018.

Solar flare

1 A massive magnetic energy release on the Sun's surface, a solar flare shows sudden concentrated brightness and emits huge amounts of radiation into the Solar System.

Coronal mass ejection

2 An eruption of solar wind caused by magnetic instabilities, CMEs can cause electrical problems to satellites and the Earth's magnetosphere.

Sunspot

3 A relatively dark and cool area of the photosphere, they have temperatures of around 3,500°C (6,330°F) and can reach over 50,000km (31,069mi) in diameter.

Geomagnetic storm

4 Caused by CMEs and solar flares, radiation-charged particles affect the Earth's magnetic field and cause auroras in the North and South Polar regions.

Solar prominence

5 Similar to a solar flare, solar prominences are loops of unstable plasma that extend from the surface to the corona, adding to the Sun's already vibrant appearance.

DID YOU KNOW? *There are two types of solar tornado: giant and small-scale magnetic. Experts are unsure whether they are linked*

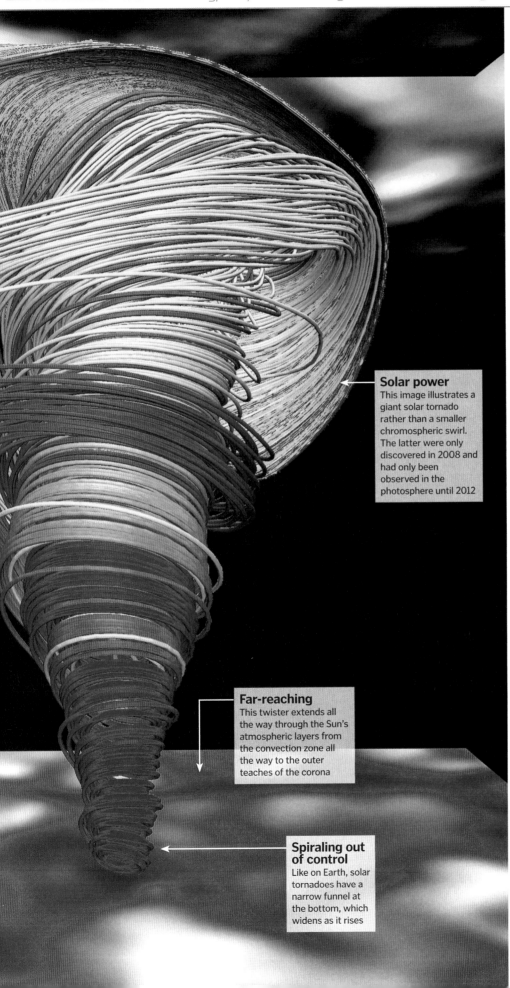

Solar power
This image illustrates a giant solar tornado rather than a smaller chromospheric swirl. The latter were only discovered in 2008 and had only been observed in the photosphere until 2012

Far-reaching
This twister extends all the way through the Sun's atmospheric layers from the convection zone all the way to the outer reaches of the corona

Spiraling out of control
Like on Earth, solar tornadoes have a narrow funnel at the bottom, which widens as it rises

Solar storm chaser

Dr Sven Wedemeyer-Böhm from the Institute of Theoretical Astrophysics explains more

How similar are solar tornadoes to tornadoes on Earth?
Aside from the visible appearance, tornadoes on Earth and on the Sun are very different phenomena. In both cases, the tornado funnel is narrow at the bottom and widens with height in the atmosphere. Particles inside tornadoes are forced to move in spirals. Tornadoes on Earth occur as a result of temperature and gas pressure differences and strong shear winds. Solar tornadoes are generated by rotating magnetic field structures, which force the plasma, ie the ionised gas, to move in spirals.

How do solar tornadoes contribute to auroras on Earth?
It has been speculated that giant tornadoes may serve as a possible trigger of solar eruptions, where they build up a magnetic field structure until it destabilises and erupts. As a consequence, ionised gas could get ejected towards Earth, which would then contribute to auroras. However, as of now, there's no direct connection confirmed.

Do you know about future planned missions to investigate this phenomenon?
There are missions such as Solar Orbiter and Solar-C, which may fly in foreseeable future. There will be also some major progress with ground-based observatories with the 4-m Daniel K Inouye Solar Telescope (DKIST, formerly the Advanced Technology Solar Telescope, ATST), which is currently built on Hawaii, and possibly the 4-m European Solar Telescope (EST), which may be built in the future. These new instruments will allow for an even closer look at our Sun and will enable us to answer the many open questions that we still have about solar tornadoes.

What is the primary difference between giant solar tornadoes and small-scale magnetic tornadoes?
It is currently not clear if these are different phenomena or not. Small-scale magnetic tornadoes have only been observed from the top so far, ie in the middle of the solar disk, whereas giant tornadoes are seen more towards the limb of the Sun, in other words: from the side. In general, magnetic tornadoes tend to have somewhat smaller diameters than giant tornadoes but it is too early to draw solid conclusions.

What is the primary difference between giant solar tornadoes and small-scale magnetic tornadoes?
There are still many questions concerning solar tornadoes and we hope to address some of the most important aspects during the next three years in a project, which has just started at the University of Oslo in collaboration with international experts.

Exploring the Moon

We've visited the lunar body several times but it still has many secrets to reveal...

The Moon has been shrouded in mystery since the dawn of time. For a start, where did it come from? The popular current hypothesis is the giant impact theory. We've learned from dating lunar rocks that the Moon formed about 4.5 billion years ago, a good 30-50 million years after the Solar System. But while the Earth was just finishing its formation, it was struck by a giant celestial body about the size of Mars, which has been christened Theia. This collision blasted material out into space near the Earth, which coalesced into the body that today we call the Moon. Whether the material came from Earth or the planetoid that caused the impact (or both) is still a matter of debate.

The Moon is the second-brightest object in our sky after the Sun and it has influenced life on Earth in countless ways. The gravitational interactions with our world and the Sun give us ocean tides and lengthen our days by a tiny amount. We've also created calendars based on its phases. Until a Soviet spacecraft landed on it in 1959, we'd only been able to study the Moon from Earth. Then in 1969, humans visited the Moon – and it remains the only other body in the universe we've actually stood upon.

Thanks to decades of study, we've learned a great deal about our satellite. For example, we know that the Moon has a differentiated interior, just like Earth – it contains a core, mantle and crust. The core is rich with iron

GO FIGURE
MOON MASSES

How many of these objects would fit into the Moon?

1.5 ▼ PLUTOS

22 MILLION ▼ DEIMOSES

4,631.6 TRILLION ▼ BASKETBALLS

DID YOU KNOW? Smoke and ash from volcanic eruptions on Earth, eg Krakatoa, have actually caused the Moon to appear blue

A closer look at the surface

The Moon's two hemispheres – the one nearest to us and the one farthest away, or the 'dark side' – have very different surface features. The nearer side is dominated by maria and highlands. The maria, or 'seas' (so-named because early astronomers assumed they were full of water) are the darker areas visible from Earth. The lighter areas are the highlands. Instead of water, the maria are dark because they contain hardened lava, left over from earlier volcanism on the Moon. The far side of our satellite, in contrast, contains almost no maria at all. Both sides of our lunar neighbour are covered with impact craters, left by meteors; they can be tiny or many kilometres across. Especially strong impacts can leave rays of dust extending hundreds of metres from the crater centre. Mountains and other volcanic features emerged shortly after the Moon's formation, as the surface cooled and buckled.

The statistics...

The Moon

Average distance from Earth: 384,403km (238,857mi)

Surface temperature:
Day: 107°C (224.6°F)
Night: -153°C (-243°F)

Mean radius: 1,737km (1,079mi)

Volume (Earth=1): 0.02 Earths

Orbit period; length of lunar year: 27.32 Earth days (tidally locked)

Rotational period; length of lunar day: 29.53 Earth days

Mass (Earth=1): 0.0123 Earths

Mean density: 3.344g/cm³ (1.94oz/in³)

Gravity at equator (Earth=1): 0.16 Earths

Mare Orientale
A distinctive target-ring shaped feature, but it's tricky to see from Earth

Oceanus Procellarum
Aka the Ocean of Storms; site of Apollo 12 landing

Archimedes
An 83km (51.5mi)-diameter impact crater

Mare Tranquillitatis
Aka the Sea of Tranquillity; site of Apollo 11 landing

Van de Graaff
Appears to be two craters merged into a figure-of-eight

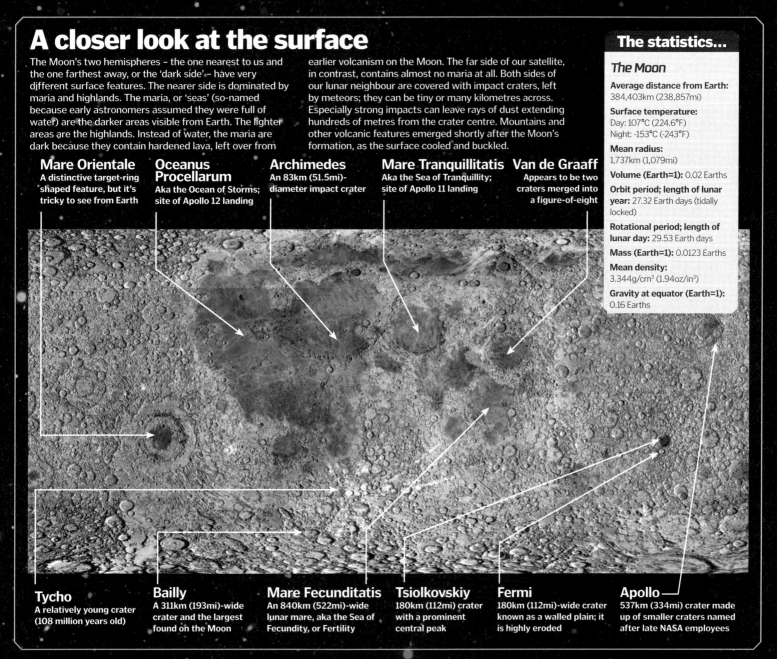

Tycho
A relatively young crater (108 million years old)

Bailly
A 311km (193mi)-wide crater and the largest found on the Moon

Mare Fecunditatis
An 840km (522mi)-wide lunar mare, aka the Sea of Fecundity, or Fertility

Tsiolkovskiy
180km (112mi) crater with a prominent central peak

Fermi
180km (112mi)-wide crater known as a walled plain; it is highly eroded

Apollo
537km (334mi) crater made up of smaller craters named after late NASA employees

– solid in the centre and surrounded by a fluid outer core. The core is small in comparison to the rest of the Moon, however – roughly 350 kilometres (217 miles) thick, about 20 per cent of the Moon's total size. Surrounding the core is a 500-kilometre (311-mile), partially melted boundary layer. This is thought to have formed when a magma ocean in the mantle cooled and crystallised shortly after the Moon's formation. The mantle is the next layer, a hard and rocky area 1,000 kilometres (620 miles) thick. The Moon's crust is also rocky, and about 60-100 kilometres (37-62 miles) in thickness. Analysing rocks has shown us that most of the lunar crust comprises aluminium and titanium, with the elements pyroxferroite and tranquillityite (first seen on the Moon and subsequently found on Earth) fairly abundant as well. The top layer is covered with dusty, broken rock that smells a bit like gunpowder and has a snowy texture, called regolith.

There's a reason why astronauts had to wear helmets on the Moon – there's very little atmosphere, and what there is doesn't contain oxygen, nitrogen or hydrogen; indeed, the atmospheric mass is less than ten metric tons. Since there's nothing to block the solar wind, it bombards the surface and causes sputtering – sprays of particles into the air. The Moon's surface also experiences outgassing, when volatile gases vent from the interior. These processes contribute sodium, potassium and compounds of argon, radon and polonium, while solar wind contributes helium-4. All of these have been found in the atmosphere and are continually replenished. Oxygen and other neutral elements found on Earth are present in the regolith, but they don't exist in the atmosphere – probably because the solar wind quickly sweeps them out into space.

Our Moon is the second-densest to be found in the Solar System, behind Jupiter's Io. It's also the fifth largest moon in diameter, only beaten, in ascending order, by Io (Jupiter), Callisto (Jupiter), Titan (Saturn) and Ganymede (Jupiter). The Moon's diameter is about one-quarter that of Earth's, but its mass is just under 0.0125 Earth masses.

© NASA, Renso

The Earth-Moon system

A closer look at the relationship between our planet and the Moon

What many people don't know is the Moon doesn't just orbit the Earth, but Earth orbits the Moon too. While the Moon is propelled around Earth in an elliptical orbit, the pull of the Moon's own gravity causes our planet to move slightly off its own centre and around in a small circle. Think of it like an Olympic hammer thrower swinging the hammer around their body while holding onto the chain: even though the hammer is many times smaller than the thrower, it's enough to pull the thrower slightly off their mark. The barycentre marks the centre of mass for this Earth-Moon relationship. The forces involved in Earth-Moon barycentre dynamics are very regular, but even so, tiny variances mean the Moon is gradually moving away from our world. When the Moon was first formed it was very close and had a powerful effect on the development of the early Earth. At first it moved away from us at a rate of ten kilometres (6.2 miles) per year, slowing down over billions of years to its current rate of just 3.8 centimetres (1.5 inches) per year.

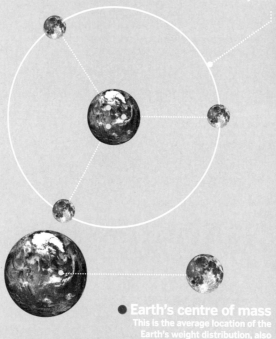

● Barycentre
This is the centre of mass at which the Earth and the Moon balance each other, located 1,710km (1,062mi) below Earth's surface

Plane of the Moon's orbit
The Moon's orbital plane is close to the ecliptic plane – the path the Earth takes as it orbits the Sun, or to be more specific, the barycentre of the Solar System

● Earth's centre of mass
This is the average location of the Earth's weight distribution, also known as its centre of gravity

The lunar body has some unique gravitational properties too. Unlike Earth, the Moon does not have a dipolar magnetic field, but it does have an external magnetic field that results in a gravity of about a sixth of that here on Earth. In addition, the Moon has 'mascons' (mass concentrations), which are large positive gravitational anomalies mostly centred around some of its largest basins. We aren't sure what causes them, although the ones in basins may come from the extremely dense lava flows filling them. We continue to search for water on the Moon, which can't exist on its surface, but might be lurking in some of the shadowy basins, deposited by comets or formed by interactions between hydrogen from the solar wind or oxygen from the regolith deposits.

The Moon is in synchronous rotation with our world. This means that its orbit and revolution periods are of equal length, so the same side of the Moon faces the Earth all of the time. We call these the near side and the far side, or the 'dark side', but the latter actually gets just as much sunlight as the former.

The phases of the Moon describe how it appears to us, which changes over the course of the Moon's orbit around our planet and Earth's orbit around the Sun. When the Sun and Moon

Apollo mission profile

We break down the key stages of a former lunar mission, from Earth to the Moon and back again

3. Trans-Earth injection
Liftoff from the Moon was timed so that when the Service Module engine fired, the midpoint of the spacecraft would be opposite the projected landing site on Earth

1. Saturn V launch
The Saturn V was a three-stage rocket that carried the Apollo Command and Service Modules to the Moon

2. Lunar orbit insertion
The spacecraft passed behind the Moon, and the Service Module engine fired briefly to insert Apollo into the Moon's orbit

4. Service Module jettison
Before re-entering Earth's atmosphere, the Service Module was jettisoned

5. Command Module rotation
The Command Module rotated 180 degrees prior to re-entry, turning its blunt end towards the Earth

6. Command Module splashdown
Parachutes helped to slow down the Command Module before it splashed down into the ocean

What a coincidence...

Many have wondered why the Moon is just the right size and distance to cover the Sun during an eclipse. The Sun is 400 times greater in diameter than the Moon; the Sun just so happens to be 400 times farther away from Earth too.

DID YOU KNOW? In 1970, two Soviet researchers theorised that the Moon was actually a hollow alien spacecraft

are on the opposite sides of the Earth, the Moon appears full. When the Sun and Moon are on the same side of the Earth, the Moon appears dark (known as a 'new moon'). The phases in between are the half and quarter-moons. Eclipses occur when the Sun, Moon and Earth all line up, also known as syzygy (pronounced siz-i-gee). A solar eclipse occurs when the Moon is between the Sun and Earth, while a lunar eclipse happens when the Earth is between the Sun and Moon. Variations in the orbits mean eclipses happen not with each new and full moon but according to the Saros cycle – a period of 18 years first identified by ancient Babylonian astronomers.

These astronomers created the first records of the Moon, in the 5th century BCE. Over the years astronomers in India, Greece, Persia and China theorised about everything from the source of moonlight to the tides and the Moon's phases. Astronomers in the Middle Ages

A focus on Apollo

On 25 May 1962, US President John F Kennedy proposed a goal of putting men on the Moon and returning them back to Earth by the end of the decade. It was a lofty ambition, but NASA achieved it on 21 July 1969 with Apollo 11. NASA sent astronauts to the Moon a total six times. Budgetary cuts and a shift to planning for the Skylab and Space Shuttle programmes led to the end of the Apollo programme after Apollo 17 returned to Earth in December 1972. No human has touched down on the Moon since.

thought that the Moon was a smooth sphere. Once the telescope was invented in 1608, we soon set our sights on the satellite. Near the end of the 17th century, many of the features on the Moon had been named by Italian astronomers like Francesco Maria Grimaldi.

The Space Race in the Fifties and Sixties between the USA and the Soviet Union ramped up interest in exploring the Moon, first by

orbiter and later by man. The USSR got there first, when the Luna 2 spacecraft smashed into the surface in 1959. It also completed the first soft landing and the first orbit of the Moon in 1966. However, the United States famously won the race of getting a man on the Moon with the seminal Apollo 11 mission in 1969.

It once seemed inevitable that we'd eventually establish a base on the Moon – but it hasn't happened yet, and with the future of NASA's manned space programme in flux, it may be up to another programme or even a private enterprise. But NASA, the European Space Agency, the China National Space Administration, the Indian Space Research Organisation and others continue to send orbiters and landers to the Moon. In January 2012, two spacecraft called GRAIL (Gravity Recovery and Interior Laboratory) began orbiting the Moon to better map it and learn more about its complex interior and gravity. ✿

© NASA; DK Images; Thinkstock

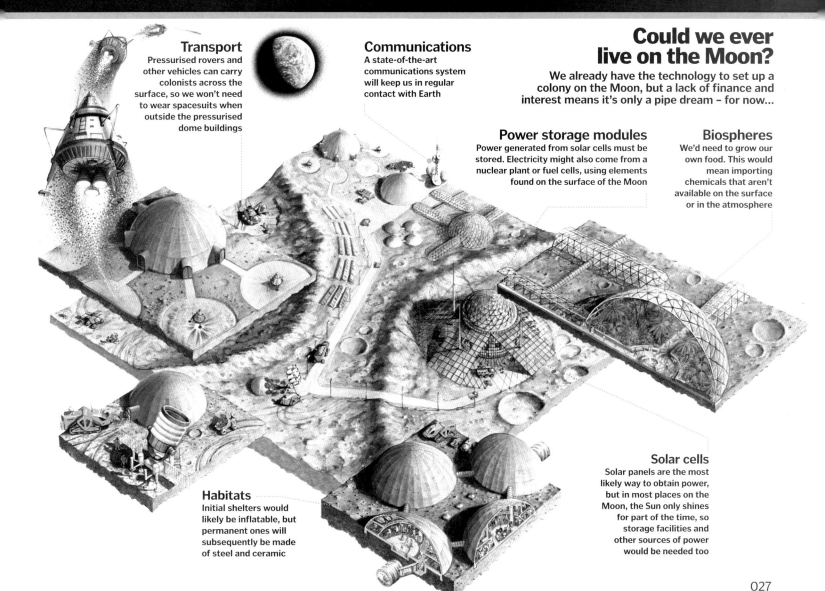

Transport
Pressurised rovers and other vehicles can carry colonists across the surface, so we won't need to wear spacesuits when outside the pressurised dome buildings

Communications
A state-of-the-art communications system will keep us in regular contact with Earth

Could we ever live on the Moon?

We already have the technology to set up a colony on the Moon, but a lack of finance and interest means it's only a pipe dream – for now...

Power storage modules
Power generated from solar cells must be stored. Electricity might also come from a nuclear plant or fuel cells, using elements found on the surface of the Moon

Biospheres
We'd need to grow our own food. This would mean importing chemicals that aren't available on the surface or in the atmosphere

Habitats
Initial shelters would likely be inflatable, but permanent ones will subsequently be made of steel and ceramic

Solar cells
Solar panels are the most likely way to obtain power, but in most places on the Moon, the Sun only shines for part of the time, so storage facilities and other sources of power would be needed too

THE FIRST MOON LANDING

Over 40 years ago on 21 July 1969 Neil Armstrong became the first person in history to set foot on the surface of a celestial body other than Earth, marking the culmination of a decade of work

In the Sixties the 'Space Race' between the USA and USSR was heating up. Russia had struck the initial blow by launching the first man-made satellite – Sputnik 1 – in 1957, and four years later they sent the first human – Yuri Gagarin – into space. The Americans followed suit a few weeks later but it was readily apparent they were playing catch-up to the Russians. To reassure the American people, President Kennedy issued an impassioned speech to Congress in 1961 announcing the ambitious goal of placing a human on the Moon before the end of the decade. As a result Project Apollo was born, and with it NASA was tasked with fulfilling Kennedy's lofty aim. An unprecedented technological marvel, the Apollo missions would come to define not only a generation, but also the standard by which all future manned space missions would be compared.

The crew

From left to right: Commander Neil A Armstrong; Command Module pilot Michael Collins; Lunar Module pilot Edwin 'Buzz' E Aldrin Jr. Collins remained in orbit while Armstrong and Aldrin explored the surface.

© NASA

The Eagle lander

The lander was a two-stage craft built to separate from the Command and Service Module then travel to and from the Moon's surface

Payload

At almost 47,000kg, (103,600lbs) the payload consisted of the Command, Service and Lunar Modules that travelled to the Moon

LEVA

The Lunar Extravehicular Visor Assembly (LEVA) contained gold-coated visors to protect against the Sun

PLSS

The Apollo Portable Life Support System (PLSS) contained the life-support apparatus including cooling water, oxygen tanks and electrical power

Third stage (S-IVB)

The final rocket stage contained just one J-2 engine and accelerated the spacecraft towards the Moon at about 39,400km/h (24,500mph) before

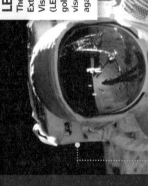

JOURNEY OF A LIFETIME

The Apollo 11 mission lasted 195 hours, 18 minutes and 35 seconds

16 July 1332 GMT
Apollo 11 launches atop a Saturn V rocket from the Kennedy Space Center and enters Earth's orbit.

19 July 1721 GMT
After a three-day journey across almost 400,000km (250,000

The rocket

The Saturn V rocket used to take Apollo into space still retains the record of being the most powerful rocket of all time

Size
The Saturn V rocket was as tall as a 36-storey building and, fully loaded, it weighed almost 3,000 tons

First stage (S-IC)
S-IC contained five F-1 engines that used liquid oxygen and kerosene fuel. They separated at an altitude of 61km (38 miles)

Second stage (S-II)
The five J-2 liquid hydrogen engines of S-II took Apollo 11 to an altitude of 185km (115 miles) before they were discarded

The flight

- Command and Service Module remains in orbit
- Lunar Module separates and lands on the Moon
- Third-stage separation
- Command and Service Module docks with third stage
- Second-stage separation
- First-stage separation

Descent stage
Equipment for use on the Moon was stored in this lower section, which also contained a rocket and landing gear for a controlled landing. It was left behind on the Moon

Ascent stage
This part of the Lunar Module (LM) contained the pressurised crew compartment and controls, and took the astronauts back to the Command and Service Module (CSM) in orbit

If the ascent stage had failed the crew would have had no hope of rescue

'...from the planet Earth first set foot upon the Moon, July 1969 AD. We came in peace for all mankind.'

Spacesuits

To walk on the Moon the Apollo 11 crew required some practical 'space clobber'

Weight
The spacesuit and backpack weighed 14kg (31lb) on the Moon, but 82kg (181lb) on Earth, due to the Moon's weaker gravity

...reduced the transfer of heat from the Moon's surface and helped to limit surface abrasion

Neil Armstrong and 'Buzz' Aldrin enter the Lunar Module (LM) and separate from the Command and Service Module (CSM).

20 July 2017 GMT
The Lunar Module lands in Mare Tranquillitatis (the Sea of Tranquillity), tracked by Collins in orbit aboard the CSM.

21 July 0256 GMT
Armstrong steps onto the lunar surface, the first human to set foot on another world. Aldrin follows 19 minutes later, and they begin deploying instruments and taking photos.

21 July 1754 GMT
Having traversed a distance of about 250m (820ft) and collected 22kg (48lb) of lunar rock and soil, the two astronauts return to the LM and launch back into orbit.

21 July 2134 GMT
The LM docks with the CSM and, once all three astronauts are safely in the CSM, the LM is jettisoned into lunar orbit.

24 July 1650 GMT
After separating from the Service Module, the Command Module splashes down in the Pacific Ocean after completing its 195-hour mission.

15 FACTS YOU NEVER KNEW ABOUT
ECLIPSES

Eclipses are one of nature's most amazing spectacles, a result of our Moon's orbit around our planet

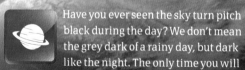

Have you ever seen the sky turn pitch black during the day? We don't mean the grey dark of a rainy day, but dark like the night. The only time you will ever see this is during a total solar eclipse, which is one of nature's most breathtaking eclipses. It happens when the Moon moves in front of the Sun for a few minutes, blocking its light and underneath the Moon's shadow darkness falls.

Total solar eclipses are rare and in a way it is an incredible stroke of luck that we have them. The Sun's distance from Earth just happens to be about 400 times the Moon's distance from our planet. The Sun also happens to be about 400 times larger than the Moon, so thanks to this

magic ratio they appear about the same size in the sky, meaning that during an eclipse the Moon can fit precisely over the Sun. We have to say 'about' a lot because Earth's orbit and the Moon's orbit are not circular but elliptical, meaning sometimes they can be a bit further away, or a bit nearer. This results in the Sun sometimes appearing larger than the Moon during some eclipses, leaving a ring of light from the Sun around the Moon's silhouette. We call this an annular eclipse.

An eclipse begins at 'first contact' when the Moon's disc first touches the Sun's disc. You won't notice a significant change in the light at this point – in fact it won't get dark until the Moon has

practically covered all of the disc – this is 'second contact' when the far limb of the Moon's disc touches the Sun's apparent disc. Totality – which is how we describe the Sun being blocked by the Moon – can last for several minutes. 'Third contact' happens when totality ends and the Moon begins to move away from the Sun and daylight returns once more. 'Fourth contact' is when the Moon moves completely off the Sun and the eclipse ends.

The Moon is very slowly moving away from Earth at a rate of 3.8 centimetres (1.5 inches) per year, so eventually it will appear too small to completely cover the Sun. Luckily, this day won't arrive for at least another 500 million years! ✿

RECORD BREAKERS
LONGEST ECLIPSE

74minutes

LONGEST ECLIPSE OBSERVATION
If you can move fast enough, you can keep up with the supersonic shadow of the Moon during an eclipse. In 1973, astronomers flew on a Concorde, moving at Mach 2, to stay in the path of totality for 74 minutes.

DID YOU KNOW? Arthur Eddington used solar eclipses to observe gravitational lensing, confirming the theory of general relativity

Earth orbit
Earth's orbit is also elliptical, with its closest point to the Sun (perihelion) 147.1mn km (91.4mn mi) and its most distant point (aphelion) at 152.1mn km (94.5mn mi).

We can still see the Moon during a lunar eclipse

01 Unlike a solar eclipse, which hides the Sun, we still see the Moon in a total lunar eclipse, as enough scattered light from Earth illuminates the lunar surface, but in a deep red.

Sunlight
Light takes eight minutes and 20 seconds to reach Earth from the Sun, and from the Moon it takes 1.3 seconds, so we always see eclipses in the past.

Shadow cone
The shadow of the Moon during a solar eclipse covers only a small part of the Earth's surface.

Partial
A partial lunar eclipse occurs when only part of the Moon is caught in Earth's shadow.

Total
A total solar eclipse occurs when the Moon moves in front of the Sun and casts its shadow on the Earth, and a total lunar eclipse will happen when the Moon moves into Earth's shadow.

Lunar orbit
The Moon's orbit is elliptical: at its closest (perigee) it is just 363,300km (225,744mi) away and at its farthest point (apogee) it reaches 405,500km (251,966mi) from Earth. This can affect the length as well as the type of solar eclipse.

Penumbral
The shadow of the Earth is split into the deepest shadow (the umbra) and lesser shadow (penumbra). A penumbral lunar eclipse is usually not as obvious to look at as an umbral eclipse is.

The length of totality can vary

02 Some eclipses are very short, with totality lasting just a couple of minutes. Others can last six or seven minutes. The reason for the difference is a result of the elliptical orbits of Earth and the Moon. When the Moon is closer to Earth in its orbit, it moves faster. The same for the Earth around the Sun, and this all affects the speed at which we see the Moon move across the Sun during a solar eclipse.

Totality – the point at which the Sun is 100 per cent covered by the Moon – can last for several minutes

You can see the Sun's atmosphere

03 The Sun has an atmosphere, split into two parts. The lower part is called the chromosphere where the temperature rises from 6,000 to 20,000 degrees Celsius (10,832 to 36,032 degrees Fahrenheit). The upper part is called the corona and can reach temperatures in excess of 1 million degrees Celsius (1.8 million degrees Fahrenheit). During totality you can see this corona as flares of light around the hidden Sun. You might also catch a glimpse of the chromosphere as a red tinge at the edge of the Moon at third contact.

The Sun's outermost atmosphere, called the corona, is made prominent during a solar eclipse

You can see the planets during an eclipse

04 If you are lucky enough to see a total solar eclipse, take a few moments to also glance around the sky. In the darkness the stars and planets will pop out. Closest to the Sun will be Venus and Mercury, but you could also see other planets, depending where in the sky they are at the time.

During a total eclipse, you should be able to see the stars and naked eye planets – depending on the time of year – as the sky turns dark

UK solar eclipses are rare

05 Total solar eclipses seen from the UK are very rare. The last one was in 1999 and the next won't be until 23 September 2090, where Cornwall will be in the umbral shadow for two minutes and ten seconds. However, there will be partial solar eclipses visible in 2018 (only Shetland, Orkney and the northern coast of Scotland), 2021, 2022 and 2026.

Solar eclipse hunters will need a passport

06 There are plenty of opportunities to view a solar eclipse over the next ten years if you are willing to travel. Following the eclipse this March, there are total solar eclipses on 9 March 2016 (Indonesia, the Pacific), 21 August 2017 (USA), 2 July 2019 (Argentina and Chile) and the same again on 14 December 2020, 4 December 2021 (Antarctica), 20 April 2023 (Indonesia and Australia) and 8 April 2024 (Mexico, USA, Canada). There are also annular eclipses in 2016, 2017, 2019, 2020, 2021, 2023 and 2024.

They can create diamond rings

07 Just at the moment totality begins or ends, a spectacular effect takes place that is called the 'diamond ring' – a bright burst of light appears, looking very much like the jewel in a diamond ring. This is caused by sunlight bursting through gaps between mountains on the edge of the Moon.

Sunlight bursting through gaps between mountains on the Moon creates a 'diamond ring'

How a solar eclipse forms

A solar eclipse is a consequence of an alignment of the Earth, Moon and Sun

Eclipses are all a result of orbits. The Moon orbits the Earth once every 27.3 days. The Earth orbits the Sun once every 365.2 days. Their orbits are elliptical, meaning their distance from their parent body can change throughout an orbit. The tilt of the Moon's orbit relative to the ecliptic (the path of the Sun through the sky) is 5.1 degrees. A solar eclipse happens only when the Moon crosses the ecliptic at the exact position that the Sun is at that moment in time.

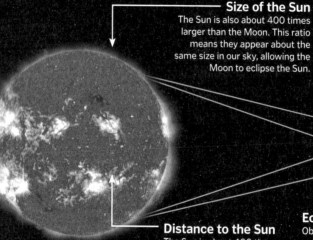

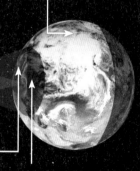

Size of the Sun
The Sun is also about 400 times larger than the Moon. This ratio means they appear about the same size in our sky, allowing the Moon to eclipse the Sun.

The Moon
We cannot see the surface of the Moon during a solar eclipse because, facing away from the Sun, it is in darkness.

Out of the shadow
Any parts of the Earth not under the shadow of the Moon will not see the eclipse.

Distance to the Sun
The Sun is about 400 times more distant from the Earth than the Moon.

Eclipse shadow
Observers in the umbral shadow of the Moon will see a total solar eclipse.

Partial eclipse
Observers in the penumbral shadow will see a partial eclipse of the Sun.

Solar and lunar eclipses come in pairs

08 There is always a lunar eclipse either two weeks before or two weeks after a solar eclipse. This is because the alignment between the Sun, Moon and Earth is still close enough that, a fortnight before or after a solar eclipse, when the Moon is on the other side of the Earth, the Moon can fall into Earth's shadow.

The characteristic reddish hue of a lunar eclipse will often appear not long before or after a solar eclipse

STRANGE BUT TRUE
LOOK TO THE SKIES

How did Columbus make use of the 1504 lunar eclipse?

A As distraction to escape from the natives B 'Predicting' it to get food C Practice his astronomy in the darkness

Answer:
After explorer Christopher Columbus became stranded in the Caribbean, he and his crew became dependent on food from the local tribes. He 'predicted' the lunar eclipse since he knew it would secure the respect of the superstitious natives.

DID YOU KNOW? Sometimes, during a total eclipse, you can see large eruptions, or prominences, from the Sun in the corona

The Moon's shadow moves very fast

09 The Moon's shadow moves quickly across the face of the Earth, from west to east, faster than the speed of sound – the eclipse shadow at the equator travels at 1,730 kilometres (1,075 miles) per hour. This is because the Moon is orbiting Earth at 3,400 kilometres (2,113 miles) per hour, counterbalanced by the Earth's rotation at 1,670 kilometres (1,038 miles) per hour. This is also why the Moon moves across the sky faster than the Sun.

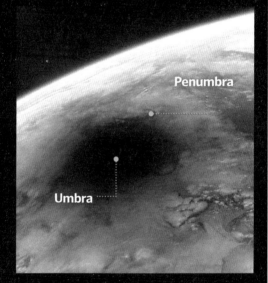

Penumbra

Umbra

You can see a lunar eclipse this year

13 Lunar eclipses are much more common than solar eclipses, occurring twice a year in different parts of the world. The next total lunar eclipse visible from the UK will be on 28 September 2015, followed by another on 21 January 2019, with several partial eclipses between those two dates.

Eclipses are relatively rare

14 On average, total solar eclipses happen every 18 months, although sometimes it can be several years between eclipses. They don't occur every month because the Moon's orbit is tilted with respect to the Earth's orbit around the Sun, so it is only rarely that the Moon's path across the sky intersects with the Sun's.

They must be observed with care

15 It is very dangerous to look direct at the Sun without using special eclipse glasses or a telescope with a specialist solar filter. This is because the Sun is so bright it can damage your eyesight, or even permanently blind you. Even if 99 per cent of the Sun's surface is blocked by the Moon, the remaining per cent is still intense enough to burn your retina. So here are some safe options for observing eclipses, or the Sun in general.

If using eclipse glasses, check they do not have any damage. Even a pinhole could damage your eyesight.

Try projecting the image of the Sun through a telescope and onto a piece of white card. Keep the finderscope covered, in case small children accidentally look through it. Gaps between leaves in trees can also act as natural pinholes to project the Sun's image

You can also use specialist solar filters and telescopes. Produced by companies such as Coronado and Lunt, these can be a bit expensive but they allow you to view the Sun at other wavelengths of light, such as hydrogen-alpha, which appears orange, blocking out the dangerous light.

There is more than one type of shadow

10 A shadow is divided into two parts – the umbra and the penumbra. The umbra is the central, deepest part of the shadow. The penumbra is where only part of the source of light is blocked. Total eclipses are seen in the umbra, while partial eclipses are seen in the penumbra.

They require syzygy

11 Eclipses occur during a particular alignment of the Sun, Moon and Earth called syzygy, which is when all three bodies are arranged in a straight line.

Ancient eclipses

12 In the past, total solar eclipses have often deemed to be bad omens or portents of doom, or the anger of the gods, prompting both wars and peace to begin. However, as far back as the ancient Babylonians and Chinese in the 25th century BCE, astronomers have been able to predict the motion of the Moon and the Sun and when eclipses would occur.

Eclipses on other planets

Solar eclipses do occur on other planets and moons in our Solar System, but as they don't have the size ratio we have between the Earth and our Moon, their eclipses are not as spectacular. Mercury and Venus cannot have eclipses as they do not have moons. Mars's two moons are too small to totally obscure the Sun, but the rovers on the Red Planet have photographed Phobos (the larger moon) moving in front of the Sun in a partial eclipse. We can witness eclipses on Jupiter with our back-garden telescopes, in the form of the shadows of its four major moons cast on the upper cloud layer of the planet. Astronomers call these 'shadow transits' and several can happen at once. We can also see Jupiter's moons go into eclipse in the shadow of Jupiter. Similar eclipses take place on all of the giant planets of the outer Solar System, and even on the dwarf planet Pluto where its largest moon Charon can eclipse the distant Sun a couple of times each century.

The shadow of the Jovian moon Ganymede can be seen transiting across the surface of gas giant Jupiter

Mercury

Compared to the other planets, we know relatively little about the smallest planet in our Solar System

Although we've been observing Mercury from Earth for thousands of years, its close proximity to the Sun – about 58 million kilometres, on average – has made it difficult for astronomers to learn much about the planet. The Hubble Space Telescope cannot observe it, because turning that close towards the Sun would damage the telescope's instruments. Most of what we know came from the 1975 Mariner 10 space probe's fly-by.

With the naked eye, Mercury can only be seen at dawn or dusk, depending on the time of year (unless there is a solar eclipse). This is due to the Sun's glare. Mercury can also be seen as a small black spot moving across the Sun at intervals of seven, 13 and 33 years. This is known as a transit of Mercury across the Sun and occurs when the planet comes between the Earth and the Sun.

Mercury has the shortest year of any planet at 88 Earth days. It also orbits around the Sun faster than any other planet, which is why it was named after the speedy Roman messenger god. Conversely, Mercury has the longest day of any planet due to its slow rotation. Because it revolves so quickly around the Sun, yet only rotates on its axis once every 59 Earth days, the time between sunrises on Mercury lasts 176 Earth days. Mercury also has the most eccentric, or stretched-out, elliptical orbit. Like our moon, Mercury can be observed going through apparent changes in its shape and size called phases. ✿

Surface
Mercury's surface is covered in tiny minerals called silicates

Outer core
It's hypothesised that Mercury has a liquid iron outer core

Atmosphere

Mercury has a very thin, almost airless atmosphere. At one time it was believed that the planet didn't have an atmosphere at all, but it does contain small concentrations of the gases helium, hydrogen and oxygen as well as calcium, potassium and sodium. Because of Mercury's size, it does not have a strong enough gravitational pull to keep a stable atmosphere. It is constantly being lost and replenished via solar wind, impacts and radioactive decay of elements in the crust.

Inside Mercury

A cross-section of the smallest planet in our Solar System

5 TOP FACTS
MERCURY

Heavily cratered surface
1 Although telescopes had revealed that Mercury looked much like our moon, the nearly 10,000 images recorded by Mariner 10 confirmed that it had a heavily cratered surface.

Lobate scarps
2 Mariner 10's images showed that Mercury was also covered in curved cliffs called lobate scarps, which formed when the planet's core cooled and shrank.

Ultraviolet radiation
3 Mariner 10 recorded large amounts of ultraviolet radiation near Mercury. It was eventually determined to come from a nearby star called 31 Crateris.

Magnetic field
4 The Mariner 10 space probe's instruments picked up a magnetic field on Mercury, which is rather similar to Earth's own magnetic field.

Exosphere
5 Mercury has an atmosphere like the exosphere on Earth – the upper layer of our planet's atmosphere. Its lightness and low density allows molecules to escape into space.

DID YOU KNOW? *Ancient Greeks believed that Mercury was two planets: one called Hermes and one called Apollo*

Terrestrial planet

Like Earth, Mercury is a rocky planet. It comprises about 70 per cent metal and 30 per cent silicate materials. Because Mercury is so dense – almost as dense as Earth, although it's much smaller – it probably has a very large, iron-rich core. Scientists believe that Mercury's core makes up almost half of the planet's total volume and three-fourths of its total radius. It also contains more molten iron than any other major planet in the solar system. The core is estimated to have a radius of about 1,800 kilometres, with a mantle about 600 kilometres thick and a crust about 300 kilometres thick. There are a few potential explanations for this large core. Mercury may have had a more substantial crust and mantle that were stripped away by high temperatures and solar wind from the Sun, or it could have been hit by a still-forming planet called a planetesimal.

Moon-like surface

The surface of Mercury looks much like the surface of our moon. The largest crater on Mercury is the Caloris Basin at 1,300 kilometres across. The impact caused lava eruptions and shockwaves that formed hills and furrows around the basin. Mercury also has two different types of plains. The smooth plains were likely formed by lava flows, while inter-crater plains may have been formed by lava or by impacts. The most unusual features are the wrinkles and folds across its plains and craters, caused by the cooling and contraction of the planet's core.

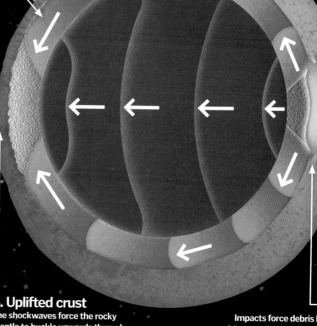

4. Shockwaves
Impacts with large meteorites actually send shockwaves through the core of the planet and around its perimeter

1. Meteorite impact
Mercury has been continually hit with comets and meteorites. The largest of these impacts have effects across the planet

2. Crater
Some craters are relatively shallow and narrow, but impacts with meteorites leave large craters

3. Ejecta
Impacts force debris high into the air on Mercury. Falling debris settles around the crater, creating an ejecta blanket

5. Uplifted crust
The shockwaves force the rocky mantle to buckle upwards through the crust, forming mountains

The Statistics
Mercury

© Science Photo Library

Diameter: 4,879 kilometres
Mass: 3.3022×10^{23} kilograms
Density: 5.427 grams per cubic centimetre
Average surface temperature: 179°C
Average distance from the Sun: 57,910,000 kilometres
Surface gravity: 0.38 g

Mantle
A rocky mantle, much like Earth's

Core
A huge iron core sits at the heart of the planet

Calori Montes
Mercury has several mountains known as montes, the tallest and largest of which are the Caloris Montes. This is a series of circular mountain ranges up to three kilometres in height located on the rim of the huge Caloris Basin. The Caloris Montes are massifs, formed when Mercury's crust flexed and fractured due to impact

Temperature extremes
While Mercury has an average surface temperature of around 179°C, temperatures on the planet fluctuate wildly depending on the location on the planet, the time of day and how close it is to the Sun in its orbit. At night, surface temperatures can go down to -170°C. During the day, they can reach 450°C. Some scientists believe that ice may exist under the surface of deep craters at Mercury's poles. Here temperatures are below average because sunlight cannot penetrate

Sizes...
Mercury's diameter is two-fifths that of the Earth, and its mass is slightly less than Earth's.

4,879km   12,756.3km

The transit of Mercury
Every seven, 13 and 33 years, Mercury can be seen as a black spot moving across the Sun

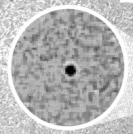

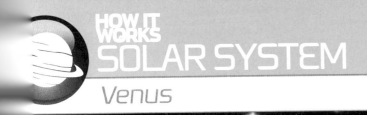
Venus

Discovering just how similar this planet actually is to Earth...

Venus has often been called Earth's sister planet because of their similarities. Both planets are terrestrial (meaning that they are made up of silicate rocks) and close in size, mass and gravity. Venus probably has a similar structure to Earth, with a crust, mantle and core. It has a diameter of around 12,000 kilometres, 650 kilometres smaller than Earth. Its mass is about 80 per cent of Earth's mass, and its gravity 90 per cent of Earth's gravity.

However, there are also many differences between Venus and Earth. Venus is about 108 million kilometres from the Sun and has an almost perfectly circular orbit, while all of the other planets have elliptical orbits. Venus completes one orbit every 225 days and has one of the slowest rotations of any planet, with one every 243 days. Venus's consistently high temperature means that it has no surface water.

The planet also has more than 1,500 volcanoes, many of which are more than 100 kilometres across. Most of the volcanoes are extinct, but some believe that there has been recent volcanic activity. Because Venus doesn't have rainfall, lightning could have been caused by ashy fallout from a volcanic eruption. These eruptions have created a rocky, barren surface of plains, mountains and valleys.

Venus is also covered with more than 1,000 impact craters. While Earth and other planets also have craters, Venus' are unusual because most of them are in perfect condition. They haven't degraded from erosion or other impacts. Venus may have experienced a massive event as much as 500 million years ago that resurfaced the planet and changed its atmosphere completely. Now bodies entering its atmosphere either burn up or are slowed down enough to avoid making a crater.

It has proven difficult to learn more about Venus, in part due to its dense atmosphere. Although probes first visited the planet in the early Sixties, it was not fully mapped by radar until the 1989 NASA Magellan probe. The Venus Express, launched by the European Space Agency in 2005, is a long-term exploration probe currently orbiting the planet and sending back

False colour view of Venus

Photographic view of Venus

5 TOP FACTS
VENUS

Venus has phases like a moon
1 When closest to the Earth, Venus appears bright and crescent-shaped. When it is further away, the planet is dim and round.

Venus rotates backwards
2 Venus has a retrograde, or west to east, rotation. This is actually the opposite direction of its revolution around the Sun.

Venus was the first 'probed' planet
3 NASA's Mariner 2 probe was launched in 1962. It passed within 30,000 kilometres of Venus and took microwave and infrared readings.

Venus doesn't have any moons
4 Venus probably had a moon billions of years ago, but it was destroyed when the planet's rotation direction was reversed.

Venus is brighter than the stars
5 Venus is brighter than any star and can be easily seen in the middle of the day, especially when the Sun is low in the horizon.

DID YOU KNOW? Because Venus shines so brightly, it has often been misreported as a UFO

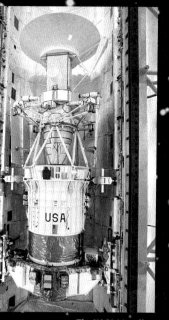
The NASA Magellan spacecraft

Venus' atmosphere
Immense pressure of the atmosphere

Venus's atmospheric pressure is greater than that of any other planet – more than 90 times that of Earth's. This pressure is equivalent to being almost one kilometre below the surface of Earth's oceans. The atmosphere is also very dense and mostly carbon dioxide, with tiny amounts of water vapour and nitrogen. It has lots of sulphur dioxide on the surface. This creates a Greenhouse Effect and makes Venus the hottest planet in the solar system. Its surface temperature is 461 degrees Celsius across the entire planet, while Mercury (the closest planet to the Sun) heats up to 426 Celsius only on the side facing the Sun.

Beneath the surface of Venus
What lies at the core of Earth's sister planet?

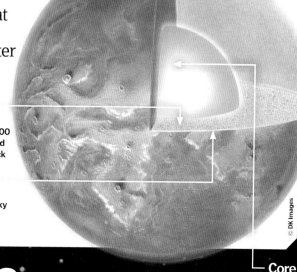

Mantle
Venus's mantle is probably about 3,000 kilometres thick and made of silicate rock

Crust
Venus likely has a highly basaltic, rocky crust about 100 kilometres thick

Core
Scientists believe that Venus's core is a nickel-iron alloy and partially liquid, with a diameter of 6,000 kilometres

© DK Images

Mapping Venus
Red indicates highland areas and blue indicates lower elevations in the false-colour view of Venus

1. Ishtar Terra
One of two 'continents', or major highland areas, on Venus, Ishtar Terra is located at the planet's North Pole. It is a little smaller than the continental United States

2. Maxwell Montes
Located on the north edge of Ishtar Terra, Maxwell Montes is the largest mountain range on Venus at nearly 11 kilometres high

3. Lakshmi Planum
This plateau in western Ishtar Terra rises about 3.5 kilometres above the surface of Venus. It is covered with lava flows

4. Guinevere Planitia
Venus is covered with regions of lowland plains such as Guinevere Planitia, which contains several volcanoes, impact craters and fissures

5. Beta Regio
Beta Regio is one of several volcanic rises on Venus' surface, more than 1,000 kilometres wide

The surface of Venus
Venus is covered in broad plains and elevated regions dotted by volcanoes

This computer-generated image shows a 7,500-kilometre-long region on the northern hemisphere of Venus known as Eistla Regio. It contains two volcanoes, Gula Mons on the right and Sif Mons on the left. Gula Mons is about three kilometres high and Sif Mons stands at two kilometres.

Sizes...
Venus and Earth are very similar in size. Venus's diameter is only 650km less than that of Earth, and the mass is 81.5 per cent of Earth's.

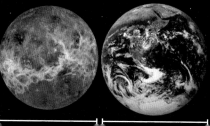

Earth   Venus

es courtesy of NASA

Olympus Mons

Ascraeus Mons

Valles Marineris

Claritas Rupes

Mars

Other than the fact that it's a planet in our Solar System, what do we really know about Mars?

To date there have been almost 50 missions to Mars, with around half of those being complete failures. Other than the Earth it is the most studied planet in the Solar System, and for centuries it has been at the heart of wild speculation and groundbreaking scientific discoveries. Observations of Mars have not only revealed otherwise unknown secrets but also posed new and exciting questions, and it is for these reasons that it has become the most intriguing planetary body of our time.

Named after the Roman god of war, Mars has fascinated astronomers since Nicolaus Copernicus first realised Mars was another planet orbiting the Sun in 1543. Its notable features such as huge impact craters, gullies and dormant volcanoes suggest it was once more geologically active than it is now, leading scientists to speculate on whether it supported water and life in the past, or indeed if it still does today. Astronomers in the 19th Century falsely believed they could see large oceans, and there were several reports of people receiving 'communications' from Martians in the form of bursts of light when they observed the planet through a telescope. Of course, we now have a better understanding of the planet, but we are still yet to unlock some of its most puzzling mysteries.

Mars sits 141 million miles (227 million km) from the Sun and takes 687 Earth days to orbit. As its orbital path is not in sync with Earth's it goes through a 26-month cycle of being closest (known as 'opposition') and furthest ('conjunction') from us, located at a distance of 35 million miles (56 million km) and 249 million miles (401 million km) respectively. This change in distance means spacecraft destined for Mars are sent in a launch window every 26 months, when Mars is closest to Earth. In November 2011, when NASA launched its new Mars rover, named 'Curiosity'. The journey time was upwards of six months, so Mars was actually closest on 3 March 2012.

Like all the planets in our Solar System, it is believed Mars formed about 4.5 billion years ago inside a solar nebula, when dust particles clumped together to form the planet. At just under half the size of Earth it's quite a small planet, which is accredited to Jupiter forming first. The gravitational forces of this gas giant consumed available material that would have otherwise contributed to Mars's growth, while Jupiter's gravity prevented another planet forming between Mars and Jupiter and instead left the asteroid belt. The northern hemisphere of Mars is significantly younger and lower in elevation than the southern hemisphere, suggesting the planet was struck by a Pluto-sized object early in its lifetime.

Mars is often referred to as something of a 'dead' planet. Indeed, its lack of folded mountains like those on Earth show that it has no currently active plate tectonics, meaning carbon dioxide cannot be recycled into the atmosphere to create a greenhouse effect. For this reason Mars is unable to retain

5 TOP FACTS
DISCOVERY OF MARS

1,500BC
1 Egyptians refer to Mars as 'Horus of the Hawk', a god with the head of a hawk. They note its retrograde motion, when it moves backwards in its orbit relative to Earth.

350BC
2 Aristotle first proposes that Mars orbits at a further distance than the Moon when he notes that the Moon passes in front of Mars in his observations.

1609
3 Galileo Galilei uses a telescope to become the first person to observe Mars, but is later vilified by the Vatican for asserting that the planets orbit the Sun and not Earth.

1666
4 Astronomer Giovanni Cassini calculates the length of a Martian day, notes the polar ice caps and even calculates its distance from Earth in his telescopic observations.

1840
5 Astronomers Wilhelm Beer and Johann Heinrich Mädler study Mars through a 3.75-inch telescope and produce the first sketched map of its surface.

DID YOU KNOW? Of the nine 21st Century missions to Mars only Beagle 2 has failed

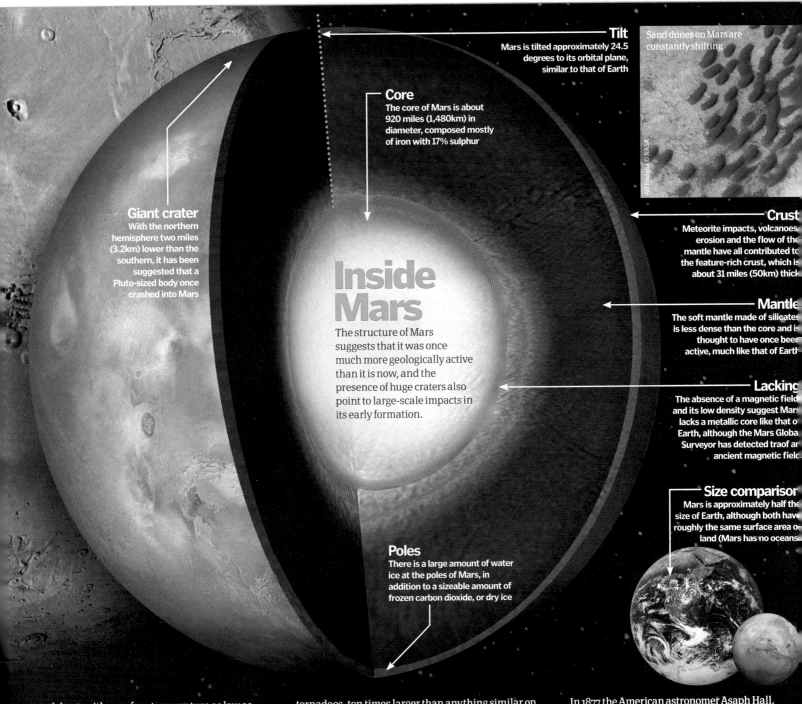

Tilt
Mars is tilted approximately 24.5 degrees to its orbital plane, similar to that of Earth

Sand dunes on Mars are constantly shifting

All images © NASA

Core
The core of Mars is about 920 miles (1,480km) in diameter, composed mostly of iron with 17% sulphur

Giant crater
With the northern hemisphere two miles (3.2km) lower than the southern, it has been suggested that a Pluto-sized body once crashed into Mars

Inside Mars
The structure of Mars suggests that it was once much more geologically active than it is now, and the presence of huge craters also point to large-scale impacts in its early formation.

Crust
Meteorite impacts, volcanoes erosion and the flow of the mantle have all contributed to the feature-rich crust, which is about 31 miles (50km) thick

Mantle
The soft mantle made of silicates is less dense than the core and is thought to have once been active, much like that of Earth

Lacking
The absence of a magnetic field and its low density suggest Mars lacks a metallic core like that of Earth, although the Mars Global Surveyor has detected traof an ancient magnetic field

Size comparison
Mars is approximately half the size of Earth, although both have roughly the same surface area of land (Mars has no oceans)

Poles
There is a large amount of water ice at the poles of Mars, in addition to a sizeable amount of frozen carbon dioxide, or dry ice

much heat, with a surface temperature as low as -133°C at the poles in the winter, rising to 27°C on the day side of the planet during the summer.

Despite this, the atmosphere of Mars offers conclusive evidence that it was once geographically active. The outer planets in the Solar System have atmospheres composed of predominantly hydrogen and helium, but that of Mars contains 95.3% carbon dioxide, 2.7% nitrogen and 1.6% argon, with minimal traces of oxygen and water. This strongly suggests that volcanoes once erupted across its surface and spewed out carbon dioxide, further evidenced by giant mountains such as Olympus Mons that appear to be dormant volcanoes.

It might not be geologically active, but Mars does play host to some extreme weather conditions, most notably the appearance of dust devils. These

tornadoes, ten times larger than anything similar on Earth, can be several miles high and hundreds of metres wide, creating miniature lightning bolts as the dust and sand within become electrically charged. The wind inside one of these, though, is almost unnoticeable, as the atmospheric pressure on Mars is so low. Interestingly, one of the reasons for the long survival rate of NASA's Mars rovers is that these dust devils have been cleaning their solar panels, allowing them to absorb more sunlight.

Mars's gravity is about 38% that of Earth, with just 10% of the mass. The surface pressure is just over 100 times weaker than ours at sea level, meaning that a human standing on the surface would see their blood instantly boil. The red colour on Mars's surface is the result of rusting, due to iron present in the rocks and soil reacting with oxygen to produce an iron oxide

In 1877 the American astronomer Asaph Hall, urged on by his wife, discovered that Mars had two moons orbiting so close that they were within the glare of the planet. They were named Phobos and Deimos, after the attendants of Ares in the Iliad. Interestingly, the moons are not spherical like most other moons; they are almost potato-shaped and only about ten miles wide at their longest axis, indicating that they are the fragments of the collision of larger objects near Mars billions of years ago. Phobos orbits Mars more than three times a day, while Deimos takes 30 hours. Phobos is gradually moving closer to Mars and will crash into the planet within 50 million years, a blink of an eye in astronomical terms. The moons have both been touted as a possible base, from which humans could observe and travel to Mars.

Farming on alien planets

Mars and the Moon could be new places to grow food

Believe it or not, the soil found on the Moon and Mars could be much more fertile than some of the dirt found on Earth. If we are ever to go on to colonise other worlds – with the Red Planet being our number-one target – then this is very good news for astronauts.

It's thanks to a team of scientists in the Netherlands, who have braved volcanoes in Hawaii and Arizona to obtain material akin to Martian dirt and lunar soil, to provide us with the information that could help humans one day settle on an alien planet. Both soils have the essential ingredients plants need to grow – nitrates and ammonium.

The experts found – by using 'fake' minerals from Mars and the Moon to try and grow carrots, tomatoes, weeds and wheat – that untreated soil found on Mars was the plant's favourite. On the other hand, Moon dirt didn't agree with them completely, with some crops struggling to grow.

All's not lost for crop farming on the Moon, though – scientists think that pumping our natural satellite's soil with nitrogen-fixing bacteria could be the ticket for growing crops on our cratered companion. ❂

Growing food on Mars and the Moon could hugely benefit plans to colonise other worlds

The V1 star

A star that changed the entire universe

In a galaxy, not too far away, resides a star that changed how we saw the universe back in the early-20th century. Its name is Hubble variable number one, or V1 for short, and it told us that there were more galaxies beyond our own. At first it highlighted Andromeda – the star's home and the closest spiral galaxy to ours – soon dubbed 'island universes' beyond the boundary of our galaxy, the Milky Way.

It was soon realised that this star was no ordinary one. Because of its predictable brightening, caused by stellar gas heating and expanding before cooling and contracting in a cycle, this object was soon dubbed a Cepheid variable. These stars help us to measure distances farther and farther out into the universe. By working out how long it takes for a variable star to brighten and dim, we can work out how bright the star would be if we were up close to it. ❂

Dec. 17, 2010
Dec. 21, 2010
Dec. 30, 2010
Jan. 26, 2011

The Andromeda galaxy (M31) hosts Cepheid variable star V1, which brightens and dims periodically

THE STATS
JUPITER

140,000km AVERAGE DIAMETER	16,500km GREAT RED SPOT SIZE	10 HOURS IN A DAY
-145°C LOWEST TEMPERATURE	AVERAGE WIND SPEED 360km/h	HIGHEST TEMPERATURE 35,500°C

DID YOU KNOW? 17th-century astronomer Giovanni Cassini called the Great Red Spot the "Eye of Jupiter"

Weather on Jupiter

The forecast is raging storms and swirling winds

If you've ever moaned about the weather, you can count yourself lucky that you don't live on Jupiter. The majority of the planet is formed of hydrogen and helium gases. The clouds, however, are made up of ammonia ice crystals.

The temperature range on Jupiter is pretty incredible. The clouds that hover above the surface of the planet are a freezing -145 degrees Celsius (-229 degrees Fahrenheit), but as you move closer to the core it reaches a scorching 35,000 degrees Celsius (63,000 degrees

Fahrenheit). And if that doesn't sound quite bad enough, then the weather conditions on the surface of the planet are almost guaranteed to put you off.

We spoke to expert Pedram Hassanzadeh, an Environmental Fellow at Harvard University: "The atmosphere of Jupiter has two prominent visible features", he explains. "These are strong winds that form multiple jets of alternating direction between the equator and the poles, and hundreds of hurricane-like swirling winds known as vortices. The average speed of the jets

can be more than 360 kilometres (224 miles) per hour. For comparison, Earth has two prominent eastward jets in each hemisphere and their average speed is about 100 kilometres (62 miles) per hour."

If, having seen the wild temperature changes, the mind-boggling winds and dramatic tornadoes, you are still keen to visit Jupiter, Hassanzadeh has one more word of advice for any potential tourists: "Jupiter does not have a solid surface, which would make life on the planet kind of hard."

The Great Red Spot

One of the best-known features of Jupiter, apart from its size, is the Great Red Spot. First recorded in 1831 and consistently observed for more than 100 years, the weather system measures about 16,500 x 14,000 kilometres (10,250 x 8,700 miles). Hassanzadeh explains what the Great Red Spot actually is: "It consists of strong swirling winds with a maximum speed of 700 kilometres (435 miles) per hour. It's not clear how the Great Red Spot was created, but vortices are common in rapidly rotating environments such as the atmosphere of the gas giants."

The Great Red Spot is notable as it has been raging for centuries, much longer than any other similar space tornadoes. However, Hassanzadeh has a theory as to how it has kept going for so long: "It has been speculated that the Great Red Spot has survived by extracting potential energy from the atmosphere and the kinetic energy of the jets, along with absorbing smaller vortices."

Temperature
The temperature of Jupiter can range from a chilly -145°C (-229°F) to a super-hot 35,000°C (63,000°F)

Composition
The majority of Jupiter is made up of hydrogen and helium gas

Ammonia crystals
Above the surface of Jupiter is a thick layer of cloud made up of ammonia ice crystals

Core
It's thought Jupiter could potentially have a solid or molten core

Rotating jets
Jets of wind move in alternating directions, whipping up storms such as the Great Red Spot

Vortices
The winds swirling in opposite directions create vortices, which are rapidly rotating tornadoes

Winds
Winds on the planet can reach up to 700km/h (435mph), driven by the rotating jets

© NASA; Corbis

041

When Galileo Galilei discovered Jupiter in 1610, it is doubtful that he was aware of the impact this giant planet had on the surrounding Solar System. From altering the evolution of Mars to preventing the formation of a ninth planet, the size and mass of Jupiter has seen it exert an influence on its neighbours second only to the Sun.

Jupiter's mass and composition almost more closely resemble a star than a planet, and in fact if it was 80 times more massive it would be classified as the former. It can virtually be regarded as being the centre of its own miniature Solar System; 50 moons to date are known to orbit the gas giant, with the four largest (Io, Europa, Ganymede and Callisto, the Galilean satellites) each surpassing Pluto in size.

The comparison of Jupiter to a star owes a lot to the fact that it is composed almost entirely of gas. It has a large number of ammonia-based clouds floating above water vapour, with strong east-west winds in the upper atmosphere pulling these climate features into dark and light stripes. The majority of its atmosphere, however, is made up of hydrogen and helium.

The strength of Jupiter's gravity is such that it is held responsible for much of the development of nearby celestial bodies. The gravitational force of the gas giant is believed to have stunted the growth of Mars, consuming material that would have contributed to its size. It also prevented a new planet forming between these two and instead gave rise to the asteroid belt.

Much of our knowledge of Jupiter comes from seven spacecraft missions to visit the planet, starting with NASA's Pioneer 10 in 1973. The only man-made object to orbit the planet is the Galileo spacecraft, which studied the planet from 1995 until 2003, when it was sent crashing into Jupiter so as not to contaminate its moons with the debris.

Jupiter

We take a look inside the most massive planet in our Solar System

NASA's Jupiter orbiter Juno launched on its five-year journey in 2011

All Images © NASA

ORBIT RADIUS 778,340,821km		**RADIUS** 69,911km		**ONE YEAR** 11.86yrs	
GRAVITY 24.79m/s²		**ESCAPE VELOCITY** 214,200km/h		**ONE DAY** 9.92hrs	

DID YOU KNOW? *The Greeks and later the Romans named the gas giant after their most important deities – Zeus and Jupiter*

Jupiter's anatomy

Metallic hydrogen
A third of the way into the planet can be found hydrogen gas that has been compressed into a metallic and electrically conducting liquid

Atmosphere
The large majority of the atmosphere is composed of hydrogen and helium gas, directly observed by the Galileo space probe that pierced its atmosphere in 1995

Core
At the core of Jupiter is an Earth-sized rock, although this has not been directly observed as it is almost impossible to see through the thick atmosphere

Aurora
An intense radiation belt of electrons and ions are trapped by Jupiter's magnetic field, influencing Jupiter's rings and its surrounding moons

Magnetic field
The magnetic field of Jupiter is 20,000 times stronger than Earth's, containing a huge number of charged particles that contribute to giant auroras at its north and south poles

Magnetosphere
The tail of Jupiter's magnetosphere (the influence of its magnetic field) stretches more than 1 billion kilometres (600 million miles) away from the Sun, out to the orbit of Saturn

Molecular hydrogen

Ring structure
The rings consist of a main, flat ring and an inner cloud-like ring, known as a halo, with both made from small, dark particles kicked up by meteorites hitting Jupiter's moons

Rings
NASA's deep-space Voyager 1 spacecraft surprised astronomers in 1979 when it found rings encircling Jupiter. The rings are only visible in sunlight

The auroras at Jupiter's poles are bigger than Earth

Gap

Halo

Main Ring

Jupiter's faint ring system was the third to be discovered in the solar system

Moons of Jupiter
Jupiter's four largest moons are known as the Galilean satellites, named after their discoverer Galileo Galilei

Io

Europa

Ganymede

Callisto

This photograph of Jupiter, with the Red Spot visible at the centre, was taken by NASA's Voyager 2 on 29 June 1979, as it flew past at a distance of almost 9 million kilometres (6 million miles)

The Great Red Spot
One of Jupiter's most iconic features is the Great Red Spot, a storm more than twice the size of Earth that has been raging for hundreds of years. The redness is believed to be the result of compounds being brought up from deeper inside Jupiter, which turn brown and red upon exposure to the Sun. Although once highly elliptical in shape, it has become squashed in recent years for unknown reasons and is expected to become circular other the next few decades, although this anti-cyclonic storm shows no sign of dying out any time soon.

Inside Saturn

Saturn is believed to have a small rocky core, with a temperature of more than 11,000°C. It is surrounded by a layer of gases and water, followed by a metallic liquid hydrogen and a viscous layer of liquid helium and hydrogen. Near the surface, the hydrogen and helium become gaseous. Saturn has no solid surface.

Inner layer
This thickest layer surrounding the core is liquid hydrogen and helium

Wave-like structures in the clouds can be seen in Saturn's atmosphere

Saturn

Only Jupiter is larger than this gas giant, best known for its ring system

 We've been viewing Saturn with the naked eye since prehistoric times, but the planet's most unique feature – its ring system – wasn't discovered until 1610. Each ring contains billions of chunks of dust and water-ice. Saturn has about 14 major ring divisions, but there are also satellites and other structures within some of the rings and gaps. Saturn's rings are believed to have come from the remains of moons, comets or other bodies that broke up in the planet's atmosphere.

The rings aren't the only fascinating thing about Saturn, however. This gas giant is less dense than any other planet in our solar system and has a mostly fluid structure. It radiates a massive amount of energy, thought to be the result of slow gravitational compression. Saturn takes about 29.5 years to revolve around the Sun, and its rotation is a bit more complex – different probes have estimated different times, the latest estimate is ten hours, 32 minutes and 35 seconds. The variations probably have something to do with irregularities in the planet's radio waves, due to the similarities between its magnetic axis and its rotational axis.

Saturn has a cold atmosphere comprising layered clouds of both water-ice and ammonia-ice. It also has winds of up to 1,800 kilometres per second. Occasionally Saturn has storms on its surface, similar to those of Jupiter. One such storm is the Great White Spot, a massive storm in the planet's northern hemisphere that has been observed about once every Saturnian year since 1876. ✿

Outer layer
The outer layer is gaseous hydrogen and helium, blending with its atmosphere

Rings in view

Saturn takes 29.5 years to orbit the Sun, and it has an elliptical orbit like most planets. The closest Saturn comes to the Sun is 1.35 billion kilometres, while at its furthest, Saturn is 1.5 billion kilometres away. Saturn has a tilt of 26.7 degrees relative to the orbital plane. During half of its orbital period, the northern hemisphere is facing the Sun, while the southern hemisphere faces the Sun during the other half. When viewing Saturn from Earth, this impacts whether we can see the rings full-on or as a thin line.

North pole tilt
The northern hemisphere is visible with the rings appearing below

Both hemispheres
Both hemispheres are visible with the rings appearing as a thin line

Orbit
Saturn has an elliptical orbit of 29½ years

South pole tilt
The southern hemisphere is visible from Earth with the rings above

DID YOU KNOW?

Discovering the rings
Galileo thought that he was seeing moons orbiting Saturn instead of rings because his telescope was not powerful enough. Astronomer Christiaan Huygens observed the rings in 1655, but thought they were a single ring.

DID YOU KNOW? Images from the Cassini probe show that Saturn has a bright blue northern atmosphere

The Statistics
Saturn

Diameter: 120,535 km
Mass: 5.6851 x 10^{26} kg
Density: 0.687 grams per cm^3
Average surface temperature: -139°C
Core temperature: 11,000°C
Moons: 62
Average distance from the Sun: 1,426,725,400km
Surface gravity: 10.44 metres per second squared

Extreme bulge
Saturn is an extreme example of an oblate spheroid – the difference between the radius of the planet at its poles and at its circumference is about ten per cent. This is due to its very short rotational period of just over ten hours.

Inner core
The inner core is likely very small and contains silicate rock, much like Jupiter's core

Cassini probe
The first spacecraft to ever orbit Saturn, the Cassini probe has provided incredible images of the planet and its ring system

Float that planet
If we had a big enough pond, we could float Saturn on its surface. Although Saturn is the second-largest planet as well as the second-most massive, it's the least-dense planet in our solar system. Its density is just 0.687 grams per cubic centimetre, about one-tenth as dense as our planet and two-thirds as dense as water.

Outer core
Saturn's outer core is much thicker than its inner core, containing metallic liquid hydrogen

Saturn's southern storm
In 2004, the Cassini space probe discovered a massive, oddly shaped convective thunderstorm in Saturn's southern atmosphere. Dubbed the Dragon Storm, this weather feature emitted strong radio waves. Like storms on Earth, the Dragon Storm emits flashes of lightning that appear as white plumes. Scientists believe it exists deep in the atmosphere and can occasionally flare up.

An artist's impression of Saturn's ring particles

Rings
Saturn's rings comprise particles of ice and dust that range from microscopic to several thousand kilometres in diameter

What are Saturn's rings?

The mysteries of how Saturn's rings were formed are only now revealing themselves to us...

While both Neptune and Uranus can boast of being encircled by a stellar crown of sorts, it's Saturn that is the true 'lord of the rings'. Neptune's five relatively thin rings are so small that they weren't definitively discovered until 1968, while Uranus's narrow bands were discovered even later, in 1977. By contrast, Galileo was the first person to view Saturn's rings over 400 years ago using a simple telescope.

Six of its seven rings span from 74,500 kilometres (46,300 miles) to 140,220 kilometres (87,130 miles) above the surface of Saturn, while its diffuse E ring is truly gigantic at around 300,000 kilometres (186,000 miles) wide – nearly the distance between the Earth and the moon.

Most of the rings are primarily composed of water ice that ranges in size from tiny droplets micrometres across to large chunks the size of houses. Icy moons like Enceladus that orbit Saturn help seed the enormous E ring by spouting water slush and organic compounds from beneath its frozen crust into the atmosphere and way beyond. Rock particles of a similar size, but much greater mass than the ice particles, can also be found within the rings.

One theory is that Saturn's main rings, A, B and C – the first ones that were discovered – were actually created much earlier than had been previously thought. Rather than at the time of the formation of the solar system, space scientists think the rings may have been formed a few hundred million years ago when a large moon or asteroid was broken apart by Saturn's gravity. ✪

Saturn's rings close up

Moonlets

The Cassini-Huygens mission has thrown new light on the formation of Saturn's moons. Some of the smallest moonlets that measure less than 50 kilometres (31 miles) across should have been destroyed by comets if they were captured by Saturn's gravity at the formation of the Solar System, as per the old theory. Using data collected by the Cassini probe, a computer simulation suggests that the ice in the rings can piece together into large enough lumps to come under the influence of their own gravity, then continue to grow as Saturn pushes them out on a gravitational tide. It also helps explain why the biggest moons are farthest from the gas giant.

2x © NASA

Uranus

Seventh planet from the Sun, third-largest and fourth most massive in the Solar System. Uranus was the first planet to be discovered by telescope

Four times the size of Earth and capable of containing 63 Earths inside it (it is only 14.5 times as dense however, as it is a gas giant), Uranus is the third largest and forth most massive planet in our Solar System. Appearing calm and pale blue when imaged, Uranus has a complex ring system and a total of 27 moons orbiting its gaseous, cloudy main body. Due to its distance from the Sun the temperature at the cloud-top layer of the planet drops to -214°C and because of its massive distance from Earth it appears incredibly dim when viewed, a factor that led to it not being recognised as a planet until 1781 by astronomer William Herschel. ⚙

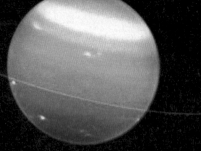

1. Atmosphere
Uranus's blue colour is caused by the absorption of the incoming sunlight's red wavelengths by methane-ice clouds. The action of the ultraviolet sunlight on the methane produces haze particles, and these hide the lower atmosphere, giving the planet its calm appearance. However, beneath this calm façade the planet is constantly changing with huge ammonia and water clouds carried around the planet by its high winds (up to 560mph) and the planet's rotation. Uranus radiates what little heat it absorbs from the Sun and has an unusually cold core

2. Rings
Uranus's 11 rings are tilted on their side, as viewed from Earth, and extend from 12,500 to 25,600km from the planet. They are widely separated and incredibly narrow too, meaning that the system has more gap than ring. All but the inner and outer rings are between 1km and 13km wide, and all are less than 15km in height. The rings consist of a mixture of dust particles, rocks and charcoal-dark pieces of carbon-rich material. The Kuiper Airborne Observatory discovered the first five of these rings in 1977

Upper atmosphere, cloud tops

Core
Made up of rock and ice

Inside Uranus
A cross-section of the blue planet

Oberon
The first Uranian moon to be discovered

Umbriel
The darkest of the major moons, reflecting only 16 per cent of light

Titania
Uranus' largest moon appears grey with an icy surface

Ariel
The brightest and with the youngest surface of

Miranda
Features a scarred, piecemeal structure

© DK Images

5 TOP FACTS
URANUS

Old man
1 Uranus is named after the Greek deity of the same name who, in Greek mythology, was Zeus's grandfather and the father of Cronus.

Passing wind
2 Uranus is one of the solar system's most windy planets, with speeds that can reach up to a monumental 250 metres per second.

Bonus
3 Upon discovering Uranus, William Herschel was gifted an annual stipend of £200 by King George III, on the condition he moved to Windsor.

Elementary
4 The element uranium was named in dedication to the discovery of Uranus eight years prior to the element's discovery in 1789.

Lone ranger
5 The only space probe to examine Uranus to date w the Voyager 2 in 1986, wh passed with 82,000km of planet's cloud-tops.

DID YOU KNOW? *Many of Uranus' moons are named after characters from the plays of Shakespeare*

Miranda is littered with impact craters and is heavily scarred with faults

Miranda

The smallest and innermost of Uranus's five major moons, Miranda is like no other moon in our Solar System

When the Voyager 2 passed by Uranus in 1986 it not only observed the planet but also many of its moons, coming close to its innermost Miranda at a distance of 32,000km. However, the images it recorded were not what were expected as on closer inspection it showed the satellite's surface consisted of a series of incongruous surface features that seemed to have been crushed together and butted up unnaturally. Miranda was an ancient terrain that seemed to have been constructed from various smaller segments from different time periods, instead of forming as one distinct whole at one time. Scientists have theorised that this was probably caused by a catastrophic collision in the moon's past that caused it to shatter into various pieces before then being reassembled in this disjointed way.

Verona Rupes
Found on Uranus' moon Miranda, this cliff face is estimated to be ten kilometres deep, almost ten times the depth of the Grand Canyon. This makes it the tallest known cliff in the entire Solar System

Atmosphere
Consists of hydrogen, helium and other gasses

Mantle
A large layer of water, methane and ammonia ices

4. Orbi
Uranus takes 84 Earth years to complete a single orbit around the Sun, through which it is permanently tilted on its side by 98 – a factor probably caused by a planetary-sized collision while it was still young. Due to its sideways tilt, each o the planet's poles points to the Sun for 21 years at a time, meaning that while one pole receive continuous sunlight, the other receive continuous darkness. The strength of the sunlight that Uranus receives on its orbit is 0.25 per cent of that which is received on Earth. There is a difference of 186 million kilometres between Uranus's aphelion (furthest point on an orbit from the Sun) and perihelion (closest point on an orbit

3. Structure
Uranus consists of three distinct sections an atmosphere of hydrogen, helium and other gases, an inner layer of water methane and ammonia ices, and a small core consisting of rock and ice. Electric currents within its icy layer are postulated by astronomers to generate Uranus's magnetic field, which is offset by 58.6° from the planet's spin axis. Its large layers of gaseous hydrogen and constantly shifting methane and ammonia ices account for the

Sizes...
Uranus' diameter is nearly five times that of Earth, with a mass that's equivalent to 14 and a half Earths

12,756.2

51,110

Neptune

The smallest and coldest of the four gas giants, as well as the most distant from the Sun, Neptune is the windiest planet in our Solar System

Over 4.5 billion kilometres from Earth and with an average temperature of -220°C, Neptune is the furthest planet from the Sun and the coldest in our Solar System, excluding the dwarf planet Pluto. It is a massive (49,532km in diameter) sphere of hydrogen, helium and methane gas, formed around a small but mass-heavy core of rock and ice that, despite its similar size and structure to its inner neighbour Uranus, differs in appearance dramatically, presenting its turbulent, violently windy atmosphere on its surface. Find out what makes Neptune so unique and volatile right here. ✿

A gigantic storm the size of Earth

Inside Neptune
A cross-section of the smallest gas giant

5. Dark spot
The Great Dark Spot, a gigantic, dark storm the size of Earth, was captured on film by the Voyager 2 spacecraft as it passed by Neptune in 1989. Storms of this size and magnitude are believed by scientists to be relatively common on this volatile, windy planet. However, when the Hubble Space Telescope tried to image the Great Dark Spot in 1996 it had disappeared

5 TOP FACTS
NEPTUNE

True blue
1 Neptune's eye-catching deep blue colouring is caused by the methane gas in its atmosphere, absorbing red light and reflecting blue.

Gale force
2 Around its equatorial region Neptune is privy to winds in excess of 1,340 miles per hour as well as extremely violent storms.

Belt buster
3 Due to the fast nature of Neptune's spin around its axis, its equatorial region is 527 miles larger in diameter than at its poles.

Son of god
4 Neptune's one major moon is actually named, funnily enough, after his Greek counterpart Poseidon's son, Triton.

The four seasons
5 Neptune undergoes seasons just like here on Earth. However, they last 40 years each instead of just the three months we're used to.

DID YOU KNOW? Neptune is not visible to the naked eye, with a small telescope necessary to discern it as a star-like point of light

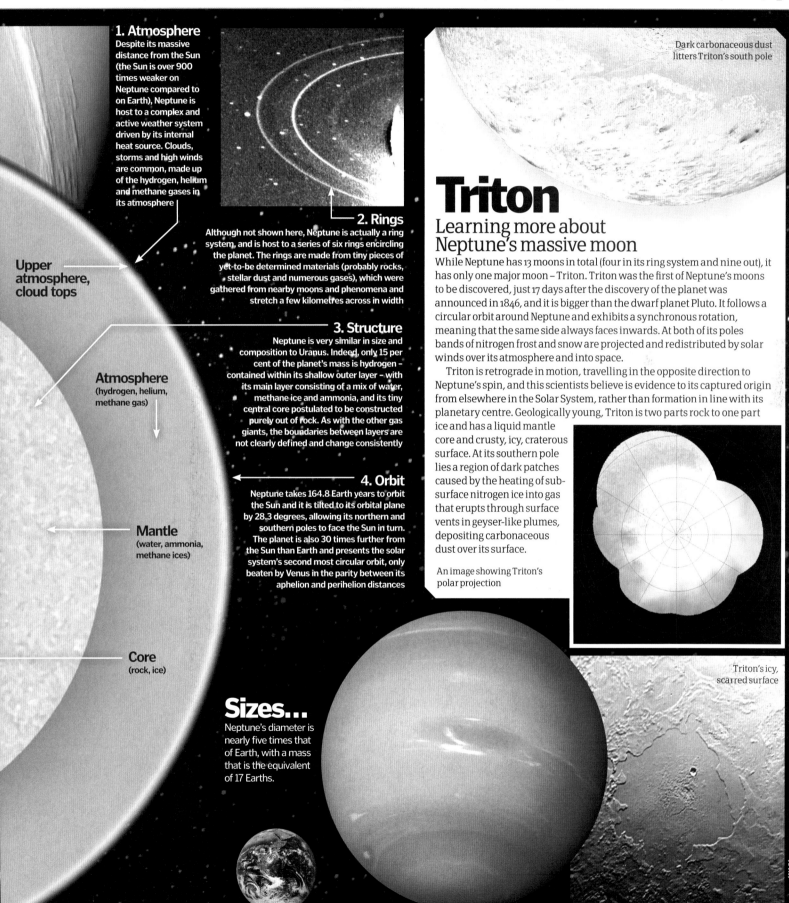

1. Atmosphere
Despite its massive distance from the Sun (the Sun is over 900 times weaker on Neptune compared to on Earth), Neptune is host to a complex and active weather system driven by its internal heat source. Clouds, storms and high winds are common, made up of the hydrogen, helium and methane gases in its atmosphere

Upper atmosphere, cloud tops

Atmosphere (hydrogen, helium, methane gas)

Mantle (water, ammonia, methane ices)

Core (rock, ice)

2. Rings
Although not shown here, Neptune is actually a ring system, and is host to a series of six rings encircling the planet. The rings are made from tiny pieces of yet-to-be determined materials (probably rocks, stellar dust and numerous gases), which were gathered from nearby moons and phenomena and stretch a few kilometres across in width

3. Structure
Neptune is very similar in size and composition to Uranus. Indeed, only 15 per cent of the planet's mass is hydrogen – contained within its shallow outer layer – with its main layer consisting of a mix of water, methane ice and ammonia, and its tiny central core postulated to be constructed purely out of rock. As with the other gas giants, the boundaries between layers are not clearly defined and change consistently

4. Orbit
Neptune takes 164.8 Earth years to orbit the Sun and it is tilted to its orbital plane by 28.3 degrees, allowing its northern and southern poles to face the Sun in turn. The planet is also 30 times further from the Sun than Earth and presents the solar system's second most circular orbit, only beaten by Venus in the parity between its aphelion and perihelion distances

Dark carbonaceous dust litters Triton's south pole

Triton
Learning more about Neptune's massive moon
While Neptune has 13 moons in total (four in its ring system and nine out), it has only one major moon – Triton. Triton was the first of Neptune's moons to be discovered, just 17 days after the discovery of the planet was announced in 1846, and it is bigger than the dwarf planet Pluto. It follows a circular orbit around Neptune and exhibits a synchronous rotation, meaning that the same side always faces inwards. At both of its poles bands of nitrogen frost and snow are projected and redistributed by solar winds over its atmosphere and into space.

Triton is retrograde in motion, travelling in the opposite direction to Neptune's spin, and this scientists believe is evidence to its captured origin from elsewhere in the Solar System, rather than formation in line with its planetary centre. Geologically young, Triton is two parts rock to one part ice and has a liquid mantle core and crusty, icy, craterous surface. At its southern pole lies a region of dark patches caused by the heating of sub-surface nitrogen ice into gas that erupts through surface vents in geyser-like plumes, depositing carbonaceous dust over its surface.

An image showing Triton's polar projection

Triton's icy, scarred surface

Sizes...
Neptune's diameter is nearly five times that of Earth, with a mass that is the equivalent of 17 Earths.

12,756.3km

49,532km

Images courtesy of NASA

Neptune's boomerang moon

Meet the natural satellite with the most eccentric orbit of any moon in the Solar System

Nereid is Neptune's third-largest moon behind Triton and Proteus. It has a diameter of approximately 340 kilometres (210 miles) and its most interesting characteristic is that it has the most fluctuating orbit of any moon in the Solar System.

The second of the planet's moons to be discovered, its orbit is so changeable it can vary from 9.65 million kilometres (6 million miles) away from the planet to just 1.37 million kilometres (854,000 miles) at its closest position.

Astronomers are divided when it comes to the reason for its eccentric trajectory but one school of thought is that the satellite was captured from the Kuiper asteroid belt in the outer Solar System, which explains its unusual orbit.

Further, Nereid, which has a surface composed primarily of ice and silicon, reflects only 14 per cent of light that it receives so human observation is problematic. It is so faint that Voyager 2 could only take a low-resolution image of it when it passed in 1989. ✿

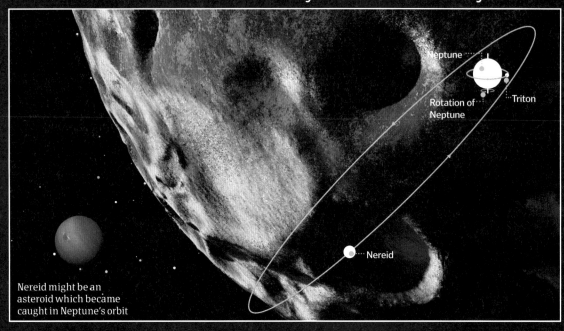

Neptune
Rotation of Neptune
Triton
Nereid

Nereid might be an asteroid which became caught in Neptune's orbit

Three of Neptune's less wayward moons

Triton
The first to be discovered and by far the largest, Triton is the king of Neptune's moons. Bigger than Pluto, it orbits the planet in a retrograde motion, which is the opposite direction to Neptune. It is made of rock and ice.

Proteus
The second largest, Proteus also has the farthest orbit of any of Neptune's six inner moons. Proteus is significantly smaller than Triton, with its diameter being a measly 440km (273mi) compared to Triton's 2,707km (1,681mi).

S/2004 N 1
New moons are still being spotted. The biggest cluster was during Voyager's visit in 1989 when almost half of the moons were found. The latest satellite – s/2004 N 1 – was only discovered in July 2013 by the Hubble Space Telescope.

Mercury's orbit

The Solar System's innermost planet travels through a curvature in the fabric of space-time

Of all the Solar System's planets, Mercury has the most eccentric orbit. Moving in an ellipse its distance from the Sun varies from 46 million kilometres (28.6 million miles) to 70 million kilometres (43.5 million miles) across its entire orbital cycle.

Not only does Mercury travel in an ellipse, but the planet's closest approach to the Sun is not always in the same place. Mercury's orbit drifts, with each ellipse around the Sun seeing it move along slightly, tracing a shape similar to the petals of a daisy (see picture).

This drifting is partially caused by the gravitational pull of local bodies; the Sun, of course, has the most influence, but other planets and asteroid belts can also have an effect, dictating its path.

However only part of Mercury's drift is accounted for by the gravitational pull of the other objects near Mercury. The orbit can only be fully explained by Einstein's general theory of relativity.

The Sun's gravitational field distorts the fabric of space and time, forming a curvature. This distorted space geometry also affects the route Mercury takes around the Sun. ✿

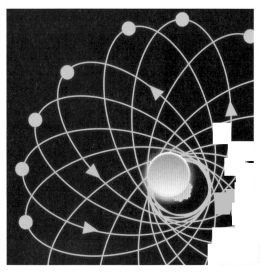

The secrets of transits

From the planet Venus to alien worlds hundreds of light years away, transits help inform us about our place in the universe

Twice every century the planet Venus does something extraordinary and appears to move, or 'transit', across the face of the Sun. It is a rare alignment of Earth's orbit with Venus' and the Sun, but in the 18th century scientists used transits of Earth's hellish cousin to measure the size of the Solar System. The most recent transits of Venus in 2004 and 2012 had relatively little scientific importance, but transits of other planets are extremely significant. These are not transits of other planets in our Solar System, but in other star systems. Astronomers detect transits of exoplanets across stars and have found over 1,000 alien worlds this way.

As the stars are so far away, planet hunters like the Kepler space telescope can't take a picture of the exoplanet's silhouette like astronomers could for Venus. Instead they monitor how much of the starlight the planet blocks as it moves across the face of its star. Kepler is able to detect dips in the star's light as small as 0.01 percent. The amount of light blocked reveals how big the exoplanet is, the length of time it takes to transit tells the astronomers what orbit the planet is on and how far away it is from its star. With this information, astronomers can work out the planet's temperature and what kind of planet it is. Astronomers have not yet found Earth's twin, but such a discovery may not be too far away. ✿

Transit of Venus
What are we seeing through the telescope?

Eight-hour transit
The speed at which a planet transits a star tells us how far from the star the planet is, assuming we know how big the star is. Venus takes less than eight hours to transit the Sun

Measuring angles
By comparing the difference in time that Venus was observed to begin transiting the Sun from different locations, 18th-century scientists were able to measure its parallax angle

Solar observing
Members of the public were able to view the recent Venus transits using solar telescopes or safe solar projection

Out in the universe
Transits don't just happen when Venus passes across the Sun, astronomers find exoplanets by watching them move across the face of their star

Sizing up the Solar System

Scientists took on the task of calculating the scale of the Solar System by observing the transits of Venus in 1761 and 1769, using a clever method called parallax. To see how this works, hold your index finger up about a foot in front of your face. Close one eye, then open it and close the other. Your finger appears to move, but in reality your eyes are seeing it from different angles. By timing the transits of Venus from different parts of the world and comparing how the times differed, they consequently estimated how far away the Sun is - about 149.6mn km (93mn mi).

Blocking out light
When a planet blocks out light, we are able to measure its size and figure out what type of planet it is – a gas giant or rocky world – through independent calculations

Kepler has used transit observations to discover almost 1,000 confirmed exoplanets

In the right place
In order for us to be able to see a transit, we – or a spacecraft – must be in the right place at the right time so the planet passes between our viewing point and its star

© ESA/CNES/D. Ducros; Alamy

Pluto

The elusive Planet X that became an ex-planet and still has many X factors

The astronomer Percival Lowell predicted the existence of a ninth planet in our solar system, beyond the orbit of Neptune. Lowell failed to find Planet X in his lifetime, but Clyde Tombaugh – using the Lowell Observatory in Arizona – confirmed his calculations. Shortly after Planet X's discovery back in January 1930 it was named Pluto. In 1978, however, it was determined that Lowell's theory based on the mass of Pluto and its effects on Uranus and Neptune were incorrect. Tombaugh's discovery was just a very lucky coincidence.

The dwarf planet Pluto takes a leisurely 248 years to orbit the Sun. Its highly elliptical orbit takes it to a maximum of 7.4 billion kilometres from the sun (at aphelion, or farthest from the Sun) to as close as 4.5 billion kilometres (at perihelion, or closest to the Sun). Twice in this orbit it is actually closer to the Sun than Neptune, as was the case from January 1979 to February 1999.

All the other planets orbit on the plane of the ecliptic, but Pluto's orbit is at an inclination of 17 degrees to this plane. Pluto is also unusual because it rotates at an angle of 122 degrees to its own axis, in a clockwise direction. This retrograde motion means it is spinning in an opposite direction to its counter-clockwise orbit around the Sun.

So far, even the Hubble Space Telescope has only obtained grainy pictures of its surface, and it is not until the arrival of the New Horizons spacecraft in 2015 that we should know more about this small, distant and very cold body. ✿

Surface
A rocky surface covered by frozen nitrogen, methane and carbon monoxide

Mantel 2
If Pluto has a hot radioactive core, then there could be a 180-kilometre thick liquid water ocean between the core and the outer mantel

Inside Pluto
So far, we know little about the composition of Pluto. Ice beneath Pluto's surface might cause movement and changes on the surface, in the same way glaciers do on Earth.

Surface details

Using observations by the Hubble Space Telescope, and maps produced since the Eighties, it has been found that the surface of Pluto undergoes many large variations in brightness and colour.

From 1994 to 2003, the southern hemisphere darkened, while the northern hemisphere got brighter. It has a slightly less red colour than Mars, with an orange cast similar to Jupiter's moon Io. It got redder from 2000 to 2002, and other colour variations of dark orange, charcoal black and white have been observed. These seasonal variations are regarded as being due to the orbital eccentricity and axial tilt of Pluto that are reflecting topographic features and the flux of the frozen surface of the planet with its rarefied atmosphere.

Core
This is about 1,700 kilometres in diameter. It is mainly composed of iron-nickel alloy and rock. At its centre might be hot radioactive material or ice

Mantel 1
Composed of rock and water ice

© DK Images

5 TOP FACTS
PLUTO

Finding Pluto
1 Clyde Tombaugh systematically photographed the sky and checked 1.5 million stars recorded by his photographic plates before he found Pluto.

Naming Pluto
2 Venetia Burney, an 11-year-old schoolgirl in Oxford, put forward the name Pluto. She picked it after the Roman god of the underworld. Her reward was a £5 note.

Nix and Hydra
3 The Hubble Space Telescope discovered these moons of Pluto in 2005. Nix orbits Pluto at a distance of 48,000 kilometres and Hydra, 65,000 kilometres.

Kuiper Belt
4 Pluto is part of a cluster of Kuiper Belt Objects (KBOs) that orbit beyond Neptune. It consists of icy and rocky objects that failed to form into planets.

Triton
5 It was thought that Pluto was a satellite of Neptune. This is no longer regarded as possible, but Pluto does have many characteristics similar to Neptune's moon, Triton.

DID YOU KNOW? *Out of 1,000 names suggested for Planet X, three were shortlisted: Minerva, Cronus and Pluto*

The Statistics
134340 Pluto

Diameter: 2,320 kilometres
Mass: 1.3×10^{22} kilograms
Density: 2 grams per cubic centimetre
Average surface temperature: -230°C or -382°F (44K)
Core temperature: Unknown
Average distance from the Sun: 5,913,520,000 kilometres (39.5 AU)
Surface gravity: 0.067g
Moons: 3

© NASA

Atmosphere

When Pluto's elongated orbit takes it relatively close to the Sun, the frozen nitrogen, methane and carbon monoxide on its surface sublimates into a tenuous gaseous form. This creates winds and clouds, but the weak gravitational force of Pluto means that it can escape into space and interact with its moon, Charon.

In the process of sublimation an anti-greenhouse effect is created, which lowers the temperature of Pluto to -230°C against the expected -220°C, which is the temperature of Charon. In the lower atmosphere, a concentration of methane creates a temperature inversion that makes the upper atmosphere warmer by three to 15 degrees every kilometre upwards. On average, the upper atmosphere is 50°C warmer than the surface of Pluto.

When Pluto's orbit takes it away from the Sun, the gaseous atmosphere freezes and falls to the surface.

An example of the anti-greenhouse effect visible on Titan, Saturn's largest moon

© NASA

Charon

Pluto's closest moon is Charon, which was discovered in 1978. It is 19,640 kilometres from Pluto, so from Earth they look like one planet. Charon has the same 6.4 day rate of rotation as Pluto so they always present the same face to each other. On Pluto, the surface facing Charon has more methane ice than the opposite face, which has more carbon monoxide and nitrogen ice.

Charon has a diameter of 1,210 kilometres, and has a grey surface with a bluer hue than Pluto. This indicates the surface could be covered in water ice rather than nitrogen ice. It is also speculated that methane has leaked from the grasp of its weak gravity to Pluto.

An artist's impression of the New Horizons craft

Sizes
Earth diameter:
8,000 miles
Pluto diameter:
1,400 miles

What is a planet?

Pluto's status as a planet was safe until the Nineties. This was when huge 'hot Jupiter' extra-solar planets were discovered, and objects were observed beyond the orbit of Neptune that rivalled the size of Pluto. Faced with the dilemma of defining a planet the International Astronomical Union (IAU) decided that it must be spherical, that it orbits the Sun and is clear of any planetary neighbours. Consequently, the IAU reclassified Pluto as a dwarf planet on the 24 August 2006.

An image of Pluto, with Charon visible to the bottom-left

© NASA

Plutoids

Plutoids, as defined by the IAU, are dwarf planets that orbit the Sun beyond Neptune, are round, have not cleared the neighbourhood of other similar bodies, and are not satellites of another planetary body. There could be at least 70 trans-Neptunian objects (TNOs) that might be plutoids.

So far only a few have been found and named. Besides Pluto, Makemake, Haumea and Eris have been classified as plutoids. Mike Brown and his Caltech team at the Palomar Observatory discovered them all in 2005. Eris is virtually the same size as Pluto and might have been regarded as a planet before the new classification system came into effect.

Europa

Our greatest chance of finding life is possibly on this moon of Jupiter

One of Jupiter's four largest moons – the others being Io, Ganymede and Callisto – Europa is notable for its icy surface with a theorised ocean underneath. The moons all keep the same face towards Jupiter as they orbit. The layer of ice that encapsulates Europa's entire surface is as little as 5-100 miles thick. It has one of the smoothest surfaces in the solar system, with its features such as valleys and hills no larger or deeper than a few hundred metres. This suggests it is young and still actively forming like Earth.

Most of Europa is made of rock, although its core has a large iron content. Gravitational forces from Jupiter and its other three largest moons have given Europa a hot interior in a process known as tidal heating, similar to how tides are created on Earth as our moon stretches and pulls the oceans. Europa has a very thin atmosphere made of just oxygen created by particles emitted from the radiation of Jupiter striking the surface and producing water vapour.

Due to there being almost no atmosphere on Europa, which is not much smaller than our moon, the temperature on the surface drops to -162°C at the equator and possibly as low as -220°C at the poles. Absolute zero is not much colder at -273.15°C. A few miles down into Europa's ocean, the temperature could still be as cold as -30°C or as high as 0°C, meaning that any life would have to adapt to these freezing temperatures.

The large amount of radiation Jupiter exerts can severely damage any probe attempting to reach Europa. One of the only missions to study the moon was the Galileo space probe, named after the astronomer Galileo who discovered Jupiter's four largest moons in one week in 1610. It journeyed between Jupiter and its moons from 1995 to 2003, providing much of the information we know about Europa today. ✿

This picture, taken by the Cassini spacecraft, shows Europa casting a shadow on Jupiter

Into the core

Composition
The core of Europa is made of metal, specifically iron and nickel

Images courtesy of NASA

THE STATS
EUROPA

| YEAR OF DISCOVERY | **1610** | ORBIT OF JUPITER | **55 days** | MEAN DISTANCE FROM JUPITER | **70,900k** |
| DIAMETER | **3,122km** | MEAN ORBITAL VELOCITY | **13.74km/second** | | |

DID YOU KNOW? The Galileo probe, which studied Europa, was sent crashing into Jupiter so it didn't contaminate nearby mo

Life on Europa

The lack of impact craters on the surface of Europa but the presence of fissures and cracks means that something other than meteorites must be fracturing and altering the ice. This has led scientists to believe there is an ocean of water beneath the icy surface of Europa. It is in this ocean where life could reside. Previously, it was thought animals required sunlight to live, but the discovery of creatures living off small bacteria at the bottom of Earth's oceans have raised the possibility that animals as large as fish could be living below Europa's surface. There are two main theories as to how Europa's ocean could look, shown in the 'Under the surface' boxout.

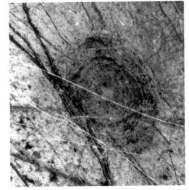

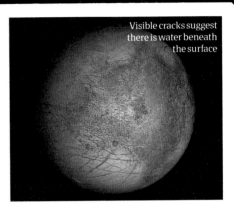

Visible cracks suggest there is water beneath the surface

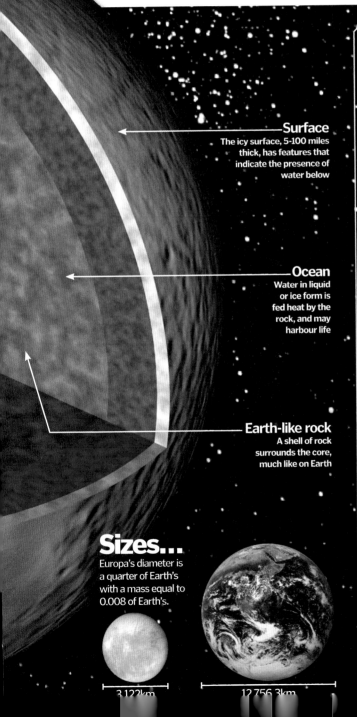

Surface
The icy surface, 5-100 miles thick, has features that indicate the presence of water below

Ocean
Water in liquid or ice form is fed heat by the rock, and may harbour life

Earth-like rock
A shell of rock surrounds the core, much like on Earth

Sizes...
Europa's diameter is a quarter of Earth's with a mass equal to 0.008 of Earth's.

3,122km

12,756.3km

Under the surface
The two theories of Europa's structure

Thin ice sheet

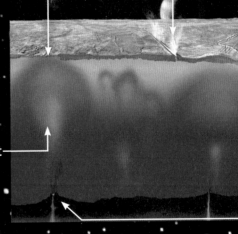

Chaos
What appear to be ice blocks on the surface of Europa, known as "chaos", may be the result of heating under the ice

Vapour
In this theory, the ice on the surface cracks and may let out water vapour as it is heated from below

Rising heat
The heat rises up through the oxygenated water, in which organisms could live

Volcanoes
The bed of the ocean may contain volcanoes, which spurt out hot gas from the core of the moon

Thick ice sheet

Tides
Additional heat is created by tidal heating, which forces the lower layer of ice into the surface

Jupiter
Europa's ecliptic orbit of Jupiter could be the cause of tidal heating in its core, moving the ocean up and down and thus releasing water vapour

Core
If the ice shell is very thick, heat from the core will transfer to this lower portion of the icy surface

Moving
This heat could move the lower ice layer like a tectonic plate and be the cause of the lines on Europa's surface, rather than simply volcanic heat

Dwarf planets

What is a dwarf planet and how is it distinguished from other celestial bodies?

When is a planet not a planet? Well, it's not as simple as you might think. Defining a planet into a particular category isn't easy, with the debate continuing to rage as to how exactly planets should be classified. According to the International Astronomical Union (IAU), dwarf planets are spherical objects in orbit around the Sun that are not moons, but they share their orbits with other debris which they have not been able to clear. It was the latter point that let Pluto down back in 2006, as it has other bodies within its orbit that it has not gathered. In addition, many bodies were discovered that were larger than Pluto, such as Eris, ultimately leading to its reclassification.

In simple terms, a dwarf planet can be regarded as a spherical object in our solar system exhibiting all or some of the properties of a planet, but lacking the necessary gravitational strength to have pulled other local objects into its influence.

There are currently five recognised dwarf planets in our solar system – these being Pluto, Eris, Makemake, Haumea and Ceres – but dozens more in the Kuiper belt, a disc-shaped region beyond Neptune, and the Oort cloud at the outer edge of the solar system, are being considered as candidates.

The five official dwarf planets and their unofficial brothers vary drastically in both composition and appearance, just as the main eight planets of the solar system do. Pluto is the only one of the five known to have its own moon – Charon, while Eris is the coldest of the bunch (and, indeed, the coldest known object in the solar system), with its surface temperature reaching as low as -250 degrees Celsius (-418 degrees Fahrenheit). Also of note is the dwarf planet Ceres, once regarded as a large spherical asteroid but recently promoted. Despite being the smallest dwarf planet, it is the largest object in the asteroid belt between Mars and Jupiter where it resides, accounting for about a quarter of the entire belt's mass. ⚙

Size
Ceres has a diameter of 942km (585mi), which is just over one quarter the size of our moon

Mantle
It is estimated that Ceres' 100km (60mi)-thick mantle contains up to 200 million cubic kilometres (48 million cubic miles) of water-ice – one-seventh of the total volume of water on Earth

© NASA

How do the dwarf planets size up to Earth?

Mercury · Venus · Earth · Mars · Jupiter · Saturn · Uranus · Neptune

Stats
Haumea

Diameter:
1,436km (892mi)

Distance from Sun:
6.5 billion kilometres (4 billion miles)

Orbital period: 283 years

Stats
Earth

Diameter:
12,742km (7,918mi)

Distance from Sun:
150 million kilometres (93 million miles)

Orbital period: 1 year

Stats
Ceres

Diameter:
942km (585mi)

Distance from Sun:
414 million kilometres (275 million miles)

Orbital period: 4.6 years

Stats
Pluto

Diameter:
2,306km (1,433mi)

Distance from Sun:
5.9 billion kilometres (3.7 billion miles)

Orbital period: 248 years

CELEBRITY

1. Pluto
Once regarded as the ninth planet of our solar system, Pluto is now classified as a dwarf planet because it lives alongside similar-sized entities in the Kuiper belt.

CHILLY

2. Eris
The coldest known planetary object in the solar system, the surface temperature on Eris (also found in the Kuiper belt) can drop as low as -250°C (-418°F).

CLOSEST

3. Ceres
Found in the asteroid belt between Jupiter and Mars, Ceres is the closest dwarf planet to Earth but also the smallest, just one-quarter the size of our moon.

DID YOU KNOW? In December 2011 the first planet smaller than Earth – Kepler-20e – was found outside the solar system

Inside Ceres
What's going on within the smallest dwarf planet in our solar system?

Surface
Ceres' surface bears marks of previous meteorite impacts and, despite having only a thin atmosphere, its surface temperature is about -38°C (-36°F) due to it being relatively near to the Sun, almost three times Earth's distance from the Sun

Core
Ceres has a solid rocky core. It is thought that it may once have had a hot and molten core like that of Earth, but its small size means it is unlikely that volatile material is still present due to its high rate of heat loss

Stats
Makemake
Diameter:
1,500km (932mi)

Distance from Sun:
6.9 billion kilometres (4.3 billion miles)

Orbital period: 310 years

Stats
Eris
Diameter:
2,326km (1,445mi)

Distance from Sun:
10.1 billion kilometres (6.3 billion miles)

Orbital period: 557 years

NASA's Dawn spacecraft will be the first to visit a dwarf planet, arriving at Ceres in 2015

WHAT TYPE OF PLANET ARE YOU?
Are you a terrestrial planet, a gas giant or a dwarf planet? Or something else? Have a go at our flowchart below to find out...

START
ARE YOU IN ORBIT AROUND THE SUN?
YES / NO

YOU ARE... AN EXTRASOLAR PLANET
You are not from our solar system, and yet to be properly classified. You could be a super-Earth, or maybe you're made entirely of diamond. Nobody knows; you'll just have to wait to be found. Mysterious.

ARE YOU SPHERICAL?
YES / NO

YOU ARE... A MOON
You are a natural satellite that orbits a planet/dwarf planet. You might be the only moon or you may be one of many. You were pulled into orbit during the planet's formation and are considerably smaller than your host. Clingy.

YOU ARE... AN ASTEROID
You are a prolific potato-shaped rocky object. You're probably located in either the asteroid belt between Jupiter and Mars or the Kuiper belt beyond Uranus, where more than 90 per cent of your kind live. Sociable.

ARE YOU ICY?
YES / NO

YOU ARE... A TERRESTRIAL PLANET
You could be one of the rocky planets Mars, Earth, Venus or Mercury. You have a molten iron core and an atmosphere. On Venus, the climate is super-hot, but Mercury's is very cold. Atmospheric.

ARE YOU ALSO IN ORBIT AROUND A PLANET?
YES / NO

YOU ARE... A COMET
You're an irregular shape made mostly of ice, which melts and forms a dust tail. You have a separate tail composed of gas that always flows away from the Sun regardless of which direction you are travelling. Breezy.

HAVE YOU CLEARED YOUR NEIGHBOURHOOD?
YES / NO

YOU ARE... A GAS GIANT
You may be Jupiter, Saturn, Uranus or Neptune, the giants composed mostly of gas. You've cleared away all objects in your vicinity and exert an influence on everything around you due to your extremely high mass. Powerful.

YOU ARE... A DWARF PLANET
You're bigger than an asteroid and spherical but generally smaller than a 'proper' planet. You don't orbit anything but the Sun, however you haven't managed to clear all local debris (or it hasn't yet formed into moons). Weakling.

ARE YOU MOSTLY MADE OF ROCK?
YES / NO

Auroras on other planets

Find out what causes these magnificent light shows on the other planets in our Solar System

For many years, the auroras seen on our planet were thought to be the souls of the dead moving to the afterlife. An aurora on Earth is actually caused by the Sun and can be thought of as a form of space weather. Solar winds hit Earth with highly charged particles, but our planet's magnetic field deflects most of them before they reach the atmosphere. Every so often these winds are boosted by solar flares or coronal mass ejections, which release huge amounts of plasma. When these intense solar winds reach Earth, some of the ionised particles get trapped in the magnetic field. These particles are then accelerated along the field lines toward the poles where they can enter the upper atmosphere, colliding with gas particles that cause them to emit bright light. This process creates the mesmerising aurora borealis and aurora australis, more commonly known as the northern lights and the southern lights respectively.

On Jupiter, Saturn, Uranus and Neptune, auroras form in a similar manner to how they form on Earth. However, on Mars and Venus they form very differently, as neither of these planets possess a significant magnetic field. ✿

You can clearly see the difference in the magnetospheres of Venus (top) and Mars (bottom) compared to Earth

NASA's Mars Atmosphere and Volatile Evolution (MAVEN) spacecraft observing the 'Christmas Lights Aurora' on Mars

Venus

Similar to Mars, Venus does not possess its own planetary magnetic field, but flashes of light from the planet have been identified as auroras. Scientists have found that the same process that causes auroras on Earth can form a gigantic magnetic bubble around Venus, allowing auroras to occur. This is possible due to Venus having a magnetotail, which was formed by ionosphere and solar wind interaction. The fact that magnetic reconnection can occur within Venus' magnetotail suggests auroras are the cause of the light that scientists have observed emitting from this planet.

Mars

On Mars, auroras appear near areas of magnetised rock within the planet's crust rather than near the poles, when charged solar particles concentrate toward them. This is because it lacks a self-generated magnetic field, possessing only 'crustal magnetic anomalies'. Scientists found that the location of the light emissions corresponded with the location of the strongest magnetic fields found on Mars. It is thought these anomalies are the last traces of Mars's planetary magnetic field, which it displayed at some time in its history. This type of aurora formation is totally unique to Mars as far as scientists are aware.

"On Jupiter, Saturn, Uranus and Neptune, auroras form in a similar manner to how they form on Earth"

Saturn's auroras occur near the planet's poles, much like they do on Earth

Saturn

Saturn's auroras differ from Earth's in their size; they can stretch to amazing heights of 1,000 kilometres (621 miles) above Saturn's cloud tops. The charged particles come from the Sun's solar winds blasting past the planet. The particles smash into hydrogen in Saturn's polar atmosphere, ionising the gaseous atoms, which causes photons to be released and leads to the aurora. This planet's auroras are actually not visible to the human eye, due to the fact that the emitted light lies in an infrared and ultraviolet spectrum we can't see. It's thought that as on Jupiter, Saturn's moons may also influence the auroras.

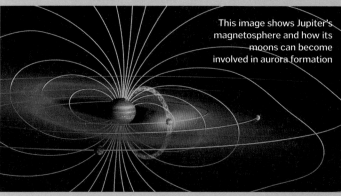

This image shows Jupiter's magnetosphere and how its moons can become involved in aurora formation

Jupiter

Although some of the auroras found on Jupiter form in a similar manner to those on Earth, many are formed due to the trapping of particles within its own magnetic environment. Unlike Saturn's main aurora that changes size as the solar winds vary, Jupiter's main auroral ring maintains a constant size. This is due to its formation through interactions within its own magnetic environment. Jupiter's moons are also believed to be able to influence auroras. Io, Jupiter's volcanic moon, is thought to produce gases that travel into Jupiter's atmosphere, where they can contribute to the planet's aurora formation.

Uranus has a mass over 14 and a half times that of Earth's

Uranus

The presence of auroras on Uranus was detected in 2011 by the Hubble Space Telescope. It is thought this was possible due to heightened solar activity during this period, which increased the amount of charged particles carried in solar winds from the Sun. The auroras formed on this giant ice planet appear far away from the north and south poles, unlike on Earth. This is because of the planet's magnetic field, which is inclined at an angle of 59 degrees to the axis of its spin. These auroras are fainter than their Earth counterparts and last only a couple of minutes, unlike those on our planet, which may last for hours at a time.

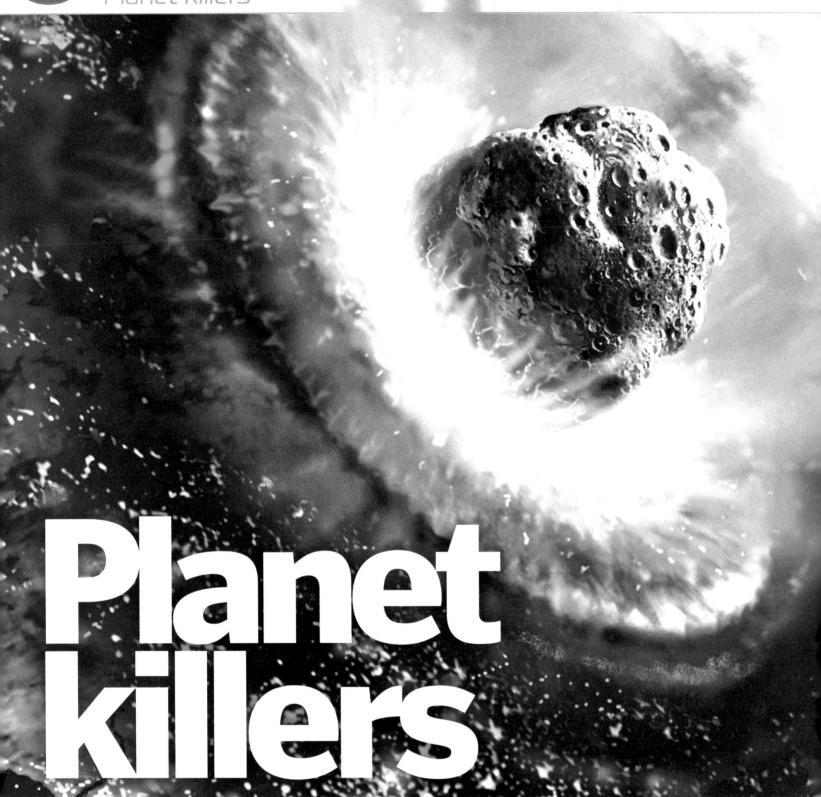

Planet killers

Remnants of failed planets, asteroids are dry, dusty and atmosphereless rocks drifting through space

Asteroids are the most numerous bodies in our Solar System, with hundreds of thousands of them orbiting around the Sun in both belts and as individuals. They far outnumber our well-documented planets (and dwarf planets, to that matter) and are being studied by space agencies world wide, each of which are trying to shed some light on what historically were written off as simple floating rocks. However, asteroids are unique in the fact that they tell us much about the conditions of the universe post-big bang, how astrophysics effect space phenomena and how planets are formed, granting the scientific community great insight into our Solar System's origins and workings.

FAIL
1. Asteroid
The city of Dallas, Texas, is going to be destroyed by an asteroid – the American government fires huge lasers to destroy it but only succeed in breaking it into small pieces that still go on to destroy the city.

BIG FAIL
2. Armageddon
Another asteroid is on course to destroy the world – the American government hatches a plan to plant a bomb in its core to split in two so it will miss Earth. However, an earlier meteorite destroys Shanghai, China.

EPIC FAIL
3. Deep Impact
Yet another asteroid is on a collision course with the Earth – the American government detonates nuclear bombs to destroy it but only succeed in splitting it in two pieces, one of which destroys ¼ of the planet.

DID YOU KNOW? The first probe dedicated to studying asteroids was the NEAR Shoemaker, launched by NASA in 1997

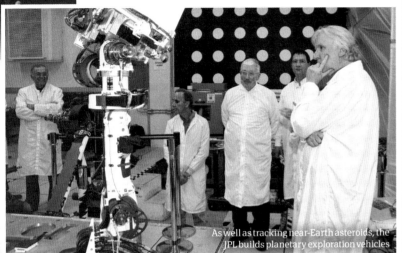

As well as tracking near-Earth asteroids, the JPL builds planetary exploration vehicles

Structures

There are three types of asteroid: carbonaceous (C-type), siliceous (S-type) and metallic (M-type) variants, each corresponding to the composition of an asteroid, be that stony, stony-iron or iron. The composition of an asteroid – be that shape or material – is dependent on when and what it was formed from, as well as if it has undergone reconstruction post collision.

Initially, at the dawn of the Solar System, most asteroids were much larger than now commonly found by astronomers, with sizes more consistent with a planet such as Mars and shapes varying wildly. However, the radioactive decay of elements within the asteroid rock melted these larger bodies, and during their fluid stage, gravity pulled them into spherical shapes before they cooled. At this point, though, many smaller asteroids – which cooled more efficiently than their larger brethren – did not reach melting point and retained their uniform rocky-metallic composition and their initial irregular shape.

This process of asteroid formation can be seen vividly when contrasting many of the asteroids that modern scientists and astronomers are currently studying. Take the asteroid Ceres (Ceres was the first asteroid to be discovered and is now considered by some astronomers as a dwarf planet) for example – this is a large asteroid (it has an equatorial radius of 487km) and, in turn, is both spherical in structure and carbonaceous composition (C-class), as it was pulled apart easily and cooled slowly. However, if you compare Ceres to Ida for example, which is a small asteroid (it has a mean radius of 15.7km), you find the latter is both irregular in shape (funnily, it looks like a potato) and heavily composed of iron and magnesium-silicates (S-class).

Orbits

The majority of asteroids in our Solar System are found in a concentration known as the main belt, which lies between Mars and Jupiter. This belt contains thousands of asteroids and takes roughly four and a half years to orbit the Sun on a slightly elliptical course and low inclination. Despite the fact that they all orbit in the same direction, collisions do occur at low velocities (for such large objects) and these cause the asteroids to be continuously broken up into smaller variants. Of this main belt, certain groups have been captured into peculiar orbits, such as the Trojan group of asteroids that follow Jupiter's orbit, or the Amor or Apollo groups, which cross the paths of Earth and Mars respectively and the Aten group, which sits inside Earth's own orbit.

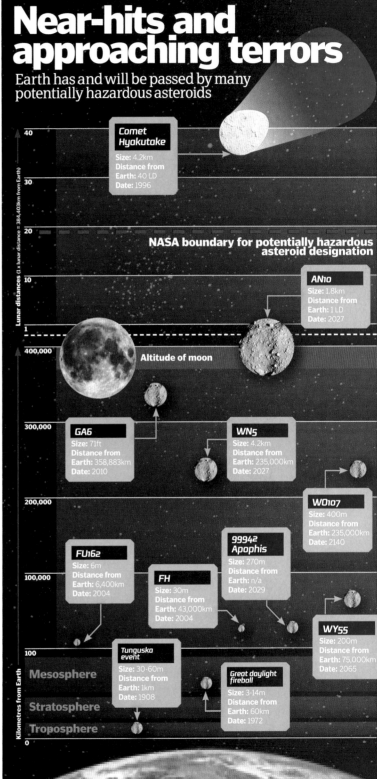

Near-hits and approaching terrors
Earth has and will be passed by many potentially hazardous asteroids

Lunar distances (1 x lunar distance = 384,403km from Earth)

Comet Hyakutake
Size: 4.2km
Distance from Earth: 40 LD
Date: 1996

NASA boundary for potentially hazardous asteroid designation

AN10
Size: 1.8km
Distance from Earth: 1 LD
Date: 2027

Altitude of moon

GA6
Size: 71ft
Distance from Earth: 358,883km
Date: 2010

WN5
Size: 4.2km
Distance from Earth: 235,000km
Date: 2027

WO107
Size: 400m
Distance from Earth: 235,000km
Date: 2140

FU162
Size: 6m
Distance from Earth: 6,400km
Date: 2004

FH
Size: 30m
Distance from Earth: 43,000km
Date: 2004

99942 Apophis
Size: 270m
Distance from Earth: n/a
Date: 2029

WY55
Size: 200m
Distance from Earth: 75,000km
Date: 2065

Kilometres from Earth

Mesosphere

Tunguska event
Size: 30-60m
Distance from Earth: 1km
Date: 1908

Stratosphere

Great daylight fireball
Size: 3-14m
Distance from Earth: 60km
Date: 1972

Troposphere

Asteroids in our Solar System

Saturn's orbit

Jupiter's orbit

Earth's

Mars's orbit

Main belt →

Direction of orbits

Most of the asteroids in our Solar System are positioned between the orbits of Mars and Jupiter, clustered in massive belts. However, some come close to Earth on their individual orbits and these are referred to as near-Earth asteroids. We take a look at some of the most notable...

A gravity map of the asteroid Eros. Blue indicates a low gravity slope, red a high slope

Eros

Dimension: 16.84km
Aphelion: 266.762Gm (1.783 AU)
Perihelion: 169.548Gm (1.133 AU)
Orbital period: 643.219 days
Escape velocity: 0.0103km/s
Temperature: -227K
Spectral type: S

With a one-in-ten chance of hitting either Earth or Mars in the next million years, Eros is one of the largest and well-studied near-Earth asteroids. In fact, Eros is one of a few asteroids to actually be landed upon by an Earth probe, and as such we have a cavalcade of information on it.

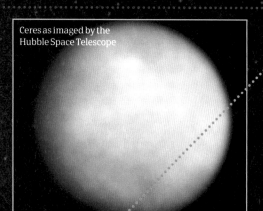

Ceres as imaged by the Hubble Space Telescope

Ceres

Dimension: 590 miles **Aphelion:** 446,669,320km (2.9858 AU) **Perihelion:** 380,995,855km (2.5468 AU) **Orbital period:** 1,680.5 days **Escape velocity:** 0.51km/s **Temperature:** -167K **Spectral type:** C

Technically classed as a dwarf planet, Ceres – named after the Roman goddess of growing plants and the harvest – is by far the most massive body in the asteroid belt. Indeed, it is so big compared to its neighbouring asteroids that it contains 32 per cent of the belt's total mass.

Icarus

Dimension: 1.4km **Aphelion:** 294.590Gm (1.969 AU) **Perihelion:** 27.923Gm (0.187 AU) **Orbital period:** 408.778 days **Escape velocity:** 0.000 74 km/s **Temperature:** -242K **Spectral type:** U

Icarus is from the Apollo asteroid sub-class of near-Earth asteroids and has the unusual characteristic that at its perihelion it is closer to the Sun than Mercury. Named after the Icarus of Greek mythology, the asteroid passes by Earth at gaps of nine, 19 and 38 years.

How to deflect an impact...

Nuclear explosion

1. Nuclear explosions
This method involves firing a nuclear bomb into the asteroid. Problems may occur if the explosion just splits the asteroid into smaller pieces.

2. Multiple explosions
Detonating multiple nuclear bombs close to impact would push the asteroid to one side and onto another, non-Earth destroying trajectory.

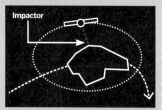

Impactor

3. Kinetic impactor
Similar to the last option, this method would involve firing a solid projectile into an asteroid in order to alter its momentum and change its course.

5 TOP FACTS
ASTEROIDS

Naked
1 The only asteroid in the main belt visible to the naked eye is Vesta, which has a mean diameter of 530km and contains nine per cent of the entire asteroid belt's mass.

Coma
2 The way comets and asteroids are distinguished relies on visual appearance, with comets displaying a perceptible coma behind them while asteroids have none.

Naming
3 Once an asteroid has been discovered it can only be named under the consultation of the International Astronomical Union, who will approve or disapprove the proposition.

Photo
4 The first true asteroids to be photographed close up were Gaspra in 1991 and Ida in 1993. They were imaged by the Galileo space probe en route to Jupiter.

New
5 The latest asteroid to be landed on is Itokawa, an S-type asteroid that crosses the path of Mars. The Hayabusa space probe returned to Earth with a surface sample.

DID YOU KNOW? The asteroid Ida has its own moon, Dactyl, which orbits at a distance of 56 miles

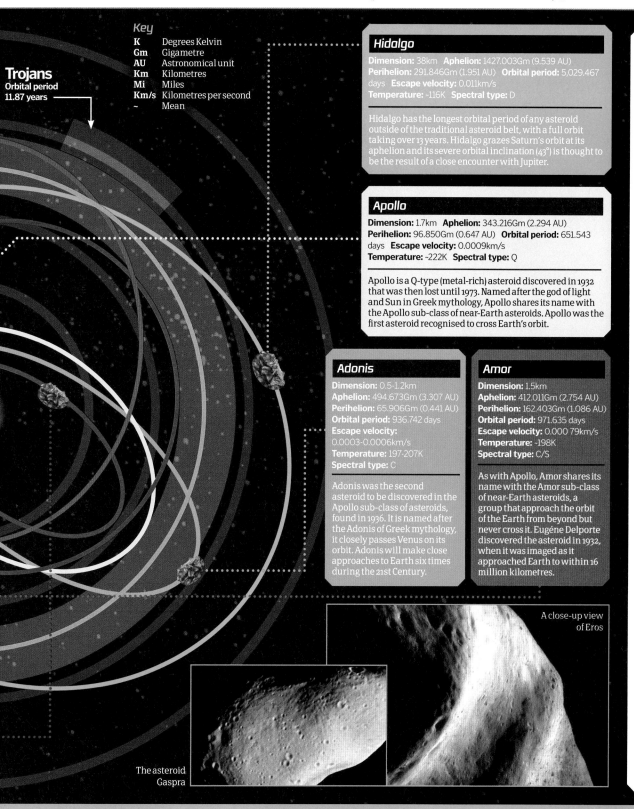

Key
K	Degrees Kelvin
Gm	Gigametre
AU	Astronomical unit
Km	Kilometres
Mi	Miles
Km/s	Kilometres per second
~	Mean

Trojans
Orbital period
11.87 years

Hidalgo
Dimension: 38km **Aphelion:** 1427.003Gm (9.539 AU)
Perihelion: 291.846Gm (1.951 AU) **Orbital period:** 5,029.467 days **Escape velocity:** 0.011km/s
Temperature: -116K **Spectral type:** D

Hidalgo has the longest orbital period of any asteroid outside of the traditional asteroid belt, with a full orbit taking over 13 years. Hidalgo grazes Saturn's orbit at its aphelion and its severe orbital inclination (43°) is thought to be the result of a close encounter with Jupiter.

Apollo
Dimension: 1.7km **Aphelion:** 343.216Gm (2.294 AU)
Perihelion: 96.850Gm (0.647 AU) **Orbital period:** 651.543 days **Escape velocity:** 0.0009km/s
Temperature: ~222K **Spectral type:** Q

Apollo is a Q-type (metal-rich) asteroid discovered in 1932 that was then lost until 1973. Named after the god of light and Sun in Greek mythology, Apollo shares its name with the Apollo sub-class of near-Earth asteroids. Apollo was the first asteroid recognised to cross Earth's orbit.

Adonis
Dimension: 0.5-1.2km
Aphelion: 494.673Gm (3.307 AU)
Perihelion: 65.906Gm (0.441 AU)
Orbital period: 936.742 days
Escape velocity: 0.0003-0.0006km/s
Temperature: 197-207K
Spectral type: C

Adonis was the second asteroid to be discovered in the Apollo sub-class of asteroids, found in 1936. It is named after the Adonis of Greek mythology, it closely passes Venus on its orbit. Adonis will make close approaches to Earth six times during the 21st Century.

Amor
Dimension: 1.5km
Aphelion: 412.011Gm (2.754 AU)
Perihelion: 162.403Gm (1.086 AU)
Orbital period: 971.635 days
Escape velocity: 0.000 79km/s
Temperature: -198K
Spectral type: C/S

As with Apollo, Amor shares its name with the Amor sub-class of near-Earth asteroids, a group that approach the orbit of the Earth from beyond but never cross it. Eugéne Delporte discovered the asteroid in 1932, when it was imaged as it approached Earth to within 16 million kilometres.

A close-up view of Eros

The asteroid Gaspra

Filling the gap

Franz Xaver von Zach (1754-1832), astronomer and leader of the Seeberg Observatory, Germany, believed that there was a missing planet orbiting the Sun between Mars and Jupiter. To prove his theory von Zach organised a group of 24 astronomers and gave them each a part of the celestial zodiac to search in an attempt to track down his errant planet. Unfortunately, despite such a large team, von Zach was beaten to the discovery by the Italian Catholic priest and mathematician Giuseppe Piazzi, who accidentally discovered the asteroid Ceres in 1801.

Franz Xaver Von Zach

Giuseppe Piazzi

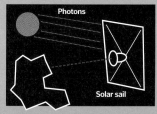
4. Solar sail
This method would involve attaching a 5,000km-wide sail to an asteroid. The constant pressure of sunlight over a large area would slowly alter its course.
Photons
Solar sail

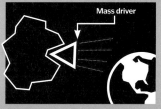
5. Mass driver
A huge space drill would be fired into the asteroid, and drill out the innards before firing them into space, altering its mass and changing the course.
Mass driver

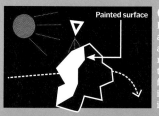
6. Paint
By coating parts of the asteroid in paint, the amounts of thermal radiation emitted by the asteroid's Sun-facing side could be increased, altering its path.
Painted surface

EXPLORATION

092
**Mega
rockets**

080
Mission to Mars

If you think you have what it takes to be an astronaut, think again

Astronauts run the systems engineering simulator in front of a full-sized projection of interactive International Space Station components

Virtual reality programs let astronauts practice mission-specific duties hundreds of times before flight

Engineers test a new extra-vehicular space suit with a partial gravity simulator

Astronaut training

It's been nearly half a century since Russian cosmonaut Yuri Gagarin became the first man in space, but with the rare exception of a few billionaire civilians, space travel is still a well-guarded privilege.

As NASA initiates a new long-term mission to return to the Moon and push on to Mars, the space agency is looking for a few good men and women who contain the rare mix of hyper-intelligence, marathon stamina and good old-fashioned guts to board the brand-new Ares I-X rocket and blast off to the uncharted depths. ✿

Applications at the ready!
Becoming an astronaut isn't easy. Firstly you'll have to be selected from thousands of applicants, and if you're successful train for two years, after which you may be chosen for an astronaut programme.

This huge centrifuge doesn't test the g-force limits of astronauts, but replicates up to 3.5g for flight simulation exercises

NASA basic training

NASA astronaut training is much like cramming for final exams at MIT while simultaneously enduring basic training for the Green Berets. Candidates begin their training in the classroom, taking advanced courses in astronomy, physics, mathematics, geology, meteorology and introductions to the Space Shuttle guidance and navigation systems. Sorry, no poetry electives.

Both pilots and non-pilots are trained to fly T-38 jets, highly acrobatic aircrafts that can reach 50,000ft. Pilots must log 15 hours of flight time a month, plus extra practice landing the Shuttle Training Aircraft (100 more hours). Non-pilots must log a minimum of four hours a month in the T-38.

But before astronaut candidates even step foot in a flight simulator, they need to be trained in military water survival. That means scuba certification and the proven ability to swim three lengths of an Olympic size pool in full flight gear and shoes. To cover all contingencies, astronaut candidates are also trained in wilderness survival, learning how to navigate by the stars and to live on nuts and berries.

The torture isn't over yet. To weed out the weaklings, candidates are subjected to extremes of high and low pressure and trained to deal with the 'consequences'. Then they're taken for a joyride in the infamous KC-135, aka 'the weightless wonder', aka 'the vomit comet', to experience 20-second shots of weightlessness. Some people love it, some people are violently sick.

After that it's time to brush up on a couple dozen equipment manuals in preparation for intense training with full-size, fully functional simulators,

everything from flight controls to hydraulic arms, even down to how to use the toilet. Every single astronaut candidate is trained in every phase of space flight, ranging from pre-launch diagnostics to emergency landing procedures.

Candidates also train in the Johnson Space Center's Neutral Buoyancy Laboratory, an immense pool that faithfully simulates near-weightlessness. Here, they prepare for both the extraordinary and mundane aspects of space life. They conduct underwater 'space walks' in full space gear and practice making freeze-dried snacks in the tiny Shuttle kitchen.

Finally comes the mission-specific training, where each member of the team runs countless simulations within his or her area of expertise. Scientists conduct their experiments over and over. Engineers do hundreds of mock space walks to make repairs to space station components. And pilots pretty much live in the flight simulators. After two years of full-time training, the candidates receive a silver lapel pin indicating they are officially astronauts. After their first flight, it's swapped for a gold one.

This centrifuge is designed to test the effects of linear acceleration on visual function in space

American and Russian astronauts train for spacewalks in the massive Hydrolab at the Gagarin Cosmonaut Training Center

So you want to be an astronaut?

In the late Fifties, when NASA began its internal search for the first seven astronauts, it drew from the ranks of the most experienced Air Force pilots. A lot has changed since the dawn of space flight, and so have the résumés of modern astronauts.

There are still some military pilots in the ranks, but they're in the minority. Today's astronauts are more likely to be academics, scientists and engineers of all stripes – particularly astronautical engineers.

Astronaut candidates are chosen through a rigorous application process and there is no career path that guarantees admission into the programme, although many current astronauts work for years within the NASA research and development ranks before suiting up themselves.

HEAD 2 HEAD
THE YOUNGEST OLDEST AND MOST EXPERIENCED ASTRONAUTS IN HISTORY

YOUNGEST

1. Gherman Stepanovich Titov
Age: 25
Facts: Only the second man in space after Yuri Gagarin, this charismatic young Russian cosmonaut was the first to make multiple orbits (17, in fact) of the Earth on 6 August 1961. He is probably most famous for his in-flight exuberance, repeatedly calling out his codename: "I am Eagle! I am Eagle!"

OLDEST

2. John Glenn
Age: 77
Facts: On 20 February 1962, John Glenn piloted NASA's very first manned orbital mission of the Earth, whipping around the globe three times in under five hours. Fast forward 36 years to 29 October 1998, when the retired US senator took his second space flight, a nine-day mission exploring – among other things – the effects of space flight on the aging process.

MOST TIME IN SPACE

3. Sergei Konstantinovich Krikalev
Total duration: 803 days
Facts: Cosmonaut Krikalev crushes all competitors in the category of most time spent in space. He flew six missions between 1985 and 2005, notching up over two years in space, including the first joint Russia/US Space Shuttle flight in 1994. The uber-experienced Krikalev now runs the Gagarin Cosmonaut Training Center in Star City, Russia.

Inside a spacesuit

What's so special about an astronaut's outfit that it can keep them alive in space?

 It's probably best to think of a spacesuit not as an item of clothing – like a jumper you'd put on when it's cold or a pair of wellies to keep your feet dry – but as a habitat or a small personal spaceship that astronauts wear when they're out in space. Two of the main threats to human life in space are the lack of oxygen and the extreme range of temperatures, which can fluctuate from below -100 degrees Celsius (-150 degrees Fahrenheit) to in excess of 120 degrees Celsius (242 degrees Fahrenheit). But they can face other dangers, too: the extremely low pressure, micrometeorites travelling several times the speed of a bullet and exposure to high levels of radiation, unfiltered by any planetary atmosphere like Earth's, travelling from the Sun and deep space.

Astronauts need protection from these dangers while on an extravehicular activity (EVA) in space, so the modern spacesuit is designed to do just that. The outer section is divided into several main pieces with flexible and rigid parts, designed to provide mechanical protection from impact and a pressurised, oxygenated environment within the suit.

Underneath that, the astronaut wears a garment that helps regulate their body temperature with tubes that are woven into it, inside which water circulates for cooling. The astronaut's chunky backpack carries the primary life support subsystem, which pumps the oxygen into the astronaut's helmet for them to breathe and 'scrubs' the excess carbon dioxide out of the air they exhale. It also holds the electricity supply required to run the suit's systems and a water tank for the cooling system. ✿

Extravehicular Mobility Unit

The space suit born in 1981 is still used outside the ISS today

Heavyweight
A complete EMU weighs over 100kg (220lb) but fortunately, the microgravity of space makes this feel nowhere near as much

Gold layer
An astronaut's visor is covered with a thin layer of gold, which is transparent but filters out harmful rays from the Sun

Protection
A Hard Upper Torso (HUT) assembly provides a rigid base for the rest of the EMU to connect to and some protection from micrometeoroids

Undergarments
Underneath the spacesuit, are Urine Collection Devices (UCDs) and a series of tubes that assist in cooling the astronaut

Life support
The heavy backpack contains power for the spacesuit, air and a water tank for cooling

Control module
The Display and Control Module gives the astronaut easy access to suit controls and communication

Jetpacks
Astronauts only use jetpacks in emergencies. The Manned Manouvering Unit (MMU) shown here was replaced by the Simplified Aid for EVA Rescue (SAFER) system in 1994

The Z-suit

NASA's prototype Z-suit is a work in progress on an update to the current incarnation of the spacesuit, whose basic structure has been used for 30 years, ever since the Extravehicular Mobility Unit (EMU) was first made in 1981. At a glance, it doesn't look radically different to contemporary space suits, but it's been designed to include several key features that will allow it to be used in both the microgravity of space and for future missions to planets such as Mars, which the Apollo-era spacesuit isn't capable of. It can be quickly put on and taken off (current spacesuits can take an hour or more to put on) and include a suitport dock, which replaces the airlock on a spacecraft. This means the spacecraft and space suit would be kept at the same pressure, so astronauts wouldn't need to pre-breathe oxygen for at least 30 minutes before an EVA as they do now to prevent decompression sickness. The Z-2 prototype is expected to undergo testing in 2015.

Space diving

There have been two successful jumps from the edge of space, but how can anyone survive such a great fall?

 Skydiving is a popular sport for thrill-seekers, but how about diving from the stratosphere? In 2012, Felix Baumgartner set a record by freefalling from 39 kilometres (24 miles) above the Earth. This puts his dive as coming from the stratosphere – not technically outer space, which is usually defined as beginning 100 kilometres (62 miles) above sea level – but who's quibbling? Baumgartner began working with a sponsor in 2005 to plan the mission, recruiting a team that included Joe Kittinger, the first man to dive from the stratosphere in 1960.

Baumgartner wore a modified version of the pressurised suit donned by astronauts and pilots that fly at high altitudes, and rode in a specially built capsule lifted by a high-altitude helium balloon. Pressure suits are necessary at heights above 19 kilometres (12 miles) because the loss of pressure can result in gas bubbles forming in body fluids, leading to a potentially fatal condition called ebullism.

The suit also protected Baumgartner from extremes in temperature on the dive. During the ascent, the capsule provided atmospheric pressure so he didn't get decompression sickness and also shielded him from the extreme cold. Once Baumgartner reached the right height he inflated his suit, opened the capsule door and made the leap. Not only did he break the altitude record, but the sound barrier as well. At 1,524 metres (5,000 feet) above the ground, he deployed his parachute – also designed for high altitudes – after hitting a speed of 1,342 kilometres (834 miles) during his four-minute, 19-second freefall. ⚙

Focus on Felix

Felix Baumgartner is an Austrian daredevil, skydiver and BASE (Building, Antenna, Span and Earth) jumper who has set records throughout his career. Baumgartner served in the Austrian military and learned skydiving as part of their demonstration and competition team before switching to BASE jumping. In 1999, he set a record for the world's highest BASE jump, from the Malaysian Petronas Towers, the tallest buildings in the world at that time at 451m (1,479ft). In the same year he also set a world record for the lowest BASE jump, from the hand of the Christ the Redeemer statue in Rio de Janeiro, which stands just 29m (95ft) tall. Having already worked as a helicopter pilot in Europe, his post-jump plans were to continue on that career path.

SURVIVE THE COSMOS
LIFE IN SPACE

Humans have had a presence in space in some form or another for half a century, but learning to live in the cosmos has been a steep learning curve. We take a look at what it's like to live in space, and how we've adapted over the years

Living in space is the ultimate mental and physical test of the human body. On Earth, the experience of being in space is almost impossible to replicate; the closest astronauts can get is to train underwater but, even then, the experience is a world away from that first journey into orbit or beyond. There's no 'up' or 'down' in space, so many of their sensory receptors are rendered useless, while materials such as water behave completely differently to how they do on

Earth. So, how do astronauts cope, and what's it like to actually live in space? We're about to find out.

Since Yuri Gagarin became the first man to leave the Earth in 1961, life in space has altered and improved dramatically. Gagarin spent the entirety of his 108-minute flight encased in a spacesuit, but nowadays astronauts can wear the same shorts and T-shirts they'd wear at home. The first space station, Russia's Salyut (launched in 1971), saw astronauts eat food from freeze-dried

packets and stay only briefly on the station in order to survive. Now, astronauts aboard the International Space Station (ISS) can eat pizza and curry, reuse and recycle many of their utilities and can stay in orbit for hundreds of days.

Before the ISS there were many unknowns about living in space. Indeed, on the earlier space stations Mir and Skylab, procedures and equipment were much less advanced than they are now. For one thing, it was quickly realised that

HEAD 2 HEAD
SPACE RECORDS

CUMULATIVE

803 days
Russian Sergei Krikalev, aged 53, has spent a grand total of 803 days, 9 hours and 39 minutes in space across six different missions.

CONTINUOUS

437 days
The record of longest single spaceflight in history is currently held by Russian Valeri Polyakov, 69, who spent 437 days and 18 hours aboard the Mir space station.

CANINE

22 days
Veterok and Ugolyok jointly hold the record of longest canine spaceflight, spending 22 days in orbit in 1966 before returning to Earth.

DID YOU KNOW? You grow taller in space because your spine elongates – some reports suggest by an inch in just ten days

Space bodies
How does living in space affect the human body?

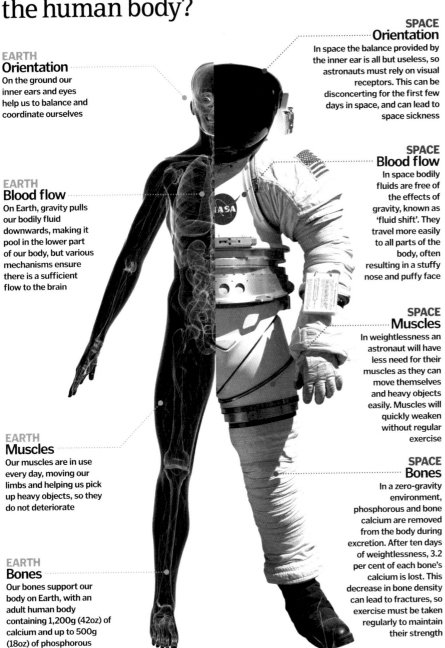

EARTH
Orientation
On the ground our inner ears and eyes help us to balance and coordinate ourselves

EARTH
Blood flow
On Earth, gravity pulls our bodily fluid downwards, making it pool in the lower part of our body, but various mechanisms ensure there is a sufficient flow to the brain

EARTH
Muscles
Our muscles are in use every day, moving our limbs and helping us pick up heavy objects, so they do not deteriorate

EARTH
Bones
Our bones support our body on Earth, with an adult human body containing 1,200g (42oz) of calcium and up to 500g (18oz) of phosphorous

SPACE
Orientation
In space the balance provided by the inner ear is all but useless, so astronauts must rely on visual receptors. This can be disconcerting for the first few days in space, and can lead to space sickness

SPACE
Blood flow
In space bodily fluids are free of the effects of gravity, known as 'fluid shift'. They travel more easily to all parts of the body, often resulting in a stuffy nose and puffy face

SPACE
Muscles
In weightlessness an astronaut will have less need for their muscles as they can move themselves and heavy objects easily. Muscles will quickly weaken without regular exercise

SPACE
Bones
In a zero-gravity environment, phosphorous and bone calcium are removed from the body during excretion. After ten days of weightlessness, 3.2 per cent of each bone's calcium is lost. This decrease in bone density can lead to fractures, so exercise must be taken regularly to maintain their strength

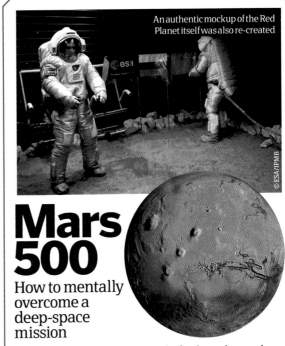
An authentic mockup of the Red Planet itself was also re-created

Mars 500
How to mentally overcome a deep-space mission

In 50 years of space exploration, the furthest a human has been from Earth is the far side of the Moon. While astronauts have spent hundreds of days aboard the ISS, the complexities of tackling a deep-space mission are relatively unknown. As a result, projects such as the Mars 500 mission have been given increasing precedence.

The Mars 500 mission was an important study to ascertain the mental and physical strain on humans in closed isolation on a long-haul trip. The mission was a joint project between the ESA and Russian Institute for Biomedical Problems, which ran from 3 June 2010 to 4 November 2011. Six candidates were sealed in an isolation chamber for 520 days, the approximate journey time for a real trip to and from the Red Planet. The chamber contained several modules designed to replicate a Martian spacecraft and the surface of Mars itself. The volunteers were subjected to some of the conditions they would experience, such as delayed communications and confined quarters. The results will be used to develop countermeasures to remedy potential problems.

The astronauts carried out the same day-to-day routine they would on a real-life mission to Mars

Space was very limited in the Mars 500 'shuttle'

2 x images © ESA/IPMB

astronauts must sleep near a ventilation fan. If they don't they run the risk of suffocation. This is because, as they sleep, warm air does not rise in a weightless environment. In a badly ventilated area they would be surrounded by a bubble of their own exhaled carbon dioxide. A regular supply of air (oxygen) is needed to allow for regulated breathing.

Over the years sleeping methods have changed, from slumbering in a sleeping bag attached to a wall, on NASA's Space Shuttle, for example, to having their own small compartment on the ISS. Sleeping isn't easy,

either. Astronauts experience a sunrise and sunset every 90 minutes as they fly at 24,945km/h (15,500mph) around the Earth, so clocks on the ISS are set to GMT and astronauts live their days just as they would on Earth. They work for over eight hours on weekdays, but on weekends they are given much more leisure time, although work must still be done to keep the ISS safe and operational, in addition to checking on experiments. Life in space isn't tough just for humans; animals have struggled as well. On NASA's Skylab space station in the Seventies, spiders were taken up

to see how they would cope in a weightless environment. While disoriented they still managed to spin a web, even if it was a little wonky. More famous was the first living animal to be sent into space from Earth, Laika the dog from Russia. Sadly, she perished in orbit, but she was said to cope well with the experience of weightlessness. At the very least, Laika proved that animals could survive in space, providing the basis for Gagarin's later mission and all future human missions into the cosmos.

Each human consumes 0.9kg (2lbs) of oxygen daily, which is enough to fill a 3.5 cubic metre (123.6 cubic feet) room, and drinks 2.7kg (6lbs) of water. Therefore, the life-support systems on board the ISS recycle as much waste as possible, including that from urine and condensed moisture in the air, both of which are purified and reused, often after being broken down by electrolysis to provide fresh oxygen. However, not all water can be reused, and thus astronauts must rely on regular re-supply vehicles to bring cargo to the station. These have been performed by several spacecraft over the years, such as NASA's Space Shuttle until its retirement in July 2011, but they are now largely carried out by the ESA's Automated Transfer Vehicle (ATV). The ATV brings fresh food, clothes, water and equipment to the station. Once the cargo has been delivered, astronauts fill the vehicle with 5,896kg (12,998lbs) of waste and it is sent to burn up in Earth's atmosphere.

These are just some of the many ways that astronauts have adapted to life in space, and as more and more time is spent on the International Space Station, our capabilities to perform in a weightless environment will no doubt improve. The ultimate goal of sending humans to an asteroid and Mars in the 2030s is looking like an increasingly achievable objective thanks to the tireless work of space agencies worldwide over the last 50 years.

A DAY IN SPACE

Astronauts aboard the ISS experience 15 'dawns' every day, but while they're on board the station they operate according to GMT so they can stay in direct contact with the ground at operational hours. Here's how a typical day pans out for an astronaut on the station

08:00
Daily conference/work

In the morning astronauts perform the first of their daily tasks assigned by ground control. They often have a daily conference where they discuss their jobs for the day. Their work consists of supervising experiments that would not be possible on Earth or performing routine maintenance on equipment to ensure the survival of the crew. On some days they take video calls from Earth. These are often simply to friends and family but, on rare occasions, they may talk to schoolchildren, the US president or even the Pope.

STS-110 crew eating on board the International Space Station

06:40
Breakfast/getting ready

Astronauts eat their first meal of the day, which is nothing like the freeze-dried food of the Apollo missions. Fresh fruit and produce are stored on the ISS, while tea and coffee are available in packets. Astronauts can wear anything from shorts and T-shirts to trousers and rugby shirts. However, there are no washing machines, so clothes must be allocated for specific days (although in such a clean environment they pick up very little dirt). Most clothes are disposed of every three days, but socks can be worn for up to a month, while a pair of underwear must be taken for each day on the station.

The ESA-built Cupola is a popular module where astronauts can get a fantastic view of Earth

All images © NASA

06:00 Post-sleep

Astronauts are woken up at 6am. On the ISS most astronauts have their own sleeping compartments, small spaces where the astronaut can lie vertically (although this doesn't matter as there is no 'up' or 'down' on the station). After waking they will get washed and dressed before eating breakfast, much like a regular day on Earth. There is a shower on the ISS, although most washing is done with a simple wet cloth. In the shower, water is squirted out from the top and 'sucked' by an air fan at the bottom, but water must be used sparingly. Grooming techniques such as shaving are difficult on the ISS, as surface tension makes water and shaving cream stick to an astronaut's face and the razor blade in globules.

10:00 & 17:00
Physical exercise
Astronauts must exercise regularly, at least 2.5 hours a day, to keep their body in optimum condition while in space. As explained previously, bones and organs can become frail and weak in a weightless environment. Therefore astronauts on the ISS have a variety of exercise machines, like treadmills and cycling machines, to keep them strong.

13:00 Lunch
Prolonged microgravity dulls tastebuds, and the white noise doesn't help (like being on an aircraft), so foods with strong flavours (such as spicy curries) are often the preferred choice for meals.

14:00
Back to work
On rare occasions astronauts will have to leave the station on an extra-vehicular activity (EVA). For this astronauts will don a spacesuit and perform work outside the ISS. Before they leave they must exercise for several hours in a decompression chamber to prevent suffering from the 'bends' on entering space. Work outside the station ranges from maintenance to installing or upgrading a component.

19:30 Pre-sleep
In the evening astronauts eat dinner in a communal area. This is an important time for social interaction, as often many hours are spent working alone on the station. Before sleep, they also have a chance for a bit of entertainment, which can range from watching a DVD to playing guitar.

21:30 Sleep
In space no one can hear you scream, right? Well, in an orbiting craft, space is actually very loud, with a multitude of fans and motors ensuring that the space station remains in the correct operational capacity. At 21.30pm astronauts head off to their designated sleeping compartments to grab some rest and, while reassuring, these noises can take a while to get used to for astronauts staying on the station for the first time, much like living next to a busy main road on Earth.

On board the
International
Space Station

What's it like to live in space?

Man has had a continuous presence in space since 2000 on the International Space Station. In 1998, the Zarya module was launched into orbit by the Russian Federal Space Agency. This was the first piece of the ISS. Now that it is complete, the ISS is the largest satellite to ever orbit the Earth. After being finished in 2012, the ISS is also arguably the most expensive single object to ever be constructed at more than $150 billion.

The ISS wasn't the first space station, however; in 1971 the Soviet Union launched the Salyut, which was the first in a series of space stations. Two years later, NASA launched Skylab. However, both of these programmes were single modules with limited life spans. In 1986, the Soviet Union launched the Mir, which was intended to be built upon and added to over time. The United States planned to launch its own space station, Freedom, just a few years later, but budgetary restraints ended the project. After the fall of the Soviet Union, the United States

began negotiating with Russia, along with several other countries, to build a multinational space station.

Until Expedition 20 in May 2009, crews on the International Space Station consisted of two-to-three astronauts and cosmonauts, who stayed for six months. Now the ISS is large enough to support a six-man crew, the stay has been reduced to just three months. The current crew consists of: NASA commander Barry Wilmore and flight engineers Alexander Samokutyaev (RKA), Anton Shkatlerov (RKA), Terry Virts (NASA), Samantha Cristoforetti (ESA) and Elena Serova (RKA).

The crew typically works for ten hours a day during the week and five hours on Saturdays. During their eight scheduled night hours, the crew sleeps in cabins while attached to bunk beds, or in sleeping bags that are secured to the wall. They also have to wear sleep masks, as it would be difficult to sleep otherwise with a sunrise occurring every 90 minutes.

All food is processed so it is easy to reheat in a special oven, usually with the addition of

water. This includes beverages, which the crew drinks with straws from plastic bags. Exercise is a very important part of daily life for the crew of the ISS because of microgravity's adverse effects on the body. The astronauts and cosmonauts may experience muscle atrophy, bone loss, a weakened immune system and a slowed cardiovascular system, among other problems. To help counteract this, the crew exercises while strapped to treadmills and exercise bicycles.

Research is the main reason for the station's existence in low Earth orbit (about 330 kilometres above the planet's surface). Several scientific experiments spanning fields including astronomy, physics, materials science, earth science and biology take place on the station simultaneously. Between September 2012 and March 2013, for example, the current expedition crew (33) and the next expedition crew (34) will be working on over 100 experiments in a wide range of fields, spanning biology and biotechnology, the

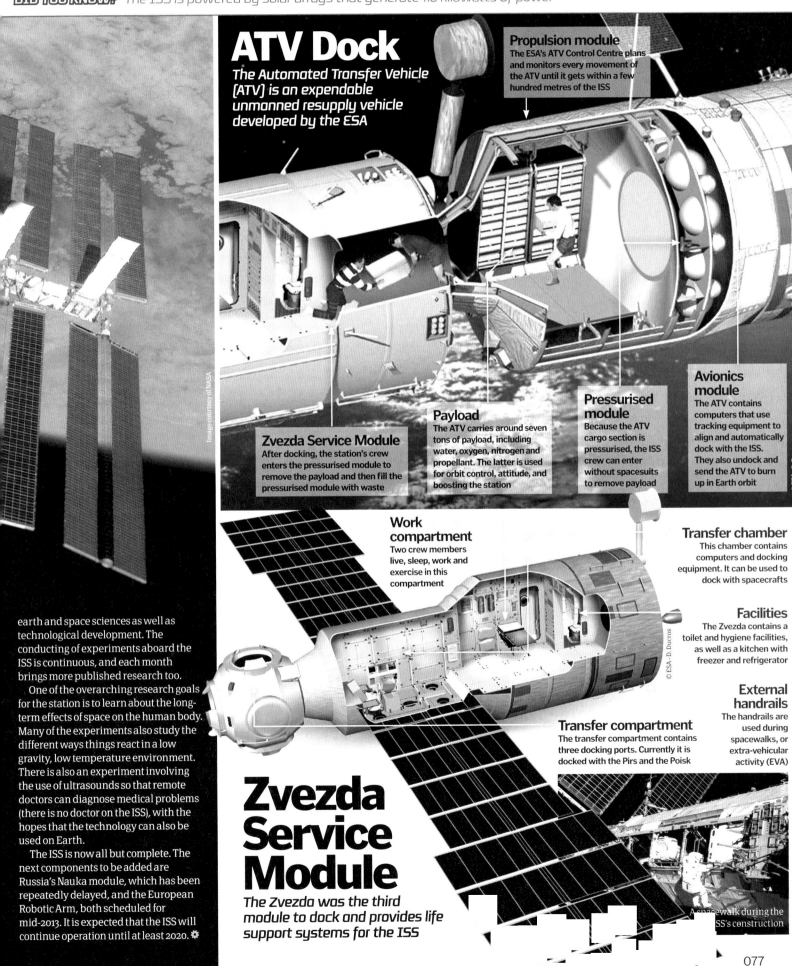

ATV Dock

The Automated Transfer Vehicle (ATV) is an expendable unmanned resupply vehicle developed by the ESA

Propulsion module
The ESA's ATV Control Centre plans and monitors every movement of the ATV until it gets within a few hundred metres of the ISS

Avionics module
The ATV contains computers that use tracking equipment to align and automatically dock with the ISS. They also undock and send the ATV to burn up in Earth orbit

Pressurised module
Because the ATV cargo section is pressurised, the ISS crew can enter without spacesuits to remove payload

Payload
The ATV carries around seven tons of payload, including water, oxygen, nitrogen and propellant. The latter is used for orbit control, attitude, and boosting the station

Zvezda Service Module
After docking, the station's crew enters the pressurised module to remove the payload and then fill the pressurised module with waste

Image courtesy of NASA

© ESA - D. Ducros

Work compartment
Two crew members live, sleep, work and exercise in this compartment

Transfer chamber
This chamber contains computers and docking equipment. It can be used to dock with spacecrafts

Facilities
The Zvezda contains a toilet and hygiene facilities, as well as a kitchen with freezer and refrigerator

External handrails
The handrails are used during spacewalks, or extra-vehicular activity (EVA)

Transfer compartment
The transfer compartment contains three docking ports. Currently it is docked with the Pirs and the Poisk

© ESA - D. Ducros

Zvezda Service Module

The Zvezda was the third module to dock and provides life support systems for the ISS

earth and space sciences as well as technological development. The conducting of experiments aboard the ISS is continuous, and each month brings more published research too.

One of the overarching research goals for the station is to learn about the long-term effects of space on the human body. Many of the experiments also study the different ways things react in a low gravity, low temperature environment. There is also an experiment involving the use of ultrasounds so that remote doctors can diagnose medical problems (there is no doctor on the ISS), with the hopes that the technology can also be used on Earth.

The ISS is now all but complete. The next components to be added are Russia's Nauka module, which has been repeatedly delayed, and the European Robotic Arm, both scheduled for mid-2013. It is expected that the ISS will continue operation until at least 2020. ✿

A spacewalk during the ISS's construction

The Columbus Module

The Columbus is a research laboratory designed by the ESA – its largest contribution to the ISS

External payload
An external payload facility houses three sets of instruments and experiments, with room for three more

In the Space Station Processing Facility at NASA's Kennedy Space Center in Florida, a crane lowers the Multi-Purpose Logistics Module Leonardo toward the payload canister

Who built the ISS?

The ISS currently comprises 15 pressurised modules and an Integrated Truss Structure. The modules are contributions from the Russian Federal Space Agency (RKA), NASA, the Japanese Aerospace Exploration Agency (JAXA), the Canadian Space Agency (CSA) and the European Space Agency (ESA), which includes 18 member countries. A series of complex treaties and agreements govern the ownership, use and maintenance of the station. A further four modules are scheduled to be added.

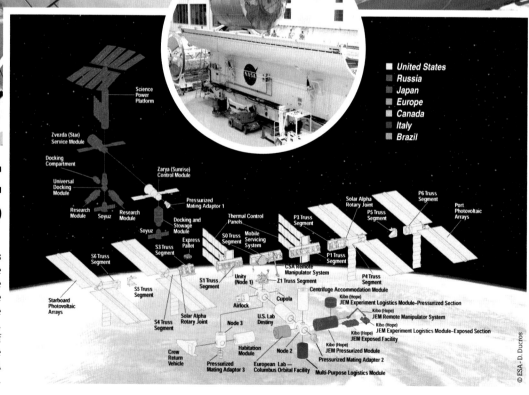

United States
Russia
Japan
Europe
Canada
Italy
Brazil

Science Power Platform

Zvezda (Star) Service Module

Docking Compartment

Universal Docking Module

Zarya (Sunrise) Control Module

Research Module
Soyuz
Research Module

Soyuz

Pressurized Mating Adaptor 1

Docking and Stowage Module

Thermal Control Panels

Express Pallet

S0 Truss Segment

Mobile Servicing System

P3 Truss Segment

Solar Alpha Rotary Joint

P5 Truss Segment

P6 Truss Segment

Port Photovoltaic Arrays

S6 Truss Segment

S3 Truss Segment

S1 Truss Segment

Unity (Node 1)

Z1 Truss Segment

CSA Remote Manipulator System

P1 Truss Segment

P4 Truss Segment

Starboard Photovoltaic Arrays

S5 Truss Segment

Cupola

Centrifuge Accommodation Module

Kibo (Hope) JEM Experiment Logistics Module–Pressurized Section

Airlock

Kibo (Hope) JEM Remote Manipulator System

S4 Truss Segment

Solar Alpha Rotary Joint

Node 3

U.S. Lab Destiny

Kibo (Hope) JEM Experiment Logistics Module–Exposed Section

Kibo (Hope) JEM Exposed Facility

Crew Return Vehicle

Pressurized Mating Adaptor 3

Habitation Module

Node 2

European Lab – Columbus Orbital Facility

Kibo (Hope) JEM Pressurized Module

Pressurized Mating Adapter 2

Multi-Purpose Logistics Module

© ESA - D. Ductos

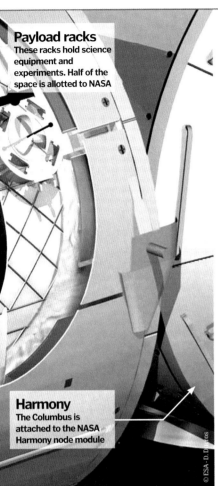

Payload racks
These racks hold science equipment and experiments. Half of the space is allotted to NASA

Harmony
The Columbus is attached to the NASA Harmony node module

© ESA - D. Ducros

Creating water in space

For the crew of the ISS it's better not to think where their next glass of water is coming from

The ECLSS (Environmental Control and Life Support System) provides water with the Water Recovery System (WRS). Water from crew member waste, condensation and other waste water is distilled, filtered and processed. This water is then used for drinking, cooking, cleaning and other functions. An Oxygen Generation System (OGS) separates water into oxygen and hydrogen. An experimental Carbon Dioxide Reduction Assembly (CReA) uses the leftover hydrogen with carbon dioxide filtered from the crew cabins to produce usable water and methane. In addition, the ECLSS filters the cabin air, maintains cabin pressure and can detect and suppress fires.

Anatomy of the Space Station

The ISS is a configuration of modules, trusses and solar arrays

© ESA - D. Ducros

1. Zarya
The Zarya, launched in 1998 and built by the RKA, is now a storage component. As the first module it provided storage, power and propulsion.

2. Unity
Built by NASA and launched in 1998, Unity was the first node module to connect to the Zarya. It provides a docking station for other modules.

3. Zvezda
The RKA-built Zvezda launched in 2000. It made the ISS habitable by providing crew cabins and environmental control as well as other systems.

4. Destiny
The Destiny is a NASA laboratory. Launched back in 2001, it also contains environmental controls and works as a mounting point for the Integrated Truss Structure.

5. Quest
The 2001 NASA-built Quest is an airlock used to host spacewalks. The equipment lock is used for storing the spacesuits, while the crew lock allows exit to space.

6. Pirs
A mini-research module called Pirs was launched in 2001 by the RKA. It can dock spacecraft and also host spacewalks by cosmonauts.

7. Harmony
Harmony, built by NASA in 2007, is a node module. It serves as a berthing point and docking station for modules and spacecraft.

8. Columbus
The Columbus, launched in 2008, is an ESA laboratory specifically designed for experiments in biology and physics. It provides power to experiments mounted to its exterior.

9. Kibo Experiment Logistics Module
This JAXA module (also known as JEM-ELM) is part of the Japanese Experiment Module laboratory and was launched in 2008. It contains transportation and storage.

10. Kibo Pressurised Module
Also launched in 2008, the JEM-PM is a research facility and the largest module on the ISS. It has an external platform and robotic arm for experiments.

11. Poisk
The RKA-built Poisk (MRM2) launched in November 2009. In addition to housing components for experiments, it serves as a dock for spacecraft and a spacewalk airlock.

12. Integrated Truss Structure
The ISS's solar arrays and thermal radiators are mounted to this structure, which is more than 100 metres long and has ten separate parts.

13. Mobile Servicing System
Also known as the Canadarm2, this CSA-built robotic system used to move supplies, service equipment and assist astronauts on spacewalks.

14. Special Purpose Dexterous Manipulator
The SPDM, or Dextre, is a robot built by the CSA and is extremely dextrous. It can perform functions outside the ISS that had previously required spacewalks to happen.

15. Tranquillity
The Tranquillity is NASA's third node module, and was successfully launched in February 2010. It contains the ECLSS as well as berthing stations for other modules.

16. Cupola
The seven windows of this observatory module, launched with Tranquility in February 2010, make it the largest window ever used in space.

17. Rassvet
Launched in May 2010, this second RKA mini-research module also serves as storage.

18. Leonardo
A pressurised multipurpose module, the Leonardo was installed in March 2011. It serves as a storage unit and frees up space in the Columbus.

19. Nauka (MLM)
Scheduled to be launched with the European Robotic Arm in mid-2013, this multipurpose research module will be a rest area for the crew as well as doubling up as a research laboratory too.

20. Solar Arrays
These arrays convert sunlight into electricity. There are four pairs on the ISS.

21. Thermal Radiators
The Active Thermal Control System (ATCS) removes excess heat from the ISS and vents it out into space via these radiators.

The ISS in early construction while in orbit in 1999

© NASA

The Statistics
The ISS

© NASA

Mass: 419,455 kilograms
Volume of habitable space: 388 cubic metres
Supplies: 2,722 kilograms per expedition
Orbit: 402 to 426 kilometres high at an angle of 51.6 degrees, travelling at 27,744 kilometres per hour, completing 15.7 orbits per day
Gravity: 88 per cent that of Earth sea level
Cost: US Government Accountability Office estimates a total of $100 billion (£62 billion). ESA estimates a total of 100 billion euros (£81 billion).
Crew support: 100,000+ ground personal, 500 contracting facilities in 37 states and 16 countries
Spacewalks: 28 shuttle-based and 127 ISS-based for more than 973 hours
Meals: About 22,000 consumed aboard
Flights: 35 NASA space shuttle, 2 RKA Proton, 27 RKA Soyuz, 1 ESA Automated Transfer Vehicle, 1 JAXA H-II Transfer Vehicle
Mission control monitoring centres: 2 NASA centres, 1 RKA centre, 1 ESA in Germany, 1 ESA in France, 1 JAXA centre, 1 CSA centre

MISSION TO MARS

REVEALED: HOW HUMANS WILL ONE DAY CONQUER THE RED PLANET

ke
ns
Mars are more
than they are on
t or moon we
ver, it is still not
umans, being
th a thin carbon
here

2 Comet crashes
One way to thicken
Mars' atmosphere is to
redirect comets and
asteroids to crash into its
surface. This would release
gases from both the
impactor and the surface,
as well as create heat

3 Thicken the atmosphere
The atmospheric surface pressure
on Mars is only 0.6 per cent of that
on Earth. The first task in
terraforming is to make the
atmosphere thicker, to warm the
planet and allow water to exist on
the surface in liquid form

4 Factories
On Earth, pollution from
factories is bad for the
environment, but if we want to
terraform Mars we need to pump
out huge amounts of greenhouse
gases to thicken the atmosphere
and trap the Sun's heat in the
greenhouse effect

5 Radiation
One thing terraforming
cannot fix is Mars' lack of a
magnetic field, which could help
block deadly radiation from
space. Colonists may have to
live in large shielded habitats to
protect themselves from the
harmful radiation

THE STATS
MARS FIGURES

AVERAGE TEMPERATURE **-63°C** DIAMETER OF MARS **6,779km** LENGTH OF MARS' YEAR **687** Earth days Minimum **4min**, maximum **24min**

24h 40min LENGTH OF MARS' DAY GRAVITATIONAL ACCELERATION **3.7m/s²** (38% of Earth's gravity) COMMUNICATION DELAY BETWEEN EARTH AND MARS

DID YOU KNOW? A day on Mars is 24 hours and 40 minutes, which means astronauts will have to use different watches

It's the planet on the bucket list of future astronauts. The world that will serve as a stepping-stone, taking humans farther out into space: It might be dry, barren and home to long-dead landers and resilient rovers that trundle along its surface, but Mars has potential. Potential to join Earth in being the only other planet in our Solar System to have life as we know it on its surface.

"Mars is the closest planet that has all of the resources to support life on it and potentially a new generation of human civilisation," says The Mars Society's Dr Robert Zubrin, an American aerospace engineer who advocates the manned exploration of Mars. "Mars can help us to discover the phenomena of life specific to Earth and general phenomena in the universe." Zubrin makes it sound surprisingly easy to colonise the Red Planet. But despite the obvious differences between it and Mother Earth, Mars also holds several similarities that make it the

most obvious option for light years around. First, there's water, mostly at the planet's poles; the gravity is only 2.6 times less than that of Earth's and what's more, a Martian day is only 40 minutes longer than a day on our planet. With an average temperature of -62 degrees Celsius (-81 degrees Fahrenheit), you'd need to wrap up against the cold, but even in these teeth-chattering conditions, it is still our best shot at attempting to venture out into the Solar System.

However, while there's a degree of familiarity, the fourth rock from the Sun harbours much of the unknown – something that could make us hesitant about setting foot on Martian soil. "The most important factor needed is the courage to try", Zubrin tells us. "Can humans live on Mars? That can only really be determined by sending people there. If Barack Obama got up tomorrow and said: 'I'm committing the nation to sending humans to Mars', we could have people on the Red Planet by the end of the decade."

Making oxygen for Mars

In 2020, NASA aims to send another rover to the Red Planet. However, while it will be built much like Curiosity, it is tipped to do something no other rover has done before: it will make precious oxygen.

The piece of technology that aims to do this is the Mars OXygen In-situ resource utilization Experiment, or MOXIE for short. Using the gas that's the most abundant on the Red Planet – carbon dioxide – the instrument will make oxygen and carbon monoxide before releasing it into the atmosphere. MOXIE should produce 22 grams (0.8 ounces) of oxygen per hour over 50 Martian days.

If MOXIE works well, we will be landing a larger instrument just like MOXIE on Mars along with a nuclear reactor to power it. This would fill an oxygen reservoir, which astronauts would breathe in when they arrive on the Red Planet. It could also be possible to use this oxygen as a rocket propellant to power their return trip to Earth.

The Mars 2020 rover mission will have a similar design to the Curiosity rover

Humans on Mars
Mars does not have a habitable environment, but terraforming could make it more Earth-like

6 Gravity
Gravity is a problem – Mars' gravity is only 38 per cent of Earth's gravity, meaning Mars finds it harder to hold onto its atmosphere. The atmosphere will have to be constantly replenished if we are to terraform Mars.

7 Martian algae
The introduction of algae could have benefits. It can break down carbon dioxide to make oxygen to breathe, and its dark colour could help lower Mars' albedo, helping Mars trap more of the Sun's heat rather than reflecting it back into space.

8 Turning the red planet blue
Mars has vast amounts of water frozen as ice, both in its polar caps as well as underground, all the way down to the mid-latitudes. Increasing the pressure and temperature on Mars will allow this ice to melt to form lakes and rivers.

9 Bringing life to a dead planet
As far as we know, Mars is a dead planet. Terraforming Mars could make it possible for us to introduce life and grow plants – and food – in the Martian dirt.

10 No more spacesuits
The aim of terraforming is to create an environment on Mars where colonists will be able to survive outside without space suits, at least for a short time.

© Mars: National Geographic

Preparing for the journey

Brave volunteers are undergoing intense experiments to discover what it takes

"Looking for life in the past, looking for life in the present and determining the future of humanity on Mars means we have to send people there," says Robert Zubrin. That means preparation is key if we're ever going to set foot on this other world. We've sent spacecraft and rovers to the Red Planet to shape our understanding of it. The Mars Reconnaissance Orbiter, which clutches the HiRISE camera, is currently in orbit around Mars, taking snaps of the landscape to identify the best possible location for future colonists.

Rovers Opportunity and Curiosity are tasting the Martian atmosphere and sampling the planet's soil in a bid to find out more details, supplying crucial information for the first Mars-walkers. "The rovers are the advance scouts, but there's nothing they can do that we could not do a thousand times faster," Zubrin adds. That's why we've had to start making some headway in preparing future Martian astronauts for a mission that will be as big as the day we first landed a man on the Moon.

That's where facilities on Earth have come in until we're fully ready to make our way to Mars. A joint effort between Russia, ESA and China, 2010's Mars500 was a project like no other. It tested the psychological mettle of its crew to the limit, squeezing six volunteers into cramped quarters of 550 cubic metres (19,423 cubic feet) for a total of 520 days on a simulated mission to Mars.

Being roughly 260 days away, astronauts to Mars would get the same treatment for real. They would need to be able to withstand the isolation, the confined space, the delayed communication between them and Earth and get along with their companions – all the while managing the general operation and scientific experimentation they would need to carry out.

While all the crew members finished the experiment in good condition, four of them had trouble sleeping or suffered mild psychological issues during the process.

500 days on 'Mars'

A multinational experiment saw potential Mars astronauts spend 520 days isolated in a mock Martian base

The surface
One chamber mimicked the Martian surface and could only be entered in space suits.

Isolation
The Russian, European and Chinese 'astronauts' were isolated from the rest of the world to mimic the loneliness astronauts would feel on Mars.

Making the trip to Mars

The journey to Mars will take astronauts around seven months, and crews could remain there for roughly two years – until Earth and Mars are closest to each other in their orbits again for the return trip. Finding out more about how such a long voyage will affect astronauts is the Hawaii Space Exploration Analog and Simulation project, also known as HI-SEAS. All alone on the slopes of the Mauna Loa volcano in Hawaii, which looks a bit like Mars, several groups of astronauts and scientists are discovering a little about what it would be like to fly to Mars and then live there. They practice Mars-walks and test freeze-dried food that astronauts will have to eat. There have been three crews take part in HI-SEAS since 2013, with the latest group of six astronauts having begun a mission in October 2014, which is set to end in June 2015.

1965
The first space mission to successfully reach Mars is Mariner 4, which shows the Red Planet is barren and lifeless.

1969
Astronauts Neil Armstrong and Buzz Aldrin land on the Moon, becoming the first humans to set foot on another world.

Buzz Aldrin stood on the Moon. Could astronauts one day stand on Mars?

1976
The Viking landers and orbiters transform what we know about Mars, finding ancient riverbeds and searching for life on the surface.

The crew of the Mars500 experiment, during their 'return' journey

Skills
Mars500 astronauts had to be between the ages of 25 and 50, have academic qualifications and be specialists in engineering, biology or medical skills, and be multilingual.

Large base
The Mars500 facility was quite large, 550m³ (19,423ft³), large enough to give six astronauts plenty of room.

Medical module
Numerous medical experiments were carried out on the crew, such as cardiac and digestion experiments, as well as research on long-term effects of weightlessness and radiation.

Communications
Astronauts could only communicate with the outside world by email or by radio, with a 20-minute delay built in.

Emergency
Emergency situations, such as air leaks, were simulated in order to test how the crew responded to danger.

Habitation module
Once they had 'landed' on Mars, the crew were able to stay in a habitation module which had all the comforts of home.

Landing craft
After they'd 'arrived' at Mars the crew had to spend 30 days in the Landing Module Simulator while 'on planet'.

The Mars500 chamber provides a homely environment for the astronauts stuck on their 'journey'

Simulating Mars on Earth

Austrian Space Forum's Gernot Groemer on the Mars2013 project

Could you briefly describe what the Mars2013 expedition entailed?
Directed by a mission support centre in Austria, a small field crew conducted experiments preparing for future human Mars missions, mainly in the fields of engineering, planetary surface operations, astrobiology, geophysics/geology, life sciences and others. We had a truly international team from 23 countries, involving more than 100 researchers and volunteers, including the United Kingdom.

What did you learn from your expedition?
We had 17 peer-reviewed research experiments and collected a large data set. One of the major outcomes was that we have gained a lot of operational experience in conducting human exploration activities on the surface of another world.

Do you think humans are ready for a trip to Mars?
Yes. It will be the most technically challenging journey our society has ever undertaken, but from an engineering and scientific point of view, we are almost ready. In all our research we haven't encountered a showstopper that told us "no, you can't go."

What do you think the future holds for manned exploration of the Red Planet?
At the Austrian Space Forum we say the first human to walk on Mars is already born. I personally believe this generation will be the first one to be able to tackle the question of life in the universe on a promising planetary surface for the first time. If you read a history book in 200 years from now, the economic crisis might only be a marginal chapter. In the long run, it will be known as the time when we left the planet to discover new worlds.

© Austrian Space Forum; Adrian Mann; NASA; ESA

1997
NASA's Pathfinder mission arrives on Mars with its little Sojourner rover. The rover provides a new, mobile method of exploring Mars.

1998
Construction begins on the International Space Station, which becomes an ideal place for training for long-duration missions such as to Mars.

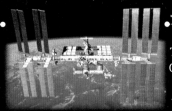

2004
The Mars exploration rovers Spirit and Opportunity land on Mars and capture the public's imagination with their exploits in exploring the Red Planet.

Getting to the Red Planet

What will astronauts face during their journey?

We will soon have the technological capability to go to Mars, thanks to NASA's latest spaceflight system that is under development, the Orion capsule and the Space Launch System, or SLS. Orion is billed as a multi-purpose crew vehicle, and has already experienced test flights with the aim of sending astronauts into space onboard it within the next decade. A little like a bigger, far more sophisticated version of the Apollo capsules that took 24 astronauts to the Moon, Orion by itself is not suitable for a long journey to Mars. However, Orion could hook up with a larger habitation module in orbit around Earth, providing the living space necessary for the astronauts before leaving Earth orbit and heading for Mars.

To get Orion and the habitation module to their destination will require a giant rocket – the biggest since the Saturn V. Simply called the Space Launch System, it will come in a couple of varieties. The first, called Block I, will be able to launch 70 tons into low Earth orbit using Space Shuttle-derived booster rockets. The next version, Block II, will dispense with the shuttle boosters for more advanced rockets, capable of launching 130 tons into space. No other rocket in history has ever been capable of launching such a large payload. The habitat module could be launched in segments and then assembled in space before leaving for Mars on the back of an SLS rocket.

The private space company SpaceX is also keen to get in on the act. Owner of SpaceX, Elon Musk, has said that he wants to start a colony on Mars, and is developing a Mars Colonial Transporter, which Musk says will be capable of launching 100 tons into space. The mission may involve some variation of SpaceX's Dragon capsule that's already ferrying cargo to the International Space Station and could one day be outfitted to carry astronauts too.

NASA's new super rocket

The Space Launch System (SLS) is set to launch astronauts to the Moon, asteroids, or Mars

Landing on Mars
Another option for SLS is to land astronauts on Mars in a semi-permanent habitat, where they will live for 540 days until the opportunity arises to return home.

Service module
This section of the exploration vehicle is home to Orion's engine, fuel and oxygen supplies.

Going to Mars' moons
NASA already has plans to use the SLS to go to Mars. One option is to go to either of its moons Deimos or Phobos, which could be used as future bases for Mars exploration.

Solar panels
Two solar panels on either side of the service module will help provide power for long-duration missions into space.

Payload
The SLS Block II rocket will be capable of launching at least 130 tons into space – the Saturn V rocket managed 118 tons.

Rockets
To give the SLS that extra punch into orbit, the Block II heavy-lift rocket will be powered by advanced boosters, the exact design of which has yet to be decided.

Expensive trip
Getting into space onboard the SLS will be expensive, costing an estimated £12 billion ($18 billion) for the development of the rocket and Orion craft, and £325 million ($500 million) for each launch.

Faster journey
The nuclear thermal rocket version of the SLS could cut travel times to Mars down to just three or four months, reducing the radiation exposure of the crew.

Hard shell
Orion's hull will be made of an aluminium-lithium alloy, which has previously been used as the main material for the Space Shuttle's large external fuel tank.

Nuclear power
The SLS will need even more power to reach Mars. NASA is currently studying nuclear thermal rocket engines, where liquid hydrogen is heated in a nuclear reactor and then spat out to provide thrust.

Emergencies
In an emergency, the crew can fire an additional thruster underneath the capsule that will take it clear of the rocket should there be an explosive accident.

2006
NASA's Mars Reconnaissance Orbiter arrives in Mars orbit, taking pictures of the surface to help choose landing sites for manned missions.

Early 2020s
NASA intends to first send its manned Orion capsule to visit a near-Earth asteroid before it sends a mission to Mars.

The first Martian astronauts will live in simple habitation modules, perhaps built out of spaceships.

2030s
For humans to survive on Mars, they will need purpose-built habitat modules and supplies that could be sent to Mars ahead of any crewed mission.

42.05km

LONGEST DRIVE ON MARS

NASA's Opportunity rover holds the off-Earth distance record after travelling 42.05km (26.13mi) across the surface of Mars, beating Soviet Lunokhod 2 lunar rover, which travelled 39km (24.2mi) in 1973.

DID YOU KNOW? Mars soil may be suitable for growing plants in, allowing colonists to grow their own food in giant greenhouses

The right trajectory

Using current space technology, it takes about seven or eight months to reach Mars. You have to leave at just the right time, when the Earth is at what we call perihelion, or the closest point to the Sun, of the orbital path to Mars. Spacecraft to the Red Planet then use a special trajectory called a Hohmann transfer orbit. This works because of a law of orbital mechanics, which says that if you can increase the spacecraft's energy at perihelion, you can increase the aphelion of its orbit, which is how far it gets from the Sun. However, you also need to make sure you arrive in position in Mars' orbit around the Sun at the same time that Mars itself does. The alignment occurs only once every two years, meaning that if you miss it, you have a long wait for the next one.

Perihelion
This is Earth's closest point in the transfer orbit to the Sun. By launching at this time, it is possible to control the size of the spacecraft's orbit.

Transfer orbit
It takes seven to eight months to reach Mars via this orbit, which uses the minimum amount of fuel.

Entering orbit
The spacecraft must then fire a retro-rocket to slow down to allow capture by Mars' gravity, or by aerobraking in the planet's atmosphere, to enter orbit.

Aphelion
The spacecraft's most distant point in its orbit is at the same distance as Mars' orbit.

Mars
The spacecraft must cross Mars' orbit at exactly the same time and position as the planet Mars itself.

Docking
Orion will have a docking system that will allow it to dock with the ISS and the habitation module.

Crew
Orion contains 50 per cent more volume inside than the Apollo capsule, able to house up to four astronauts.

Effects of long-term space travel

Staying fit and healthy during a long flight will be harder than actually getting there

Astronauts headed to Mars will face an uphill battle to stay healthy because space has lots of ways to make you poorly. Microgravity affects the blood circulation, causing bone loss and muscle atrophy, meaning the astronauts must constantly exercise to combat muscle wastage. While the gravity on Mars is just 38 per cent of Earth's gravity, many of these problems will be alleviated once the astronauts land. More deadly is radiation, from both the Sun and from cosmic rays coming from deep space. Because Mars does not have a magnetic field to deflect space radiation and keep it from the surface, astronauts will have to live inside shielded habitats. There is also the worry of psychological effects resulting from the strange environment and isolation from everyone on Earth.

Radiation
Solar flares from the Sun and cosmic rays from deep space would expose astronauts to potentially deadly levels of radiation during a Mars mission.

Blood
Microgravity slows down your blood circulation, increasing blood pressure and heart rate.

Bones
In microgravity your bones are not required to support your body weight, so bone tissue is broken down much faster than it is replenished.

Balance
In the microgravity of space, as well as the reduced gravity on Mars, the human body will take time to adjust.

Psychology
Isolation, boredom and living in close quarters to other crew members could cause psychological effects ranging from insomnia to depression.

Kidneys
Higher levels of calcium in the blood due to bone loss can lead to an increased risk of kidney stones.

Muscles
In space, under low gravity, your muscles can waste away without frequent exercise.

2030s
The 2030s are probably the earliest that the space agencies of the world will launch a manned mission to Mars, although the Mars One project wants to do so in 2024.

2100s
Terraforming Mars will require the atmosphere to be thickened and warmed. This could be accomplished by releasing greenhouse gases from factories.

Over hundreds of years terraforming could transform Mars into a more Earth-like world

FAR FUTURE
After hundreds or even thousands of years, the atmosphere could grow thick enough for liquid water to survive on Mars' surface.

The Mars Hopper

The Martian vehicle that will hop, skip and jump its way around the Red Planet

British scientists have designed a robot that could roam the Red Planet by jumping over 0.8 kilometres (half a mile) at a time. The Mars Hopper will tackle the rocky landscape by leaping over obstacles.

The Hopper measures 2.5 metres (8.2 feet) across and weighs 1,000 kilograms (2,205 pounds), which is slightly more than NASA's Curiosity rover. One hop could launch the vehicle up to 900 metres (2,953 feet) at a time. To achieve this, a radioactive thermal capacitor core will provide thrust through a rocket nozzle. The Martian atmosphere, thick in carbon dioxide, would provide the fuel as it is compressed and liquefied within the Hopper.

If successful, the Hopper would allow rapid exploration of Mars with tricky terrains like Olympus Mons and other hills, craters and canyons much easier to navigate. On current vehicles such as the Exploration rovers, the wheels have become stuck on slopes and the sandy, rocky texture of the planet's surface. The Hopper will use magnets in its four-metre (13-foot) leg span to allow it to leap again and again. The magnets will create an eddy current to produce a damping effect.

Proposed by experts from the company Astrium and the University of Leicester, the concept was first designed in 2010. A slight issue lies in the rate of CO_2 gathering, with the current system taking several weeks to fill the fuel tank. However, the vehicle will more often than not be at a standstill as it thoroughly scours the Martian landscape, so this should not pose an immediate problem. ⚙

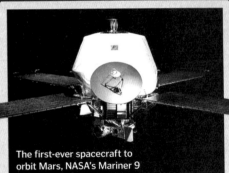

The first-ever spacecraft to orbit Mars, NASA's Mariner 9

Martian exploration programmes

The first craft to attempt to explore Mars was launched way back in 1960 when the USSR's 1M spacecraft failed to leave Earth's atmosphere. After various unsuccessful launches by the USA and the Soviet Union, NASA's Mariner 9 became the first craft to orbit the planet in 1971. In 1975 the Viking 1 lander was the first to successfully touch down on the surface. The USSR managed to orbit Mars only weeks after the Mariner with their Mars 2 spacecraft but have not yet landed on the planet. The most recent lander is NASA's Curiosity, which was launched in 2011 and is tracking the Martian surface as you read this. The third organisation to get in on the act was the ESA (European Space Agency) who launched the Mars Express and Beagle 2 Lander in 2003. The Express has successfully orbited the planet but unfortunately communication was lost with Beagle 2 after its deployment. The most recent NASA craft is MAVEN, the Mars Atmospheric and Volatile EvolutioN, which launched in 2013 and entered Martian orbit in September 2014. Also in 2013, the Indian Space Research Organization (ISRO) launched its Mars Orbiter Mission (MOM) in its bid to become the fourth space agency to reach the red planet.

1. NEW

Spirit
Both the Spirit and Opportunity crafts have found evidence of hydrothermal vents, ancient lakes of acid and evidence of wind on Mars.

2. NEWER

Curiosity
Locating ancient waterbeds and digging into the Martian surface have helped the Curiosity to reignite humanity's interest in the Red Planet.

3. NEWEST

Hopper
Using legs to traverse the rough environment instead of slow-rolling wheels, it is predicted the Hopper will make new discoveries at a rapid rate.

DID YOU KNOW? *The first manned mission to Mars is planned to launch as early as 2030*

Galileo Space Probe

The first man-made object to ever enter Jupiter's atmosphere

NASA launched the Galileo spacecraft, which comprises the Galileo Orbiter and Space Probe, atop a space shuttle in 1989, using a 38-month orbit of Venus and the Earth's gravitational pull to gain the necessary speed to reach Jupiter.

While the Galileo Orbiter was designed to orbit and study Jupiter and its moons, the Galileo Probe was released near Jupiter and was sent into the gas giant itself. It entered the atmosphere of Jupiter at 30 miles per second (47kmps), the highest impact speed ever achieved by a man-made object. Amazingly, Jupiter's gravitational forces slowed the craft to 0.07 miles per second (0.12 kmps) in just four minutes.

The Probe's heat shield, made of carbon phenolic, was able to withstand the 15,500°C ball of plasma caused by this sudden deceleration, producing light brighter than the Sun's surface. It remained active for about 78 minutes as it passed through Jupiter's atmosphere, losing more than half its mass in the process before being crushed by the huge pressure.

Wrapped in black and gold blankets to provide insulations and protect against micrometeorites, the Probe conducted nine experiments that measured Jupiter's atmospheric structure. It discovered the presence of a large amount of argon, krypton and xenon. For these to form Jupiter would need to be at a temperature of -240°C, suggesting it once orbited much further from the Sun. ❀

Technicians prepare Galileo for liftoff at the Kennedy Space Center

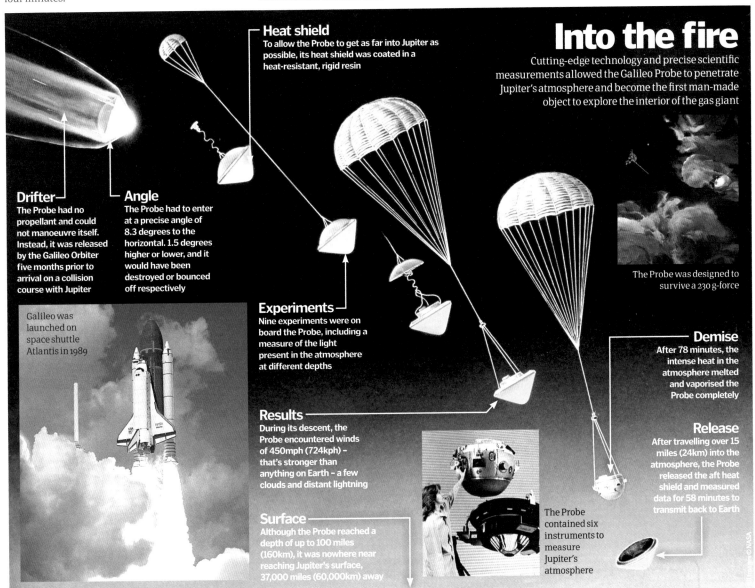

Heat shield
To allow the Probe to get as far into Jupiter as possible, its heat shield was coated in a heat-resistant, rigid resin

Into the fire

Cutting-edge technology and precise scientific measurements allowed the Galileo Probe to penetrate Jupiter's atmosphere and become the first man-made object to explore the interior of the gas giant

Drifter
The Probe had no propellant and could not manoeuvre itself. Instead, it was released by the Galileo Orbiter five months prior to arrival on a collision course with Jupiter

Angle
The Probe had to enter at a precise angle of 8.3 degrees to the horizontal. 1.5 degrees higher or lower, and it would have been destroyed or bounced off respectively

The Probe was designed to survive a 230 g-force

Galileo was launched on space shuttle Atlantis in 1989

Experiments
Nine experiments were on board the Probe, including a measure of the light present in the atmosphere at different depths

Demise
After 78 minutes, the intense heat in the atmosphere melted and vaporised the Probe completely

Results
During its descent, the Probe encountered winds of 450mph (724kph) – that's stronger than anything on Earth – a few clouds and distant lightning

Release
After travelling over 15 miles (24km) into the atmosphere, the Probe released the aft heat shield and measured data for 58 minutes to transmit back to Earth

The Probe contained six instruments to measure Jupiter's atmosphere

Surface
Although the Probe reached a depth of up to 100 miles (160km), it was nowhere near reaching Jupiter's surface, 37,000 miles (60,000km) away

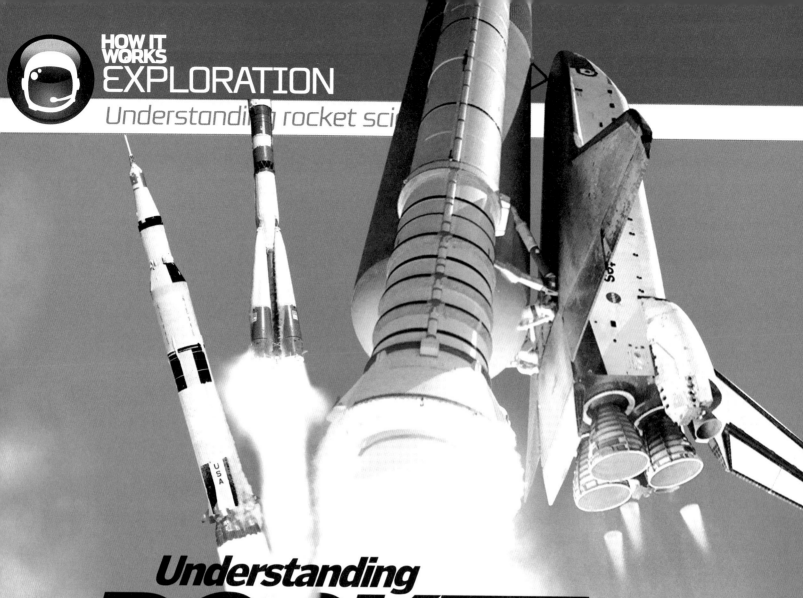

Understanding
ROCKET SCIENCE

Modern rocket science was used in entertainment and weaponry, long before the realms of space travel

 Rocket science has been around since the 280s BCE, when ancient Chinese alchemists invented gunpowder. Initially used in fireworks, gunpowder was soon put to use in weaponry as fire-arrows, bombs and more. Through the centuries, rockets continued to be used as weapons until the early-20th Century. In 1912, Robert Goddard built the first liquid-fuel rocket (previous rockets were solid-fuel) and began the age of modern rocketry. To date, there have been about 500 rocket launches from NASA's Cape Canaveral, and more than five thousand satellites launched by rockets from spaceports around the world.

While the term 'rocket' can be used to describe everything from cars to jet packs, most of us think 'space travel' when we see 'rocket'. Most rockets follow the same basic design.

Typically they are tube-like, with stacks of components. Rockets carry propellants (a fuel and an oxidiser), one or more engines, stabilisation devices, and a nozzle to accelerate and expand gases. However, there's a lot of variation among those basic elements.

There are two main types of rockets: solid-fuel and liquid-fuel. The former have some similarities to those early gunpowder rockets. For space applications, solid-fuel rockets are often used as boosters to lower the amount of needed liquid fuel and reduce the overall mass of the vehicle as a whole. A common type of solid propellant, used in the solid rocket boosters on the NASA space shuttles, is a composite made of ammonium percholate, aluminium, iron oxide and a polymer to bind it. The propellant is packed into a casing. Solid-fuel

5 TOP FACTS
ROCKET FIRSTS

Liquid-fuel rocket
1 Robert Goddard built and launched the first liquid-fuel rocket on 26 March 1926. It was fuelled by gasoline and liquid oxygen, the flight lasting 2.5 seconds.

True rocket
2 In 1232 BC, the Chinese used rocket-arrows propelled by burning gunpowder in their war with the Mongols. While not very effective, they were likely a frightening sight.

Launch into Earth orbit
3 On 4 Oct 1957, the R-7 ICBM was the first rocket to launch an artificial satellite – Sputnik 1 – into orbit. This marked the start of the Space Race between the US and the USSR.

Launch into space
4 Germany launched the first rocket capable of reaching space, the V-2 rocket, in 1942. The missile was launched at sites in England and Belgium as part of the WWII effort.

Private launch, Earth orbit
5 Space X, a company pioneering commercial space travel, launched Falcon 9 on 10 Dec 2010. With an unmanned capsule, it orbited Earth twice before landing in the Pacific.

DID YOU KNOW? *Advances in gunnery left rockets forgotten until an Indian prince used them in the Mysore Wars (late 1700s)*

rockets are used alone sometimes to launch lighter objects into low-Earth orbit, but they cannot provide the type of overall thrust needed to propel a very heavy object into Earth orbit or into space. They can also be difficult to control and to stop once ignited.

The difficulty in getting off the ground is due to the strength of Earth's gravity. This is why thrust – a rocket's strength – is measured in pounds or Newtons. One pound of thrust is the amount of force that it takes to keep a one-pound object at rest against Earth's gravity. A rocket carries fuel that weighs much more than the object that it's trying to move (its payload – a spacecraft or satellite). To understand why, think about what happens when you blow up a balloon and then release it. The balloon flies around the room

because of the force exerted by the air molecules escaping from it. This is Newton's third law in action (see boxout on the following page). But the balloon is only propelling itself; rockets need to generate thrust greater than their mass, which includes the weight of the fuel. For example, the space shuttle in total weighs about 4.4 million pounds, with a possible payload of about 230,000 pounds. To lift this, rocket boosters provided 3.3 million pounds of thrust each, while three engines on the main tank each provided 375,000 pounds of thrust.

Liquid-fuel rockets have the benefit of losing mass over time as their propellant is used up, which in turn increases the rate of acceleration. They have a higher energy content than solid-fuel rockets. Typically they

consist of a fuel and an oxidiser in separate tanks, mixed in a combustion chamber. Guidance systems control the amount of propellants that enter, depending on the amount of thrust needed. Liquid-fuel rockets can be stopped and started.

Launch location can also help rockets become more efficient. European Space Agency member country France chose to build a spaceport in French Guiana not only for its location near water, but also its location near the equator. Launching a rocket near the equator, in an easterly direction, makes use of energy created by the Earth's rotation speed of 465m per second. This also means that putting a rocket into geosynchronous orbit is easier, because few corrections have to be made to its trajectory.

Liquid-fuel rocket

The components of a liquid fuel rocket and how they work

Fuel
Common fuels used today include kerosene (RP-1), liquid hydrogen and hydrazine

Oxidiser
The oxidiser may be liquid hydrogen, or in the case of hydrazine, nitrogen tetroxide

Pumps
These pumps move the fuel and oxidiser into the combustion chamber

Combustion chamber
Jets of fuel and oxidiser meet here, where their ignition creates a high-pressure stream of gases

Nozzle
The gases are further accelerated in the nozzle, which directs them from the engine

© DK Images

Escape velocity How rockets break free of Earth's gravity

Throw an apple into the air and it will keep travelling away from planet Earth until gravity overcomes the force of your throw. At this point the apple will fall back down to the

ground. If, however, you launched that apple from a cannon at a speed of 25,000mph (40,000kph) – that's a nippy seven miles (11km) per second – the apple will reach what's known

as escape velocity. At this speed, the force of gravity will never be stronger than the force causing the apple to move away from Earth, and so the apple will escape Earth's gravity.

Escaping other bodies

Escape velocity depends on the mass of the planet or moon, meaning that each planet's escape velocity is different

Ceres
Mass (Earth = 1): 0.00015
Escape velocity: 1,430mph (2,301kph)

The Moon
Mass (Earth = 1): 0.012
Escape velocity: 5,320mph (8,561kph)

Earth
Mass (Earth = 1): 1
Escape velocity: 25,038mph (40,000kph)

The Sun
Mass (Earth = 1): 333,000
Escape velocity: 1,381,600mph (2,223,469kph)

1. Gravity
An object fired from a cannon is returned to Earth by gravity, in the direction of Earth's core

2. Mid-range
The greater the object's speed, the further it travels before returning to Earth (falls at the same rate of acceleration)

3. Long-range
With enough velocity, the object reaches the horizon, at which point the ground 'falls away' (due to Earth's curve) and the object travels further before landing

8. Escape velocity
At escape velocity, the object will break free of Earth's gravitational pull

5. Orbital velocity
At this speed the object's gravitational fall is balanced with the curvature of the Earth

6. Circular orbit
The object travels so fast it falls all the way around the world. It is now in orbit

7. Elliptical orbit
Object speed is greater than orbital velocity but less than escape velocity. The object continues to circle the Earth

Newton's cannon
How an object's velocity helps it escape Earth's gravitational pull

4. Half orbit
Earth's surface falls away from the object nearly equal to gravity's rate of acceleration

The three laws of motion

Rockets have been around for thousands of years, but the science behind them wasn't understood until Isaac Newton's 1687 book *Philosophiae Naturalis Principia Mathematica*. In it, Newton explained three laws that govern motion of all objects, now known as Newton's Laws of Motion. Knowing these laws have made modern rocketry possible.

FIRST LAW

The first law states that objects that are at rest will stay at rest, while objects that are in motion will stay in motion unless an external, unbalanced force acts upon it. A rocket is at rest until thrust unbalances it; it will then stay in motion until it encounters another unbalanced force.

SECOND LAW

Force equals mass times acceleration. Force is the pressure from the explosions. It accelerates the rocket's mass in one direction and the mass of the expelled gases in the other. Mass decreases as it burns up propellants, while acceleration increases.

THIRD LAW

The third law states that for every action, there is an equal and opposite reaction. When a rocket launches, the action is the gas expelling from its engine. The rocket moves in the opposite direction, which is the reaction. To lift off, the thrust must be greater than the rocket's mass.

Saturn V: The biggest and most powerful

Rockets like Saturn V, the one used to launch NASA's Apollo and Skylab programs, are multi-stage liquid-fuelled boosters. The Saturn V is considered to be the biggest, most powerful and most successful rocket ever built. It was 110.6m tall, 10.1m in diameter and had a payload of 119,000kgs to low-Earth orbit.

There were three stages, followed by an instrument unit and the payload (spacecraft). The total mission time for this rocket was about 20 mins. The centre engine was ignited first, then engines on either side ignited. The first stage lifted the rocket to about 70km and burned for 2.5 mins. When sensors in the tanks sensed that the propellant was low, motors detached the first stage. The second stage continued the trajectory to 176km and burned for six mins. About halfway through this stage's ignition, the instrument unit took control of calculating the trajectory.

Second stage complete, solid-fuel rockets fired it away from the third stage. The third stage burned for 2.5 mins and stayed attached to the spacecraft while it orbited the Earth, at an altitude of 191.2km. It continued to thrust and vent hydrogen before ramping up and burning for six more minutes, so the spacecraft could reach a high enough velocity to escape Earth's gravity.

Launch Umbilical Tower

Built as part of the MLP (but removed and installed permanently at the launch site for the shuttle missions), the Launch Umbilical Tower contains swing arms to access the rocket, a crane and a water suppression system

Payload

The Saturn V payload was either Apollo spacecraft or the Skylab space station. With the former, it carried both the Command Service Module (CSM) and the Lunar Module (LM)

Instrument unit

The instrument unit, containing telemetry and guidance systems, controlled the rocket's operations until the ejection of the third stage

Third stage

The third stage is S-IVB. It only had one engine but also used liquid hydrogen and liquid oxygen. Fully fuelled, it weighed 119,000 kilograms

Second stage

The second stage, or S-II, also contained five engines and was nearly identical to the first stage. However, it was powered by liquid hydrogen and liquid oxygen and weighed 480,000 kilograms

First stage

The first stage was also known as S-IC. It contained a central engine, four outer engines, RP-1 fuel (kerosene) and liquid oxygen as the oxidiser. Fully fuelled, it weighed 2.3 million kilograms

© DK Images

Crawler Transporter

This tracked vehicle moved spacecraft from the Assembly Building to the launch complex along a path called the Crawlerway, and then moved the empty MLP back to the VAB

Mobile Launcher Platform (MLP)

A three-story platform designed to support and launch the Saturn V (and later, the space shuttle). Spacecraft are built vertically, in a ready-for-launch configuration, in the Vehicle Assembly Building (VAB)

SPEED NEEDED TO ESCAPE EARTH'S GRAVITY	**11.3kps**	GALLONS OF FUEL ON BOARD	**500,000**
TIME IT TAKES TO REACH SPACE	**8mins**	SPEED NEEDED TO REMAIN IN EARTH ORBIT	**28,000kph**

DID YOU KNOW? In 100 BCE the Greek inventor Hero created the aeolipile, a rocket-like jet engine that ran on steam

6. Payload launched
Ariane's payload, a satellite, is released by steel springs. The rocket is also capable of carrying and launching dual satellites and also delivered a spacecraft to the International Space Station

4. Third stage
This third stage is known as the storable propellant stage. It contains two propellant tanks of nitrogen tetroxide and hydrazine, which feed an engine that provides the energy to release the payload

Here the Apollo 6 flight is shown between its first and second stage

© NASA

5. Fairing
The fairing protects the upper stages and payload from thermodynamic and acoustic pressure during launch. It falls off about three minutes after liftoff, at an altitude of about 100km

3. Main stage
Ariane's main, or second, stage comprises two separate compartments, containing liquid oxygen and liquid hydrogen. These power an engine that burns for ten minutes until the stage separates, at an altitude of 145km

2. Solid rocket boosters
These solid rocket boosters provide 110 tons of thrust. At an altitude of 60km, about 130 seconds after liftoff, the boosters are spent and detach from the main stage

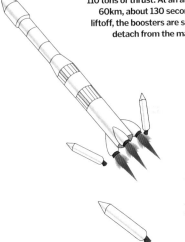

Multi-stage rockets

Multi-stage rockets are essentially multiple rockets (each with their own engines and fuel systems) stacked on top or beside each other. Sometimes this assembly is known as a launch vehicle. As the fuel burns, the container holding it becomes dead weight. When a stage separates from the main body, the next stage is capable of generating more acceleration. The downside of a multi-stage rocket is that they're more complex and time-consuming to build, and there are multiple potential failure points. However, the fuel savings are worth the risk. This example shows the ESA's Ariane rocket launching a satellite in Earth orbit.

1 Payload packed
Any external features of a payload (such as solar panels) will remain folded up until it reaches orbit

THE FINAL COUNT DOWN
Liquid-propellant rockets have come a long way since their inception...

1981
STS
NASA's Space Transportation System, which took the shuttle into orbit, was retired in July 2011 after a mighty 135 missions.

1967
Saturn V
The most powerful space rocket to date, Saturn V was taller than a 36-story building and launched every Apollo Moon mission.

1957
Sputnik
The Soviet Union's Sputnik Rocket launched the world's first satellite, Sputnik 1, a major landmark at the start of the 'Space Race' with the USA.

1944
V-2 Rocket
Developed by Germany for use at the end of WWII, the V-2 was the first rocket to achieve sub-orbital spaceflight.

1926
The first modern rocket
American Robert Goddard built the first successful liquid-propellant rocket. It climbed 12.5 metres before landing in a nearby cabbage patch.

Propellant injection
Ion engines use a propellant fuel, which is injected into a discharge chamber and bombarded with electrons

Collision
The collision of propellant atoms and electrons results in the release of positively charged ions

Ion engine propulsion

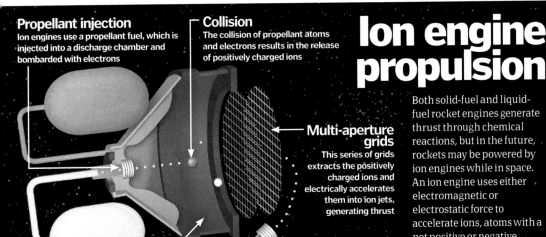

Multi-aperture grids
This series of grids extracts the positively charged ions and electrically accelerates them into ion jets, generating thrust

Magnetic field
Magnetic rings generate a magnetic field that facilitates the ionisation process

Cathode
A hollow cathode injects negatively charged electrons into the positively charged ion beam to render it neutral

Both solid-fuel and liquid-fuel rocket engines generate thrust through chemical reactions, but in the future, rockets may be powered by ion engines while in space. An ion engine uses either electromagnetic or electrostatic force to accelerate ions, atoms with a net positive or negative charge. While the amount of thrust generated is comparatively low, the engine is more efficient and can last for a very long time.

© NASA

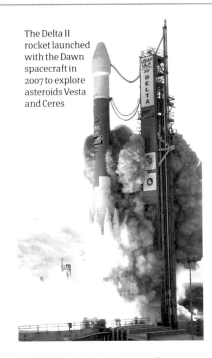

The Delta II rocket launched with the Dawn spacecraft in 2007 to explore asteroids Vesta and Ceres

The new breed of propulsion system that will take us to Mars and beyond

MEGA ROCKETS

The hardest part of exploring the final frontier is actually getting there in the first place. While mankind has been undertaking space-faring missions for over 50 years now, our methods of propulsion to escape Earth's influence have barely changed at all, and the fundamental problem of overcoming our planet's gravity is still readily apparent. When, years ago, people dreamed of regular space planes flying every week or space elevators lifting cargo into orbit, limitations and complexities have seen our forays beyond Low Earth Orbit (LEO) rely solely on vertically launching rockets. Unfortunately, these themselves bring with them a number of limitations – notably the amount of thrust that is needed to transport cargo into orbit and the cost considering that most rockets are almost entirely non-reusable. And so, as is the way with most things, the solution to take more cargo into orbit was relatively simple: make the rockets bigger. Much bigger.

Giant rockets are used predominantly to take loads such as satellites into orbit. Different rockets can travel to differing heights, with larger payloads unable to be transported into further orbits, while smaller payloads can be taken out to geosynchronous orbits over 32,000 kilometres (20,000 miles) above the surface of the Earth, and even beyond.

One of the major problems with rocket-powered flight is the sheer cost involved in taking even just a single kilogram into orbit. Most rockets that fly today are all but wholly non-reusable. This means the boosters that are

BIG

1. Johannes Kepler ATV
This unmanned ISS resupply vehicle is Europe's heaviest ever space payload, weighing almost 20,000kg (44,092lb).

BIGGER

2. Apollo 16
The penultimate manned mission to the Moon was also the heaviest, at 47,000kg (103,607lb), owing to the lunar rover and satellite it carried.

BIGGEST

3. Skylab
NASA's first space station weighed in at a mighty 77,100kg (169,976lb). Incredibly, the entire thing was launched in one go by a Saturn V rocket in 1973.

DID YOU KNOW? The Delta IV Heavy holds 483,500 gallons of fuel but only does the equivalent of 0.00087mpg

The ESA's Ariane 5 heavy-lift rocket

jettisoned as the rocket makes its way to the cosmos are left to burn up in the atmosphere or, occasionally, are recovered from the sea where they have splashed down, but they are rarely designed to be flown again and again.

One company planning to tackle this problem is SpaceX, a US-based manufacturer that has been developing its own rockets for several years. The first of these, the Falcon 9, has already flown several times, but the next development will be the Falcon Heavy, a giant rocket employing three of the Falcon 9's Merlin engines to take about 50,000 kilograms (110,231 pounds) of mass into orbit. The ultimate goal of SpaceX is to make the rocket fully reusable. Their plan is to use rockets attached to each stage to carry out controlled ground landings and recover each component of the rocket. This has never been done before, but for good reason, as making a rocket that can survive the forces of re-entry intact is incredibly difficult.

Other innovations in the world of heavy-lift rockets have largely focused on new propulsive fuels and advanced technologies to make better use of what is already available. One example of this is NASA's new J-2X engine. The original J-2 engine was used on the Saturn V Moon rocket, the most powerful rocket of all time, but the new J-2X engine employs advanced capabilities to harness the power of this old workhorse and turn it into a modern marvel.

The only way for humans to venture beyond LEO, where the International Space Station (ISS) currently resides, is to use a heavy-lift rocket. NASA's long-term plan is to use its new Space Launch

Inside NASA's Space Launch System

Payload
Preliminary specifications allow for a payload of 70 tons, but eventually this will be closer to 130 tons, equivalent to 75 SUVs

J-2X
In advanced versions of the Space Launch System, NASA will attach a J-2X engine (an upgraded version of the J-2 engine used on the Saturn V rocket) to achieve even more power

Solid
Some heavy-lift rockets, like the Space Launch System, use two or more additional solid fuel rockets to harness a greater amount of thrust

Liquid
The core of NASA's heavy-lift rocket uses five of the engines that powered the Space Shuttle for thrust, fuelled by liquid hydrogen and oxygen

"One major benefit of heavy-lift rockets is the ability to lift a satellite to geostationary orbit"

Heavy lifting
How do giant rockets differ from the norm?

There are three major classes of rocket that are used to reach space. Light and medium launch vehicles are generally used for smaller satellite launches to LEO, whereas heavy-lift launch vehicles are used for deep-space missions and to haul larger objects into higher orbit. These rockets can do what others cannot, namely taking mega payloads into orbit. NASA's Saturn V rocket lifted an entire space station – the Skylab – in 1973.

One major benefit of heavy-lift rockets is the ability to lift a satellite to geostationary orbit. At this height – 35,406 kilometres (22,000 miles) above Earth – satellites stay in the same position, which is crucial for communications satellites. Heavy-lift rockets can also take vehicles, or even humans, to other planetary bodies. The Saturn V rocket could take 130 tons to Earth orbit or 50 tons to the Moon, and was imperative in the Apollo missions. NASA's next mega rocket, the Space Launch System, will be able to lift a comparable load and is planned to take astronauts to the Moon, an asteroid and Mars.

However, not all heavy-lift rockets can travel these large distances. NASA's Space Shuttle, although extremely powerful, did not have the propulsion to escape LEO, and thus it was used to take large payloads into orbit such as the Hubble Space Telescope and many modules for the ISS.

©NASA

System to take astronauts first to the Moon, then to an asteroid, and finally to Mars by the 2030s. SpaceX aims to challenge NASA's deep-space exploration plans by launching its own variant of the Falcon Heavy in the coming years. Known as the Red Dragon mission, this would see the soon-to-be completed Falcon Heavy taking a specially designed Dragon capsule, SpaceX's human transportation vehicle, to Mars by the 2020s. It all depends who finishes their heavy-lift launch vehicle first, but its entirely possible that the first human on Mars will be flown by a private technology company, which would be no small feat, to put it mildly.

Heavy-lift launch vehicles have a number of advantages over their smaller brethren, not least their size. Were it not for NASA's Space Transportation System rocket, used to take the Space Shuttle into orbit, the ISS would be some way from completion. It was thanks to the high operating capabilities of this launch system that NASA was able to contribute more than 90 per cent of the orbiting outpost and ensure that it reached completion this year.

Heavy-lift rockets, like regular-sized rockets, have a number of stages to take the vehicle into orbit. The first stage gets the rocket off the ground. This is usually composed of several booster rockets strapped together, like the Delta IV Heavy which uses three of the boosters seen on the smaller Delta III.

The advancement of launch vehicles promises to usher in an exciting era for space exploration. Bigger, more powerful rockets will enable us to visit once unreachable worlds. A human mission to Mars looks more and more likely, and as the rockets are developed further, the goal of landing humans on the Red Planet in the next decade or two might just be achievable.

NASA's J-2X engine, being tested here, will play a key role in the Space Launch System

THE PAST
How man's most powerful rocket took astronauts to the Moon

The Saturn V is the most powerful rocket of all time… for the time being

© NASA

To date there has been no rocket that has matched, let alone exceeded, the lifting capabilities of the Saturn V Moon rocket. Of course, this will change in the future with the arrival of several new super-heavy-lift rockets, but for now the Saturn V retains the title of most powerful rocket of all time. Capable of lifting 130 tons into orbit, the Saturn V was used to take Apollo astronauts to the Moon throughout the Sixties and Seventies.

Undeniably the most well-known heavy-lift launch vehicle of all time, though, is the Space Transportation System (STS), used to take the Space Shuttle into orbit. The Space Shuttle could take a payload weighing 30 tons into orbit, and it was pivotal in the construction of the ISS. Now retired, the STS was one of the most powerful rockets of the modern era. It used solid rocket propellant and its initial rocket boosters were recoverable when they landed in the ocean, allowing for up to 20 more uses before they were deemed unsafe to fly.

THE PRESENT
The modern workhorses that lau satellites and resupply the ISS

Russia's heavy-lift Proton rocket is currently the longest-serving rocket in activity, completing its firs flight in 1965. It has a formidable success rate: 88 per cent across over 300 launches. It has been one of the few successes of Russia's Space Program, which has otherwise been riddled with failures and a lack of advancement, particularly in missions beyond LEO.

Another hugely successful rocket has been Boein Delta series. The largest of these, the Delta IV Heavy, can take over 20 tons of cargo into orbit. The Delta IV

The Delta IV can take 21,772kg (48,000lb) of cargo into Low Earth Orbit (LEO)

© NASA

Heavy uses two strap-on rocket boosters to achiev higher orbits and greater payload capabilities. In Europe, the ESA's Ariane rocket continues to make great strides to being the most reliable heavy-lift rocket around. It uses a cryogenic main stage, holding liquid oxygen an hydrogen, to produce a thrust of 115 ton-forces, while two solid rocket boosters provide additio thrust. These heavy-lift vehicles have been instrumental in the modern space era and w continue to launch countless satellites and craft into the cosmos.

One of the huge boosters used on the Delta rockets

ROCKET SIZE COMPARISON

Height (metres) — 120, 90, 60, 30, 0

Saturn V
Manufacturer: NASA
Payload: 118,000kg
Operation: 1967-1972
Launches: 13

Space Transportation System
Manufacturer: NASA
Payload: 24,400kg
Operation: 1981-2011
Launches: 135

Delta IV Heavy
Manufacturer: United Launch Alliance
Payload: 22,950kg
Operation: 2004-present
Launches: 4

Titan IV
Manufacturer: Lockheed Mart
Payload: 21,682k
Operation: 1989-2005
Launches: 35

Inside the Ariane 5

Take a look at the inner workings of this ESA rocket

Payload
The Ariane 5 rocket used to take up to ten tons of large cargo into orbit, most often satellites. Although it is capable of carrying humans, it never has

Stats
The Ariane 5 rocket weighs about 700 tons, one-tenth of the weight of the Eiffel Tower, is as high as a 15-storey building and reaches 8,047km/h (5,000mph) in just 120 seconds

Jettisoned
Two or three minutes after launch the boosters are jettisoned to lighten the rocket and allow it to reach a high orbit

Booster
Inside each of the 30-metre (98-foot)-tall boosters is 230 tons of solid rocket propellant

Vulcan
The central Vulcan engine takes liquid propellant from the central cryogenic main stage to propel the payload out into space

© DK Images

THE FUTURE
Which rockets will take us to the Red Planet and beyond?

With NASA's Space Shuttle retired in July 2011, the next step for the agency is to build a rocket comparable in size and power to the Saturn V. This comes in the form of the Space Launch System (SLS).

One of the major advancements of NASA's new mega rocket is its shift to liquid propellants over solid ones. Liquid propellants, while more expensive, allow for a greater power yield. In addition, solid propellants cannot be stopped burning when lit, a potential problem if a disaster were to occur, whereas liquid propellants can be throttled for the required speed. NASA is reusing old, tried-and-tested components to keep costs down. For example, the main booster core of the SLS will use five of the main engines that had been used to take the Space Shuttle into orbit. This booster core uses a liquid hydrogen/oxygen combination, a very efficient way of getting to orbit with minimal toxic waste produced. The second stage of the SLS will use a modified version of the engine used to take astronauts to the Moon aboard the Saturn V rocket. This will be the J-2X engine, an advancement of the

The predecessor to the Falcon Heavy, the Falcon 9

Concept art of SpaceX's Falcon Heavy mega rocket

© SpaceX

old Saturn V J-2 engine. At first the SLS will be able to carry 70 tons to orbit, but eventually it will be able to handle 130 tons.

American manufacturer SpaceX is also making strides with heavy-lift rockets. Having already successfully flown the smaller Falcon 9 rocket, they plan to begin flying their Falcon Heavy in the coming years. With twice the payload capability of NASA's Space Shuttle, the Falcon Heavy promises trips to space at a fraction of the cost of current rockets.

It will use three Merlin engines – the Falcon 9 rocket only uses one – and with 1.7 million kilograms (3.8 million pounds) of thrust it will be equivalent to 15,747 jumbo jets operating at full power. The ultimate goal of SpaceX's Falcon Heavy is to make the rocket fully reusable. The company's plan is to use rockets attached to each stage to carry out controlled ground landings and recover each component. If successful, the Falcon Heavy will be one of the cheapest rockets to launch of all time.

A visualisation of NASA's Space Launch System due to be completed by 2017

© NASA

Proton
Manufacturer: Roscosmos
Payload: 21,682kg
Operation: 1965-present
Launches: 326

Ariane 5
Manufacturer: EADS Astrium
Payload: 21,000kg
Operation: 1996-present
Launches: 56

Falcon Heavy
Manufacturer: SpaceX
Payload: 53,000kg
Operation: Due in 2013
Launches: 0

Space Launch System
Manufacturer: NASA
Payload: 130,000kg
Operation: Due in 2017
Launches: 0

The Orion spacecraft

How the replacement for NASA's Space Shuttle will take us to the Moon and beyond

The primary goals of the Orion spacecraft, which has been contracted to technology company Lockheed Martin by NASA, are to deliver crew and cargo to the International Space Shuttle and return astronauts to the Moon after almost a 50-year wait. Orion made its first test flight in 2014 and is on course to complete a lunar mission by the early 2020s.

The Orion crew module is similar in design and appearance to the Apollo Command Module that first took astronauts to the Moon. It is three times the volume of the Apollo module with the same 70° sloped top, deemed to be the safest and most reliable shape for re-entering Earth's atmosphere at high velocity. The Orion module has a diameter of five metres and a total mass of about 9,000kg including the cargo and the crew, which increases or decreases slightly for missions to the International Space Station and the Moon respectively. Unlike the Apollo module, which had a crew capacity of three people, the Orion module can carry between four and six astronauts.

Attached to the crew module is the service module, responsible for propulsion, electrical power, communications and water/air storage. The service module is equipped with a pair of extendable solar panels that are deployed post-launch in addition to batteries to store power for times of darkness. Like the Orion crew module, the service module is also five metres in diameter to provide a clean fit between the two, and has a mass of about 3,700kg in addition to 8,300kg of propellant.

Exerting 33,000 newtons (7,500 pounds) of thrust, the engine of the service module uses hypergolic fuels monomethyl hydrazine and nitrogen tetroxide, which are propellants that ignite on contact with each other and require no ignition source. Another benefit of these propellants is that they do not need to be cooled like other fuels; they can be stored at room temperature. 24 thrusters around the service module will also give it control to change its orientation in all directions, but these are almost 30 times weaker than the main booster.

Upon descent to Earth the Orion crew module will use a combination of parachutes and air bags to allow a cushioned touchdown on land or sea. The service module will detach in space and disintegrate in the atmosphere. The entire Orion crew module will be reusable for at most ten missions except for its ablative heat shield, which burns up on re-entry into Earth's atmosphere to protect the astronauts from the extreme heat.

The first Orion missions will see it dock with the ISS to test its systems

The Orion spacecraft will transport a lunar lander to the Moon

©NASA

Orion
1 Although Orion is currently still on schedule, there are several other private companies that are clamouring to provide NASA's transportation to the ISS.

SpaceX Dragon
2 One of the competitors, the Dragon capsule is currently undergoing advanced testing and should be ready to transport crew members to the ISS within a few years.

Boeing CST-100
3 After losing the Orion contract to Lockheed Martin, Boeing's capsule (similar in design to Orion) has been helped by $18m of funding from NASA and could launch by 2015.

Dream Chaser
4 Under development by the Sierra Nevada Corporation, this space plane won $20m from a NASA competition. It could land on almost any runway in the world.

X-37B
5 This US military space plane returned from a seven-month orbit in December 2010 and made the first ever spacecraft landing by autopilot, but its intentions were unknown.

DID YOU KNOW? An Orion test module will use over 150,000 ping-pong balls to stop it sinking after splashing down in the ocean

Launch abort
In a launch pad emergency, this rocket will lift the crew module and allow it to parachute safely to ground

Heat shield
The ablative (burns on re-entry) heat shield protects the crew module as it returns to Earth alone before the parachutes deploy

Airlock
The top of the crew module allows docking with other vehicles such as the ISS and lunar landers

The Launch Abort System will carry the crew module to safety in an emergency

Crew module
Able to accommodate up to six crew members, this module provides a safe habitat for them to stay in during their journey

Service module
This module supports the crew throughout their journey, providing life support and propulsion, before detaching upon Earth re-entry

Cargo
Inside the service module, unpressurised cargo for the ISS and science equipment are stored

Spacecraft adapter
Connects the Orion spacecraft to the launch rocket, and also protects components in the service module

When and where will Orion be going?*

2015 Low Earth orbit

Journey time: Ten minutes
Distance: 350km

Journey time: Three days
Distance: 380,000km

2019 First lunar mission

Journey time: One year
Distance: 54 million km

2031 First mission to Mars

*Provisional dates from NASA, subject to change

Spacecraft re-entry

How do spacecraft survive the journey from space to the ground?

While not all spacecraft are designed to return home after completion of a mission, those that do must overcome intense heat and forces as the spacecraft passes through our atmosphere. Almost all spacecraft undergo a ballistic entry, travelling directly through the atmosphere until parachutes slow their descent. Only a few – NASA's space shuttle and the US Air Force's secretive unmanned space plane X-37B – are capable of performing a glide landing and touch down on a runway like an aeroplane.

The dense gas in our atmosphere is useful for slowing down a spacecraft on re-entry, allowing it to land safely without the need for extra fuel to reduce its velocity when approaching our planet. This is a problem scientists must overcome when a satellite lands on a celestial body with little to no atmosphere, such as Mars or an asteroid. Spacecraft must take care when re-entering the atmosphere of Earth and ensure they approach at a specific angle of entry. Too shallow and they will bounce back off the atmosphere, but too great and they will burn up during re-entry.

Most ballistic re-entry spacecraft return to Earth at approximately 25,000mph (40,000kph), encountering temperatures up to 3,000 °C (5,400 °F). As most metals would melt at this temperature, the base of the spacecraft is made of an ablative material that burns as re-entry occurs and radiates heat away from the spacecraft. These are often made of materials such as phenolic resins and silicone rubbers.

After surviving atmospheric re-entry, spacecraft that cannot glide to the ground use parachutes to slow their descent. Russian Soyuz spacecraft usually perform a soft landing on the ground, but most spacecraft touch down in the sea, where they are recovered. A rare few unmanned spacecraft containing sensitive cargo such as photographic film are recovered in midair by an aircraft.

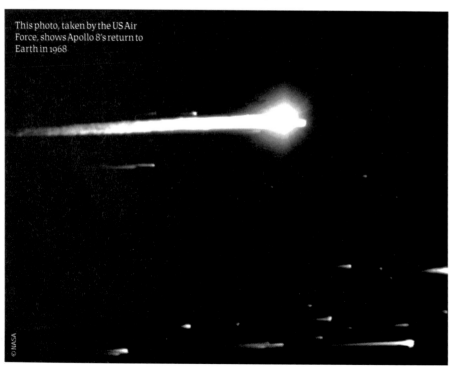

This photo, taken by the US Air Force, shows Apollo 8's return to Earth in 1968

Heat shield

During re-entry a spacecraft will typically experience a temperature that rises past 3,000°C (5,400°F), which would melt standard metals such as aluminium and steel. To overcome this problem the heat shield was developed, to dissipate heat from the spacecraft by burning on re-entry. Ablative heat shields, such as those that were used on NASA's Apollo and Mercury spacecraft, are normally made of a carbon phenolic resin that completely burns on re-entry, carrying heat away from the spacecraft as it deteriorates and keeping the occupants inside relatively safe from heat outside. This is not re-usable but some spacecraft, such as the space shuttle, use fibreglass tiles capable of absorbing heat, which do not need to be replaced after every flight.

NASA's space shuttle used thermal soak tiles to absorb heat upon re-entry

5 TOP FACTS
RE-ENTRY DISASTERS

Soyuz 1
1 Lone cosmonaut Vladimir Komarov perished in 1967 when the parachutes of Soyuz 1 tangled during re-entry following some problems in orbit.

Soyuz 5
2 In 1969 when a module failed to separate, Boris Volynov's spacecraft re-entered in a ball of fire until it righted itself and crash landed, Volynov suffered only broken teeth.

Soyuz 11
3 In 1971 the Russian Soyuz 11 spacecraft failed to depressurise properly in orbit, killing all three of the crew prior to re-entry, the only astronauts to die in space.

Columbia
4 In 2003 a piece of foam pierced the left wing of the space shuttle Columbia during launch. Atmospheric gases tore it apart during re-entry, killing a crew of seven.

Genesis
5 The sample return capsule of NASA's unmanned Genesis spacecraft failed to deploy its parachutes during re-entry in 2004, and crashed in the Utah desert.

DID YOU KNOW? NASA's Stardust capsule is the fastest man-made object to ever re-enter Earth, at 7.95 miles per sec, in 2006

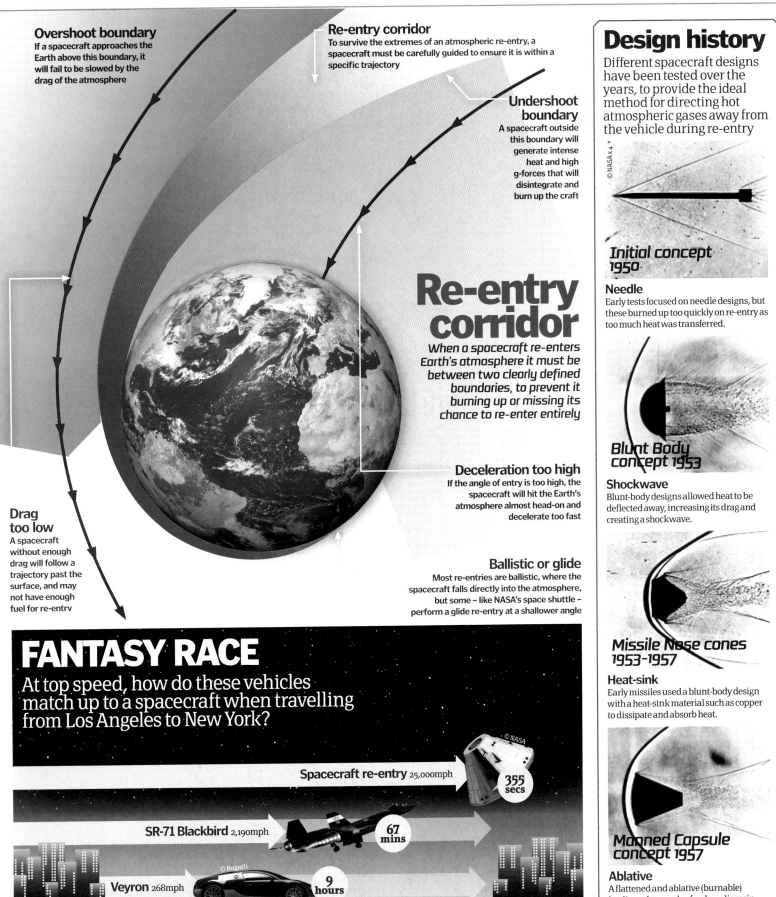

Overshoot boundary
If a spacecraft approaches the Earth above this boundary, it will fail to be slowed by the drag of the atmosphere

Re-entry corridor
To survive the extremes of an atmospheric re-entry, a spacecraft must be carefully guided to ensure it is within a specific trajectory

Undershoot boundary
A spacecraft outside this boundary will generate intense heat and high g-forces that will disintegrate and burn up the craft

Re-entry corridor
When a spacecraft re-enters Earth's atmosphere it must be between two clearly defined boundaries, to prevent it burning up or missing its chance to re-enter entirely

Deceleration too high
If the angle of entry is too high, the spacecraft will hit the Earth's atmosphere almost head-on and decelerate too fast

Drag too low
A spacecraft without enough drag will follow a trajectory past the surface, and may not have enough fuel for re-entry

Ballistic or glide
Most re-entries are ballistic, where the spacecraft falls directly into the atmosphere, but some – like NASA's space shuttle – perform a glide re-entry at a shallower angle

Design history
Different spacecraft designs have been tested over the years, to provide the ideal method for directing hot atmospheric gases away from the vehicle during re-entry

© NASA x 4

Initial concept 1950
Needle
Early tests focused on needle designs, but these burned up too quickly on re-entry as too much heat was transferred.

Blunt Body concept 1953
Shockwave
Blunt-body designs allowed heat to be deflected away, increasing its drag and creating a shockwave.

Missile Nose cones 1953-1957
Heat-sink
Early missiles used a blunt-body design with a heat-sink material such as copper to dissipate and absorb heat.

Manned Capsule concept 1957
Ablative
A flattened and ablative (burnable) leading edge, made of a phenolic resin, subjected the spacecraft to even less heat.

FANTASY RACE
At top speed, how do these vehicles match up to a spacecraft when travelling from Los Angeles to New York?

© NASA

Spacecraft re-entry 25,000mph — **355 secs**

SR-71 Blackbird 2,190mph — **67 mins**

© Bugatti

Veyron 268mph — **9 hours**

Los Angeles - - - - - - - - - 2,462 miles - - - - - - - - - **New York**

099

Radar dishes at the ESA's ESAC headquarters in Villanueva de la Cañada, Spain

An image of the ESA's headquarters in Paris, France. While centred at the heart of Europe, the ESA has bases all over the world, and co-operates on many missions undertaken by NASA, the FKA and the CNSA

European Space Agency

Europe's gateway to space, the European Space Agency is revealing the wonders of our Earth, solar system and the universe

The purpose of the European Space Agency (ESA) is to develop and advance Europe's space capability, while ensuring such research directly benefits those who fund it – the citizens of Europe. As such, the ESA is an international organisation comprised of 19 member states, which collectively pool their resources, be that financial or intellectual, in order to draw up the European space programme and carry it through – something that would be impossible to achieve if they simply worked as singular nations.

The ESA draws up programmes designed to explore, analyse and actuate information garnered from the Earth's immediate space environment, our solar system and even further afield into distant galaxies, in addition to developing satellite-based technologies and services constructed by European companies and industries. The size and financial/intellectual commitment a member state makes to the ESA is directly proportional to the amount of service contracts for technological construction and mission funding it receives, ensuring that the money spent by the county's government

The average investment per person per annum of an ESA member state is roughly ten pounds, which collectively provides the yearly budget for space expenditure. In 2012 the budget for the ESA was just over £4 billion and it was spent across a wide gamut of missions, divisions and departments, including: the European Astronauts Centre, European Space Astronomy division, European Space Operations Centre, the ESA Centre for Earth Observation, and the European Space Research and Technology Centre.

The majority of space launches occur at the ESA's launch base in French Guiana (a 96,000 hectare base employing 1,500 people), where probes, satellites and rockets carry astronauts and equipment into space either to dock with the International Space Station, orbit the Earth and collect and transmit data, or on a far-off trajectory to monitor distant phenomena. Indeed, the ESA boasts one of the most active and successful mission profiles in the world and is currently embarking on a host of cutting-edge programmes – including the notable launch of CryoSat-2, an orbiting satellite designed to monitor the effects of global warming on

1. NASA
Established: 1958
Budget: £11.4 billion / $17.6 billion
Divisions: 15
Primary spaceport: Kennedy Space Center

EUROPE

2. ESA
Established: 1975
Budget: £3.3 billion / $5.4 billion
Divisions: 5
Primary spaceport: Guiana Space Centre

CHINA

3. CNSA
Established: 1993
Budget: £850 million / $1.3 billion
Divisions: 4
Primary spaceport: Jiuquan Satellite Launch Center

DID YOU KNOW? ESA's first mission was launched in 1975 and was a space probe designed to monitor gamma-ray emissions

The ESA's primary launch vehicle, the Ariane 5 rocket, blasts off

1. Upper stage
The rocket's payload is housed here, which in the case of most Ariane 5 launches, are satellites

2. Solid rocket boosters
Each of the Ariane 5's rocket boosters deliver 6,470kN of thrust and burn for 129 seconds

3. Cryogenic main stage
This main, first stage delivers 1,114kN of thrust over 589 seconds burning a mixture of liquid hydrogen and oxygen

The Statistics
Ariane 5
Function: Heavy launch vehicle
Height: 46-52m (151-170ft)
Mass: 777,000kg
Stages: 2
Max payload: LEO – 21,000kg / GTO – 10,500kg
Maiden flight: 4 June 1996

An aerial shot of the sprawling ESTEC division in Noordwijk

ESA budgets
Breakdown of the ESA budgets (using 2009 figures)

- LAUNCHERS – 18.35%, €659m
- NAVIGATION – 10.78%, €387m
- HUMAN SPACEFLIGHT – 10.77%, €386m
- SCIENCE – 12.10%, €434m
- EARTH OBSERVATION – 16.32%, €586m
- TELECOMMUNICATIONS – 8.89%, €319m
- EXPLORATION – 3.22%, €115m
- TECHNOLOGY – 3.14%, €112m
- MICROGRAVITY – 2.61%, €93m
- GENERAL BUDGET – 6.67%, €239m
- ASSOCIATED TO GENERAL BUDGET – 5.48%, €196m
- FINANCED BY THIRD PARTIES – 1.33%, €47m
- SPACE SITUATIONAL AWARENESS – 0.25%, €9m
- ECSA – 0.09%, €3m

Divisions of the ESA

The ESA employs over 2,000 individuals, including scientists, engineers, information technology specialists and administrative personnel, across its five main divisions. These divisions are based all over Europe and are linked by the ESA's headquarters in Paris, France. Two of its larger divisions include ESOC, the European Space Operations Centre in Darmstadt, Germany, which since its creation in 1967 has operated more than 50 satellites, ensured spacecraft meet their objectives and co-ordinated ground-based communications. There's also the ESTEC in Noordwijk, The Netherlands, whose remit includes being the primary test centre for European space activities and all technical preparation and management of ESA space projects (ESTEC is the largest division of the ESA). Other divisions can be found in Frascati, Italy (ESRIN), Villanueva de la Cañada, Spain (ESAC) and Cologne, Germany (EAC).

Member countries
- ESA member countries
- ECS (European Co-operating state)
- Signed Co-operation Agreement countries

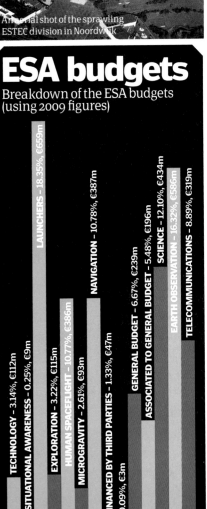

1. Site
An Ariane 5 heavy launch vehicle stands on-site

2. Access
The large approach road is necessary considering the size of the equipment being transported

Europe's spaceport, the Guiana Space Centre, covers 96,000 hectares and is operated by more than 1,500 personnel

Space for Europe

Learn about the three main missions currently being undertaken by the ESA

CryoSat-2

The ESA's most recent launch, CryoSat-2, is imaging and analysing the effects of global warming like never before

The ESA's Earth Explorer CryoSat-2 mission, which was launched on 8 April 2010 on a Dnepr rocket, is concerned with the precise monitoring of the changes in the thickness of marine ice floating in polar oceans and variations in the thickness of Greenland's ice sheets. This is a highly important and timely mission as currently Earth's ice fields are diminishing at an expediential rate.

The CryoSat-2 satellite – which boasts a state-of-the-art SAR/Interferometric Radar Altimeter, which measures ice by sending a series of cloud-piercing radar pulses down to Earth – is orbiting Earth from an altitude of just over 700km and latitudes of up to 88 degrees, a record for this type of platform. It is powered by two angled sheets of solar panels, which each contain hundreds of highly sensitive gallium arsenide solar cells that supply power for the batteries.

The CryoSat-2's technique of transmitting a series of radar pulses works as when they reach Earth they are scattered off the variable slopes of the ice sheet margins and the returned echo comes from the closest surface location with respect to the satellite. These are then received by the CryoSat-2's antennas – which are wrapped in multi-layer insulation – and decoded.

The dedicated control room for CryoSat-2 operations at ESOC, Darmstadt

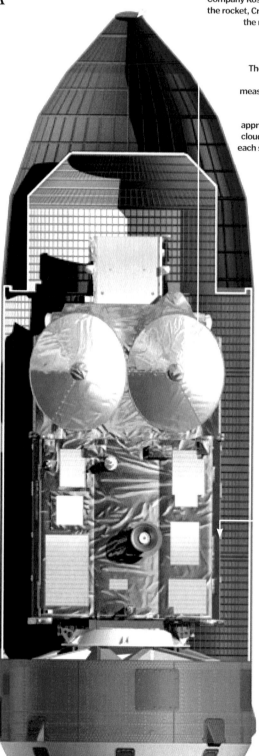

1. Dnepr rocket head
The launch vehicle for the CryoSat-2 satellite was a Dnepr rocket, provided by the International Space Company Kosmotras. Housed in the top section of the rocket, CryoSat-2 separated successfully from the rocket after 17 minutes of vertical lift

2. SAR/Interferometric Radar Altimeter
The primary payload of the CryoSat-2 is designed to meet the nuanced measurement requirements for ice-sheet elevation and sea-ice freeboard data acquisition. This highly advanced approach works by sending thousands of cloud piercing radar pulses to the ground each second and then measuring the time it takes for their echoes to return to CryoSat-2's antennas

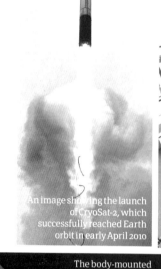
An image showing the launch of CryoSat-2, which successfully reached Earth orbit in early April 2010

The body-mounted solar arrays of the CryoSat-2

The Statistics
CryoSat-2

Operator: ESA
Launch vehicle: Kosmotras Dnepr rocket
Payload: SAR/Interferometric Radar Altimeter
Orbit altitude: 717km (approx)
Mass: 720kg
Power: 2 x GaAs body-mounted solar arrays (1700 W)

3. Solar panels
In order to power the imaging and data recording systems on the CryoSat-2 satellite, it is covered with two large sheets of solar cells, which produce power for the on-board batteries. Unlike many other satellites, these panels are fixed and non-deployable, however they are positioned on optimal angles for the capturing of solar energy throughout an orbit

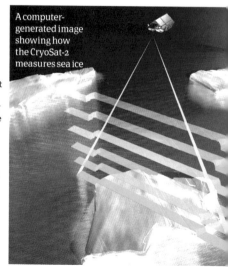
A computer-generated image showing how the CryoSat-2 measures sea ice

5 TOP FACTS
ESA

Jobbing
1 Out of 10,000 people who registered back in 2008 for an ESA astronaut recruitment drive, only six made the cut. That's just a one in 1,666 chance of being successful.

Year-on-year
2 Since 2005 the annual budget of the European Space Agency has grown rapidly from £2.5 billion to the £3.3 billion it currently has at its disposal today.

Canada
3 Since 1 January 1971, Canada has acted as an associate member to the ESA. This means it takes part in the decision-making processes and its programmes.

Corps
4 There are currently 14 astronauts in the European Astronaut Corps, 13 of which are men and only one is a woman. The sole Brit is Timothy Peake.

Spot-on
5 The European Space Agency's spaceport in French Guiana is ideally positioned for space launches due to its proximity to the Earth's equator.

DID YOU KNOW? *The original CryoSat mission failed in 2005. The separation mechanism on its carrying rocket broke at launch*

Mars500
The mission that simulated humanity's journey to Mars

The Mars500 mission was an important study to ascertain the mental and physical strain on humans in closed isolation on a long-haul trip to Mars. The mission was a joint project between the ESA and Russian Institute for Biomedical Problems, beginning on 3 June 2010 and culminating on 4 November 2011. In it, six candidates were sealed in an isolation chamber for 520 days, the approximate journey time for a real mission to and from the Red Planet.

The isolation facility in which they were held was based in Moscow and consisted of five modules: three to replicate the spacecraft (where the volunteers spent the majority of their time), one to replicate the Mars-lander in which the astronauts would travel to the surface and another to simulate the Martian surface, with a total combined area of 550m³ (19,423 ft³).

To accurately simulate a mission to Mars, the volunteers were subjected to the same conditions that would be apparent for astronauts making the trip for real. For example, all communications outside the pod were given a time delay, ranging from 1 minute when near "Earth" to 20 minutes at "Mars", while the crew were also given a diet identical to that of astronauts on board the International Space Station.

The volunteers carried out the same tasks that astronauts would in a real-life Mars trip, including simulating a Martian landing and performing experiments. The participants were able to talk to friends and family via video link at various points in the mission, albeit with the aforementioned time delay.

With the mission finished, future astronauts making the long-haul trip will have useful knowledge of the conditions they might expect when being in isolation for such a long period of time and at such a great distance from home.

An image showing the multiple parts of the Mars500 simulated spacecraft

The members of the 2010 stage of the experiment prepare to go into isolation

Training facilities were included to help keep the astronauts fit and healthy

An artist's impression of the XMM-Newton as it orbits Earth

All uncredited images © ESA

XMM-Newton
The primary x-ray telescope of the ESA, the XMM-Newton is increasing our knowledge of black holes, the formation of galaxies and the origins of the universe

X-ray telescopes

Camera radiators

Telescope tubes

Launched from the ESA's Guiana spaceport in 1999 on an Ariane 5 rocket, the XMM-Newton is the ESA's largest and most active x-ray observatory and orbiting satellite. It orbits the Earth on a highly eccentric and elliptical orbit of 40 degrees and boasts three x-ray telescopes each containing 58 Wolter-type concentric mirrors. It is powered by twin extendable solar arrays that give the XMM a span of 16 metres. In addition to its three x-ray telescopes, the XMM also includes two reflection-grating spectrometers (used to measure light intensity) and a 12-inch in diameter Ritchey-Chrétien optical/UV telescope (a specialised telescope used to mitigate aberration in images).

The XMM-Newton's name comes from the design of its mirrors, the highly nested x-ray multi-mirrors, and in dedication to the great scientist Sir Isaac Newton. These mirrors are enabling astronomers to discover more x-ray sources than with any of the previous space observatories. In one day, for example, the XMM-Newton sees more sources in one small area than lesser satellites managed in years. Thanks to its orbit, the XMM-Newton has been able to measure the influence of the gravitational field of a neutron star on the light it emits. This was a first in astronomical observation and helped give a valuable insight into these super-dense objects.

ELS launch site

A look around the ESA's incredible, history-making launch pad

The sight of a rocket igniting and blasting off is one of the most awe-inspiring things anyone can ever watch. For the lucky people in Kourou, French Guiana, this is a regular occurrence, thanks to the European Space Agency's (ESA) multi-rocket launch pad. With the birth of the ESA, the French-built launch pad was selected as the place from where all European-funded missions take off.

The Ensemble de Lancement Soyouz (ELS) is made up of three specific sections. There is the preparation area, where rockets are put together, the launch control centre, a safe bunker, which houses the scientists and engineers involved in the launch, and finally the launch platform, the 53-metre (174-foot) high tower that holds the rocket steady and vertical until the moment it takes off. The site is fairly spread out, with the control centre one kilometre (0.6 miles) away from the launch pad, which is connected to the preparation area by a 700-metre (2,300-foot) long railway.

In 2011, history was made at ELS as a Soyuz rocket, the most famous Russian-made rocket, was launched from the site. It was a momentous occasion as it was the first of the flagship Russian rockets ever to be launched outside of Kazakhstan or Russia.

Looking to the future, plans are being made for Skylon, a British spaceplane, to launch from the site. The exciting thing about Skylon is that parts are reusable and can be turned around in hours, making huge savings. Although the runway at Kourou would need strengthening, the ESA has already shown active willingness to pump money into the site, having already spent €1.6 billion (£1.3 billion/$2.2 billion) on improving and upgrading the site. There is also the option to store liquid hydrogen at the site, as there are plans to use it as a fuel for future Soyuz rockets. ✿

KEY DATES
TIMELINE OF KOUROU

1964
France commissions the building of Kourou. Completed four years later, it costs 25 million francs.

1970
The Diamant-B rocket is launched, carrying the DIAL satellite. It is Kourou's first rocket launch.

1986
Ariane 3 is the first rocket to set off from ELA-2, the second launch pad at the site.

2003
An agreement between France and Russia paves the way for Soyuz rockets to launch from Kourou.

2011
A Soyuz rocket is successfully launched from the site, with more launches planned for the future.

DID YOU KNOW? *French Guiana was the seventh country to launch a satellite after the USSR, USA, France, Japan, China and Britain*

The remote location at Kourou on French Guiana makes it perfect for space launches

What makes Kourou perfect?

Kourou is an ideal site for a range of launches. French Guiana is one of the northernmost countries in South America. It sits at latitude 5°3', which means it's only 500km (311mi) north of the equator, ideal for geostationary orbit launches as the rocket won't need to make many adjustments to get the satellites into their planned orbit.

Other pros to being near the equator include the slingshot effect. As the equator is the widest point of the Earth, it has the largest distance of rotation of any part of the planet. Spacecraft can use this rotation to vastly increase the speed of the rocket and save fuel on launch.

French Guiana is ideal because 90 per cent of the land is covered in uninhabitable forests so the population is low. This means disruption to the locals is minimal.

Ready for Soyuz

A huge coup in the history of ELS was in 2003 when the Russian and French governments came to an agreement to begin launching Soyuz rockets from Kourou.

Updates were required to make it suitable for the Soyuz rockets to launch there. One of the key changes was the construction of a moveable tower, which could be placed next to the launch pad, providing access for engineers up to a height of 36m (118ft). However, the tower itself rose 53m (174ft) high and was the cause of delays to the programme.

The first rockets scheduled for launch arrived in November 2009 and in October 2011 the first Soyuz rocket ever to be launched outside of Kazakhstan and Russia took off on its maiden voyage.

© ESA

SPACE TRAVEL

We take a look at the ten most important space missions of all time

Since Russia's Sputnik 1 satellite entered space on 4 October 1957, thousands of manned and unmanned spacecraft, including Earth satellites and deep-space probes, have launched into the cosmos.

In those five decades, space travel has truly come on leaps and bounds, with the development of liquid and solid fuels, as well as the use of solar panels and radioactive power sources among many of the impressive innovations, allowing space agencies across the planet to undertake evermore ambitious missions that would once have never been thought possible. Here, we've compiled ten of the most successful missions that have advanced the field of space travel to a whole new level. ✿

1969
Apollo 11

Probably the most well-known space mission of all time, Apollo 11 was launched atop the most powerful rocket to date, the Saturn V. The spacecraft was composed of two sections – the Lunar Module and the Command Module – the latter of which remained in orbit around the Moon with Michael Collins on board while the former took astronauts Neil Armstrong and Buzz Aldrin to the surface. Apollo 11 paved the way for a further five successful missions to the Moon, each spending several days on the lunar surface.

▷ 1960s •
▷ 1970s •
▷ 198

1961
Vostok 1

In 1961 Yuri Gagarin became the first man to travel to space, and the spacecraft that took him there for 68 minutes, was a fairly rudimentary sphere known as Vostok 1. As this was the first manned craft to leave Earth orbit, lots of extra precautions were taken, eg Gagarin was not able to freely move around the cabin, nor was he able to manually control the spacecraft. Nonetheless, in the timeline of space exploration, Vostok 1 is without a doubt one of the most important spacecraft of all time.

1977-present
Voyager 1 and 2

The Voyager programme was originally designed to explore Jupiter, Saturn, Uranus and Neptune, but the mission was extended to include the boundary into interstellar space, which they are currently entering. The Voyager probes both receive power from three radioisotope thermoelectric generators, fed by plutonium-238. On board each probe is a variety of sounds and images known as the Golden Record, which also contains instructions on how to find Earth for any passing aliens.

1961-1984
Venera probes

The Venera missions have been Russia's most successful space exploration missions to date. In total, 23 separate probes were launched to the hottest planet in our solar system, Venus, between 1961 and 1984, with ten of these landing on the surface. Each Venera lander was a technical marvel, withstanding incredible temperatures of up to 462 degrees Celsius (864 degrees Fahrenheit) to remain operational for up to two hours. They returned key data about the surface of Venus, including detailed information on the planet's atmospheric structure

1972-2003
Pioneer 10 and 11

The purpose of the Pioneer missions was to learn about the outer reaches of the solar system. These two spacecraft were, at the time of their launch, the most advanced vehicles to venture into space. They contained a number of technical tools never used before, including a charged particle instrument to measure the extent of the Sun's influence. While comms were lost in 1995 (Pioneer 11) and 2003 (Pioneer 10), the probes continue to make their way out of the solar system, with each possessing an on-board plaque detailing their origins.

1981-2011
Space Shuttles

NASA's five cosmos-faring Space Shuttles were the largest spacecraft of all time, and each completed numerous missions that defined them as some of the most important vehicles to enter Earth orbit. Their many accolades include taking the Hubble Space Telescope into orbit (and later repairing it) and launching more than 80 per cent of the modules for the ISS. There were 135 missions in total, but two of these ended in tragedy. The Challenger spacecraft exploded 73 seconds after launch in 1986, while in 2003 the Columbia spacecraft was torn apart on re-entry. While the Shuttles are remembered largely as a success, these two disasters serve as a reminder of just how dangerous space travel is.

2003-2010
Hayabusa

Japan's Hayabusa probe was the first spacecraft to return a sample from an asteroid, but it wasn't without its problems. A fuel leak rendered its chemical engines unusable and, coupled with a variety of mechanical failures, the probe was forced to limp home on its weaker ion engines. It eventually arrived three years behind schedule in 2010, but the mission was still a success. Ion engines on spacecraft have become more and more popular due to their longevity, rather than relying on an initial big 'push'.

▷1990s ▷2000s

1997-present
Cassini-Huygens

The Cassini-Huygens probe was a joint mission between NASA, the ESA and ASI (Italian Space Agency) and is often regarded as the most successful deep-space probe of all time. The orbiting component of the probe flew by Jupiter and became the first spacecraft to orbit Saturn. The landing vehicle was the Huygens Probe, which landed on Saturn's moon Titan in 2005, the first and only successful landing in the outer solar system. As with most probes, it is powered by plutonium-238, which has enabled its mission to be extended to 2017.

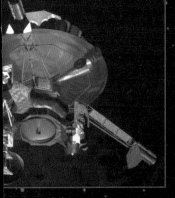

1989-2003
Galileo probe/spacecraft

NASA's Galileo spacecraft was taken into space in 1989 and went on to study Jupiter after flybys of Venus and Earth. It was the first spacecraft to orbit Jupiter, in addition to performing the first flyby of an asteroid. It also carried the Galileo Space Probe, which it released into Jupiter's atmosphere in 1995, providing unprecedented data about the gas giant. In 2003 the orbiting spacecraft was sent crashing into our solar system's biggest planet to prevent it colliding with a nearby moon and causing contamination.

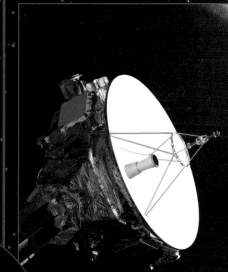

2006-present
New Horizons

NASA's New Horizons spacecraft will become the first probe to fly by Pluto in 2015. While its primary mission is to study the (now) dwarf planet, it has also studied Jupiter and its moons. New Horizons is the fastest probe to have left Earth's orbit. It is currently more than 21 times further from the Sun than Earth; at that distance it takes almost three hours to send or receive a signal.

Voyager spacecraft

How the furthest man-made objects from Earth work

PLUTO (DWARF PLANET)

Distance from Earth today: 19 billion

NEPTUNE

Date reached: 25/8/89

On 20 August 1977 Voyager 2 launched from Cape Canaveral in Florida aboard a Titan-Centaur rocket, heralding the start of one of the most ambitious deep space exploration missions of all time. Two weeks later Voyager 1 was sent up in an identical launch, although its greater speed meant that it eventually overtook Voyager 2. The list of accomplishments by the two probes is astounding. Between them they have studied all of the major planets of the solar system past Mars, in addition to some moons of Jupiter and Saturn, making countless new discoveries in the process. Now, as the furthest man-made objects from Earth, they are on their way out of the solar system.

The launch of the mission coincided with a favourable alignment of the planets in the Seventies that would allow Voyager 2 to visit Jupiter, Saturn, Uranus and Neptune. The list of achievements by the two Voyager spacecraft is extensive. The Voyager mission was only the second – after Pioneer 10 and 11 in 1974 and 1975, respectively – to visit Jupiter and then Saturn, but it also discovered the existence of rings around Jupiter, while Voyager 2 was the first mission to visit Uranus and Neptune.

The primary objective of the mission was to study Jupiter and Saturn, but once it became apparent that the spacecraft could continue working, the mission was extended to include Neptune and Uranus for Voyager 2. Voyager 1 could have travelled to Pluto, but NASA decided to extend its mission to Saturn and its moon Titan, leaving the dwarf planet Pluto one of the largest bodies in the solar system yet to be explored.

The Voyager probes obtain power from their radioactive generators, which have kept them running even at such a great distance from Earth and will continue to do so until about 2020, when they will no longer be able to power their instruments. Voyager 1 is roughly now over 17 billion kilometres (10.6 billion miles) from the Sun, while Voyager 2 is at a distance of over 14 billion kilometres (8.5 billion miles).

After making so many groundbreaking discoveries, both spacecraft are now on their way out of the solar system. They are both expected to pass out of the Sun's influence and into interstellar space in the coming years, although it is not entirely clear when this will happen as no machine has yet experienced the conditions that the Voyager probes are about to endure.

In 40,000 years, Voyager 1 should be within 1.6 light years (9.4 trillion miles) of a star in the constellation of Camelopardalis thought to harbour a planetary system. 256,000 years later, Voyager 2 will be 4.3 light years (25 trillion miles) from Sirius, which is the brightest star other than the Sun in our night sky. ✿

Voyager 2 launched atop a Titan III-Centaur rocket on 20 August 1977

Inside Voyager
What's going on inside the long-distance probes?

Data
A single 8-track digital tape recorder (DTR) and Flight Data Subsystem (FDS) handle data and calibrate instruments too

Golden Record
The Golden Record is a collection of sounds and imagery from Earth, intended to provide any passing extraterrestrial race with information about our home planet

Thrust
The probes manoeuvre via Hydrazine thrusters, although since leaving the planets they have stopped doing so

Instruments
On board both probes is a science payload with ten instruments, including those to measure solar wind and those that can detect low-energy particles

Antenna
The high-gain antenna (HGA) transmits data to Earth

Communication
It takes 16 hours for a message from the Voyager probes to reach Earth. However, they're not in constant communication, and only periodically send data back to our planet

Phone home
Each of the identical spacecraft use celestial or gyroscopic attitude control to ensure that their high-gain antennas are constantly pointed towards Earth for communication

Weight
Each Voyager probe weighs 773kg (1,704lbs), with the science payload making up about 105kg (231lbs) of this

Power up
Three radioisotope thermoelectric generators (RTGs) supply electrical power, which will eventually diminish but currently supply about 315 watts

Power down
To conserve energy as the probes continue their journeys, many instruments deemed unnecessary have or will be switched off

Magnetometer
This instrument enables the probes to measure nearby magnetic field intensities, which was used to study the magnetospheres of the outer planets

5 TOP FACTS
VOYAGER DISCOVERIES

Moons
1 Around the outer planets the Voyager probes discovered 23 new moons, including five around Saturn and 11 around Uranus, in addition to imaging our own.

Interstellar medium
2 Both of the Voyager probes are now in a region where the Sun's influence is increasingly waning, and soon they will enter the interstellar medium.

Atmospheres
3 Voyager probes 1 and 2 both provided unprecedented information about the atmospheres of the following planets: Jupiter, Saturn, Uranus and Neptune.

Jupiter
4 The probes discovered for the first time a ring system encircling Jupiter, and they also observed hurricane-like storms in the planet's atmosphere.

Io
5 Voyager 1 discovered the only known body in the solar system other than Earth to be volcanically active: Jupiter's moon Io. This moon also affects the surrounding Jovian system.

DID YOU KNOW? *Voyager 1 is now travelling at 38,000mph, while Voyager 2 is slightly slower at 35,000mph*

The journey so far...

What path have the Voyager probes taken through the solar system, and where are they now?

Distance from Earth today: 17 billion km

Date reached: 5/3/79

URANUS

Date reached: 12/11/80

JUPITER

SATURN

VOYAGER 1 launch: 5/9/77

EARTH

Date reached: 24/1/86

Heliopause
This is where the Sun's influence is almost non-existent and the Voyager probes will enter the interstellar medium, the matter between stars in our galaxy. No one is sure how far the probes are from this point

Date reached: 25/8/81

Termination shock
At the edge of the heliosheath, the Sun's influence in the form of solar wind slows dramatically and heats up at an area known as the termination shock, which Voyager 1 passed in 2004

Voyager 1

Bow shock

VOYAGER 2 launch: 20/8/77

Date reached: 9/7/79

On 16 November 1980, Voyager 1 looked back at Saturn and snapped this picture four days after it had passed the planet

Heliosphere
Our solar system is contained within an area of space where the Sun exerts an influence, known as the heliosphere

Voyager 2

What lies ahead...

All images © NASA

The Herschel crater

Mimas, Saturn's closest moon, looks like the Death Star with its massive impact crater

Of Saturn's major moons, Mimas is the closest to the planet at 185,520 kilometres away. The moon is believed to have created the Cassini Division, a 4,800-kilometre gap between Saturn's A and B rings. Mimas has an average diameter of 396 kilometres, with an ovoid shape. This is due to its low surface gravity – about one 25th that of Earth's moon – as well as the strong gravitational pull from Saturn. The same side of Mimas always faces Saturn, and it has an asynchronous rotation (meaning that it takes the same amount of time to both orbit and rotate on its axis) of 22.5 hours.

Mimas has a very low density, about 1.17 times that of water, so astronomers believe that it probably comprises a small rocky core with an outer layer of ice. It appears to be solidly frozen at about 64 Kelvin. The moon's main geological features are chasms and impact craters. Mimas is best known for its massive Herschel crater, however. This crater has a diameter of 130 kilometres, about a third of the moon's own diameter. Its walls are about five kilometres high, and it has areas that are 10 kilometres deep. If a crater of the same scale were found on Earth, it would be wider than the entire country of Canada. ✿

The Herschel crater mystery

Mimas's most distinguishing feature is also something of a mystery. Astronomers cannot figure out why the force necessary to create such a wide, deep crater didn't destroy the moon completely. The massive impact appears to have left fissures on the opposite side of the moon, although these may also be the result of cracking in its icy surface. If Mimas had been destroyed, its remaining pieces might have become other Saturnian moons or even formed another ring around the planet. It is not known exactly what caused the crater, which has an unusual, hexagonal shape. It could have been a massive meteor, or rubble that broke away during the formation of Saturn's moons.

Ellipsoid moon
Due to the forces acting upon it. Mimas is not perfectly spherical. Its longest axis is about ten per cent longer than the shortest

Exploration
Mimas has been imaged several times by the Cassini orbiter. The closest flyby occurred on 13 February 2010, when Cassini passed by Mimas at 9,500km

All images © NASA

Saturn's major icy moons

Although Saturn has more than 60 named moons, the majority of them are very small satellites. Mimas is one of the seven major icy moons in Saturn's orbit. It is in resonance with two of its neighbours, Dione and Enceladus. The orbits of these three moons speed up when they get closer to each other and slow down as they separate.

Mimas
Diameter: 396 kilometres
Orbital period: 22.5 hours
Distance from Saturn: 185,520 kilometres
Fact: Mimas is best known for its massive, Death Star-like impact crater

Enceladus
Diameter: 505 kilometres
Orbital period: 1.37 days
Distance from Saturn: 238,020 kilometres
Fact: Enceladus is a bright white moon with widely varying terrain

Tethys
Diameter: 1,066 kilometres
Orbital period: 1.9 days
Distance from Saturn: 294,660 kilometres
Fact: The terrain on Tethys is dominated by both a massive crater and a wide, deep valley

Dione
Diameter: 1,123 kilometres
Orbital period: 2.7 days
Distance from Saturn: 377,400 kilometres
Fact: Dione orbits Saturn at about the same distance that our moon orbits Earth

Rhea
Diameter: 1,528 kilometres
Orbital period: 4.5 days
Distance from Saturn: 527, 040 kilometres
Fact: Has a region of craters larger than 40km and another with smaller craters

Antstronauts

Learn how a microgravity study of ants could lead to better robots

Several hundred ants are currently in orbit on the International Space Station, in an experiment to see how they adapt to microgravity environments. The way ant colonies work is fascinating. They don't have a central control; no single ant can force another to do something. Instead, they use information gathered locally to assess situations, which means the behaviour of the colony depends on the local cues each ant produces. Colonies send out worker ants to search and assess new areas. This can help them find food, map foreign terrain and identify potential threats.

By studying the ways ants assess an alien environment, scientists believe they will be able to develop better search algorithms for robots. They want to create autonomous search robots that do not need a central control, much like ant colonies. These would then be more effective at tasks such as finding survivors immediately after a disaster takes place. This research could also impact mobile phone networks, helping to solve problems of interference. ✿

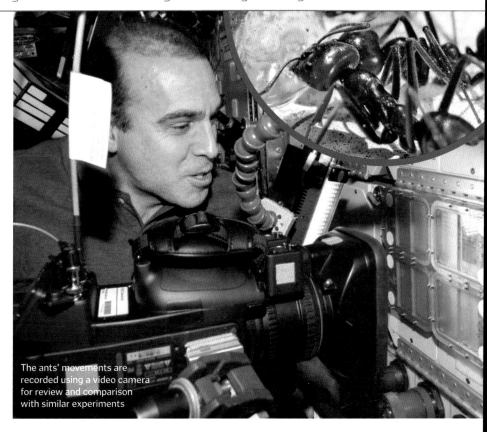

The ants' movements are recorded using a video camera for review and comparison with similar experiments

How robots keep astronauts company

Meet Kirobo, the Japanese robot living on the ISS

Feelings of loneliness are often hard to avoid when you're in space. Astronauts on the International Space Station (ISS) for long periods often struggle with this. Sometimes, their psychological issues can be harder to deal with than living in microgravity or sleeping upright.

To combat this, Japanese scientists designed a robot with the aim of providing psychological support. It was named Kirobo, which is derived from the Japanese word for hope ("kibo") and robot. Kirobo stands 34 centimetres (13.4 inches) tall and weighs one kilogram (2.2 pounds). It has a clever voice-recognition system and can produce its own sentences with the help of an advanced language-processing system, and its own built-in voice synthesis software.

These innovative systems were actually designed by Toyota, which plans to use the technology to develop other robots' conversational abilities. The Kirobo experiment also aimed to see how humans and robots might live alongside each other during longer space missions, which may take place in the future. Kirobo has now returned to Earth after an 18-month stay aboard the ISS as its astronauts' robotic buddy. ✿

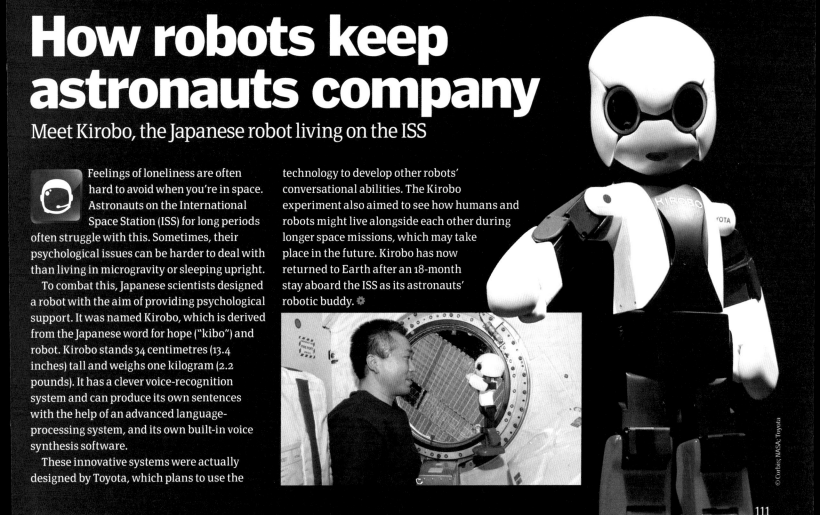

UNIVERSE

152
Search for
extraterresrial life

148
Black holes

124 Zombie stars

10 secrets of space

Our universe is full of odd phenomena to which we don't have all the answers – here we look at the science of the most intriguing

Answering questions and solving puzzles has been the driving force behind astronomy for thousands of years, even if it often seems that for every mystery solved, a new one springs up. Today, astronomers like to think they have a fairly good understanding of the way our universe works, and processes from the life cycle of stars to the evolution of galaxies, and it's certainly true that we know a lot more than we did a century ago. But there are still plenty of loose ends and new ones are still constantly emerging.

Some of these mysteries are recent discoveries that may seem at first to break the established rules.

Of course, we can't be sure until these particular enigmas are resolved, but often the solution to puzzles like this is just a matter of time; once a mystery object such as the 'impossible star' SDSS J102915+172927 or the rectangular galaxy LEDA 074886 is announced to the world, scientists can turn their collective efforts and a huge array of observational techniques to learning more about it and understanding why it defies convention.

Others require more patience – for instance, new images of Uranus's satellite Miranda would certainly reveal more about its turbulent history, but we're sadly unlikely to be sending another probe that way any time soon. The long-standing

mysteries of the Sun's corona have had to await the development of new techniques for studying it. And the ins and outs of 'dark matter' that permeates the entire cosmos still remain frustratingly elusive.

But perhaps the most exciting mysteries of all are those that come completely out of the blue, such as the dark energy accelerating the expansion of the universe. Two decades ago, astronomers didn't even know there was a puzzle to be solved, yet now dark energy is one of the hottest topics in the field. It's discoveries like this and 'unknown unknowns' that will doubtless be discovered in the future that help drive forward our understanding of not just space, but also our place within it. ✿

HEAD 2 HEAD

SPACE PARTICLES

1. FAST

Solar particles
Particles blown from the Sun take approximately two to three days to reach us here on Earth, moving at hundreds of kilometres per second.

2. FASTER

Galactic cosmic rays
Accelerated by the energy released in massive supernova explosions, these rays can travel at over half the speed of light.

3. FASTEST

Ultra-high-energy rays
The fastest rays of all, with speeds of up to 99 per cent of light, have probably been ejected from active galaxies.

1. Most of the universe is missing

For the past decade, astronomers have been getting to grips with a mystery that has undermined a lot of what we previously thought we knew about the cosmos. We once thought the universe was dominated by two substances: normal, or 'baryonic', matter (matter that interacts with light and other forms of radiation), and invisible 'dark' matter that is transparent to light and only makes its presence felt through gravity (see Mystery 8).

But in the late-Nineties, cosmologists found an unexpected twist: the expansion of the universe (which should be slowing down due to the gravitational drag of the matter within it) is speeding up. The evidence for this comes from distant supernova explosions in galaxies billions of light years from Earth, which appear fainter than we would expect if we relied on previous models of cosmic expansion.

The phenomenon responsible is called 'dark energy' and seems to account for a staggering 70 per cent of the universe. Nobody knows exactly what dark energy is, but perhaps the most intriguing – and even alarming – aspect to the discovery is that it seems to be increasing. Until around 7.5 billion years ago, expansion was slowing; then the strength of dark energy overcame gravity and the expansion picked up again.

If the growth of dark energy continues, some predict that the universe might end in a 'Big Rip' many billions of years from now, when it becomes so powerful that galaxies, stars and even individual particles of matter are torn apart.

Centres of mass
Normal and dark matter tend to concentrate in and around galaxies, holding them together despite cosmic expansion

Energy field
Dark energy seems to be a force field of some sort that extends across the universe, driving the expansion of spacetime

Spacetime
The four dimensions of space and time can be represented as a sheet that can be distorted by concentrations of mass and gravity

Dark energy is pulling the universe apart in unexpected ways, but will its influence continue to grow?

2. The origin of cosmic rays

Cosmic rays are high-speed, high-energy particles from space, which we usually detect via the less energetic particles they produce as they enter Earth's upper atmosphere. Astronomers divide them into several classes depending on their speed and energy, and most seem to originate from distant supernovas. Perhaps the most troublesome, however, are the ultra-high-energy rays – tiny subatomic particles that can carry the same amount of energy as a baseball travelling at 100 kilometres (62 miles) per hour.

For some years, the likeliest origin for ultra-high-energy particles seemed to be gamma-ray bursts (GRBs) – enormous blasts of energy linked to dying stars or merging black holes. But recent studies using the IceCube Neutrino Observatory, a particle detector buried beneath Antarctica, failed to find the predicted neutrino particles that would indicate this origin. Astronomers are now revisiting the idea that they are formed by natural particle accelerators around supermassive black holes in the heart of distant active galaxies.

If exploding stars or colliding black holes can't create high-energy cosmic rays, astronomers need to find something even more powerful...

3. Impossible stars

Occasionally, astronomers come across a star that seems to break all the rules and forces them to rethink long-cherished theories. In 2011, scientists at the European Southern Observatory (ESO) made one such discovery in the form of SDSS J102915+172927 (Caffau's star) – a star roughly 4,000 light years from Earth in the constellation of Leo.

This star has about four-fifths the mass of our Sun, and is composed mainly of hydrogen and helium, the two lightest elements in the universe. Together, they make up around 99.99993 per cent of its entire composition, with heavier elements – known as metals – almost entirely absent.

Such a pure lightweight star must have formed more than 13 billion years ago from the raw cosmic materials remaining after the Big Bang, but the problem is that according to accepted models of star formation it shouldn't have ever been born.

In order to produce enough gravity to collapse and form a star, astronomers believe a protostellar cloud needs either to have a significant amount of heavier metals or a larger overall mass – small, low-density stars simply shouldn't exist.

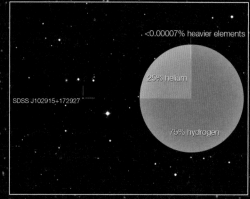

<0.00007% heavier elements

25% helium

75% hydrogen

SDSS J102915+172927

4. The moon that shouldn't exist

When Voyager 2 flew past Uranus in 1986, its close-up views of the ringed planet's inner satellite Miranda surprised everyone. This small 470-kilometre (292-mile)-diameter moon shows a huge variety of different surface features that seem to break the rule that smaller worlds don't show geological activity. Astronomers soon nicknamed it the 'Frankenstein moon', since it looks like it has been broken up and reassembled, perhaps in some ancient interplanetary impact. But there's a problem with this theory: Miranda's orbit is too close to Uranus for it to have pulled itself together again after breaking up. Instead, some scientists think it was reshaped by extreme tides.

Miranda's patchwork appearance is evidence of a turbulent past, but did it really break apart and reform?

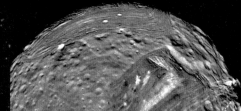

Nicknamed the 'Emerald-cut Galaxy', LEDA 074886 is a rare star cloud that appears to be rectangular

5. Rectangular galaxies

The laws of orbital mechanics mean that stars always follow elliptical (stretched circular) orbits when influenced by gravity, so in large groups they form either flattened disc-like spirals or ball-shaped ellipticals. The corners of a rectangle should be impossible, but astronomers have found several galaxies with apparently rectangular features. For example, LEDA 074886 in the constellation of Eridanus is a compact, rectangular galaxy within a nearby galaxy cluster. The big question is whether its shape is a long-lived structure or brief coincidence. Astronomers who studied it with the giant Japanese Subaru telescope think the latter is more likely, and a collision and merger between two could have scattered outlying stars into the box-like distribution, triggering starbirth at the new centre.

6. The rogue planet

According to the standard definition, a planet is a substantial object in orbit around a star, formed from the debris left behind in the aftermath of starbirth. So how do some planets end up floating alone through the galaxy, far from any stars? Astronomers have discovered several of these, of which the closest and most intriguing goes by the catalogue name of CFBDSIR J214947.2-040308.9. First spotted in 2012, this rogue planet sits about 100 light years away in the AB Doradus Moving Group – a cluster of young stars. With a surface temperature of around 400 degrees Celsius (752 degrees Fahrenheit), it is probably a gas giant much heavier than Jupiter, either still warm from the events of its formation, or perhaps with its own internal energy source driven by gravitational contraction. Too far from a star to shine by reflected light, the planet was only detected due to the infrared glow from its surface. As with all rogue planets, astronomers aren't sure if it started life orbiting a star before being flung off into space (perhaps in a close encounter with another star), or if it formed independently from the same nebula as the surrounding cluster, making it a 'sub-brown dwarf star'.

Floating in the midst of the AB Doradus cluster, this rogue world gives astronomers a rare look at a planet far from any stars

7. The Sun's corona shouldn't be hotter than its surface

The Sun's visible surface is one of its coolest regions, with an average temperature of around 5,800 degrees Celsius (10,472 degrees Fahrenheit). But while it's no surprise that temperatures towards the core rise to around 15 million degrees Celsius (27 million degrees Fahrenheit), the fact that the Sun's thin outer atmosphere, known as the corona, rapidly soars to more than 2 million degrees Celsius (3.6 million degrees Fahrenheit) is more puzzling. This huge rise in temperature takes place across a 'transition region' less than 1,000 kilometres (621 miles) deep, and solar physicists still aren't sure what drives it. The leading contenders are shocks caused by sound waves rippling across the surface, and 'nanoflares' – bursts of energy released by changes to the Sun's magnetic field. New imaging technology on board NASA's Solar Dynamics Observatory (SDO) mission is helping map these phenomena in unprecedented detail, and may soon provide definitive answers to this enigma.

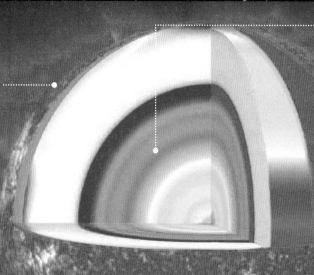

Outer corona
The Sun's outer atmosphere extends for millions of kilometres into space, reaching temperatures of up to 2mn°C (3.6mn°F)

Solar interior
The Sun's interior consists of increasingly hot layers referred to as the convective zone, radiative zone and core

Visible surface
The thin opaque layers known as the photosphere and chromosphere have temperatures of 'just' a few thousand degrees Celsius

DID YOU KNOW? Using the SWIFT satellite, astronomers traced bursts of radiation to collisions of black holes and neutron stars

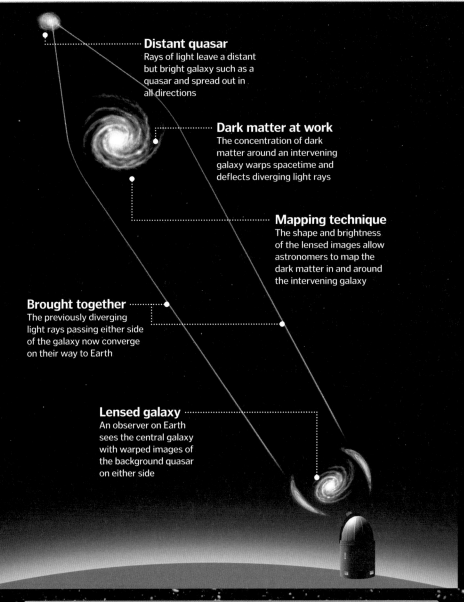

Distant quasar
Rays of light leave a distant but bright galaxy such as a quasar and spread out in all directions

Dark matter at work
The concentration of dark matter around an intervening galaxy warps spacetime and deflects diverging light rays

Mapping technique
The shape and brightness of the lensed images allow astronomers to map the dark matter in and around the intervening galaxy

Brought together
The previously diverging light rays passing either side of the galaxy now converge on their way to Earth

Lensed galaxy
An observer on Earth sees the central galaxy with warped images of the background quasar on either side

8. The quest to find dark matter

Since the Thirties, astronomers have understood that there's a lot more to the universe than just the material we can see. Normal – or baryonic – matter can't help but interact with light and other forms of electromagnetic radiation – stars emit visible light, hot gas emits X-rays, and even the coldest material in the universe emits radio waves and infrared, and clouds made up of this type of matter also absorb radiation that passes through them.

But there's another class of matter that ignores light completely – so-called 'dark matter' that is not just dark but entirely transparent to all types of radiation. It gives itself away only through its gravitational influence on visible objects around it – for example, affecting the orbits of stars within galaxies and galaxies within galaxy clusters. More recently, astronomers have also developed techniques to map the distribution of dark matter through 'gravitational lensing' – the way in which large concentrations of matter deflect the passage of nearby light waves.

Evidence suggests that dark matter outweighs visible matter by roughly six to one. But what is it made of? Astronomers used to think that 'massive compact halo objects', or MACHOs – normal matter in forms too dark and faint to detect, such as lone planets and black holes – might make a contribution, but as our telescopes have improved, it's become clear that these objects don't exist in sufficient quantities. Instead, cosmologists now believe dark matter consists largely of 'weakly interactive massive particles', or WIMPs – exotic subatomic particles that don't interact with radiation or normal matter, but possess considerable mass. But what exactly WIMPs are is still to be worked out.

Astronomers can map the distribution of dark matter across the universe, but it's more likely they'll discover its true nature via particle experiments closer to home

9. Unpredictable pulsars

Pulsars are supposed to be the most reliable timekeepers in the universe. These collapsed neutron stars (the super-dense cores of once-massive stars that long ago destroyed themselves in supernovas) channel intense beams of radiation into space along their powerful magnetic fields, creating a 'cosmic lighthouse' that appears to switch on and off many times each second from our point of view on Earth. Most pulsars emit either X-rays, radio waves, or both, but in early-2013 astronomers discovered a pulsar known as PSR B0943+10 emitting both radio and X-ray wavelengths, changing from one type of radiation to the other in seconds. This behaviour could be due to 'starquakes' on the neutron star's surface, which astronomers believe can also cause glitches when a pulsar's period changes speed, or due to strange activity around the pulsar.

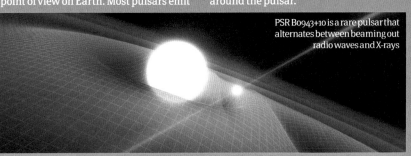

PSR B0943+10 is a rare pulsar that alternates between beaming out radio waves and X-rays

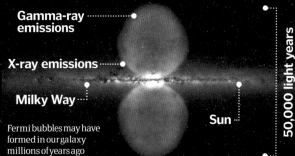

Gamma-ray emissions

X-ray emissions

Milky Way

Sun

50,000 light years

Fermi bubbles may have formed in our galaxy millions of years ago

10. Galactic bubbles

Two bubbles of superhot gas, some 25,000 light years in diameter, extend above and below our Milky Way. Found in 2010 via the Fermi Gamma-ray Space Telescope, the 'Fermi bubbles' are some of the largest structures in our part of the universe, but how did they form? The bubbles have sharp edges and are hollow inside, suggesting expansion from a single-event, perhaps millions of years ago.

One theory is that they are remnants of shockwaves generated when the centre of our galaxy underwent a burst of star formation followed by a wave of supernovas. Another is that they were ejected by activity in our central supermassive black hole.

© NASA; SPL; ESO; ESA; AWM Graham

117

As an elegant explanation of the origins of both atoms and galaxies, the Big Bang is the ultimate theory of everything

The Big Bang theory begins with a simple assumption: if the universe is expanding and cooling – something Edwin Hubble and company proved at the beginning of the 20th Century – then it must have once been very small and very hot. From then on, the simple becomes infinitely complex. Big Bang theory is nothing less than the summation of everything we've learned about the very big (astrophysics) and the very small (quantum physics) in the history of human thought.

Cosmologists – people who study the origin and evolution of the universe – theorise that 13.7 billion years ago, a bubble formed out of the void. The bubble, many times smaller than a single proton, contained all matter and radiation in our current universe. Propelled by a mysterious outward force, the bubble instantaneously expanded (it didn't explode) by a factor of 1,027, triggering a cosmic domino effect that created the stars, the galaxies and life as we know it.

The Big Bang

The Planck era
Time: Zero to 10^{-43} seconds

The Planck era describes the impossibly short passage of time between the absolute beginning of the universe (zero) and 10^{-43} seconds (10 trillionths of a yoctosecond, if you're counting). In this fraction of an instant, the universe went from infinite density to something called Planck density ($1093g/cm3$), the equivalent of 100 billion galaxies squeezed into the nucleus of an atom. Beyond the Planck density, rules of General Relativity don't apply, so the very dawn of time is still a complete and utter mystery.

ERA

Inflation era
In the Eighties, cosmologists theorised a period of spontaneous expansion in the very early moments of time. Instantaneously, every point in the universe expanded by a factor of

Quark era
After the explosive inflation period, the universe was a dense cauldron of pure energy. Under these conditions, gamma rays of energy collided to briefly form quarks and anti-quarks, the fundamental building blocks of matter. Just as quickly, though, the quarks and anti-quarks collided in a process called annihilation, converting their mass back to pure energy.

TIME | 10^{-36} to 10^{-32} after Big Bang | 10^{-32} to 10^{-12}

1,027. The universe didn't get bigger, it just was bigger. Because the universe got so big, so fast, its naturally spherical shape appeared flat to objects on the surface, solving one of the early problems with Big Bang theory.

Quark

Antiquark

Quark - antiquark pair

X-boson

Particle soup
If you turn the heat up high enough, everything melts. When the universe was 10-32 seconds old, it burned at a magnificent 1,000 trillion trillion degrees Celsius. At this remarkable temperature, the tiniest building blocks of matter – quarks and anti-quarks, leptons and anti-leptons – swirled freely in a particle soup called the quark-gluon plasma. Gluon is the invisible 'glue' that carries the strong force, binding quarks into protons and neutrons.

3 TOP FACTS
EVIDENCE FOR THE BIG BANG

Background radiation

1 Cosmic microwave background radiation (CMB) – which fills the universe uniformly – is well explained as the super-cooled afterglow from the original Big Bang.

Expanding universe

2 Galaxies outside of the Milky Way move away from us at a rate that is proportional to their distance from us, pointing to a continual expansion from a single source.

Big Bang nucleosynthesis

3 Big Bang theory predicts that the earliest atoms to emerge from the dense particle soup were hydrogen and helium in a 3:1 ratio. Using powerful telescopes and spectrometers, cosmologists confirm that the observed universe is 74 per cent hydrogen, 25 per cent helium and one per cent heavier elements.

DID YOU KNOW? *None of the essential elements of human life (carbon and oxygen) were created during the Big Bang*

Let there be light

The primordial soup of the early universe was composed of pairs of particles and anti-particles (mostly quarks, anti-quarks, leptons and anti-leptons). Picture this ultra-hot, supercharged environment as the original super collider. Particles and anti-particles smashed together in a process called annihilation, producing beams of photons (light radiation). As more particles collided, more light was generated. Some of those photons reformed into particles, but when the universe finally cooled enough to form stable atoms, the spare photons were set free. The net result: the (observable) universe contains a billion times more light than it does matter.

X-bosons

A funny thing happened at 10^{-39} seconds after the beginning of time. The universe produced huge particles called X-bosons (1,015 times more massive than protons). X-bosons are neither matter nor anti-matter and exist only to carry the Grand Unified Force, a combination of the electromagnetic, weak and strong forces that exist today.

The Grand Unified Force drove the early expansion of the universe, but rapid cooling caused X-bosons to decay into protons and anti-protons. For reasons that aren't clear, a billion and one protons were created for every billion anti-protons, creating a tiny net gain of matter. This imbalance, forged during a short blip in time, is the reason for our matter-dominated universe.

Recreating the Big Bang

CERN's Large Hadron Collider (LHC) is the world's largest particle accelerator. At full power, trillions of protons will travel at near light speed through super-cooled vacuum tubes buried 100 metres below the surface. As the protons smash into each other – at a rate of 600 million collisions per second – they will generate energy 100,000 times hotter than the Sun, a faithful recreation of the cosmic conditions milliseconds after the Big Bang. Using ultra-sensitive detectors, scientists will scour the debris trails for traces of quarks, leptons and even the Higgs boson, a highly theoretical particle believed to give mass to matter.

A computer simulation of the decay path of a Higgs boson after two protons collide in the LHC

Separation of the Electroweak force

During the Planck era, the four forces of nature were briefly unified: gravity, the strong force, electromagnetism and the weak force. As the Planck era ended as the universe cooled, gravity separated out, then the strong force separated during the inflation. But it wasn't until the end of the Quark era that the universe was cool enough to separate the electromagnetic and weak forces, establishing the physical laws we follow today.

110^{-9} to 10^{-62}

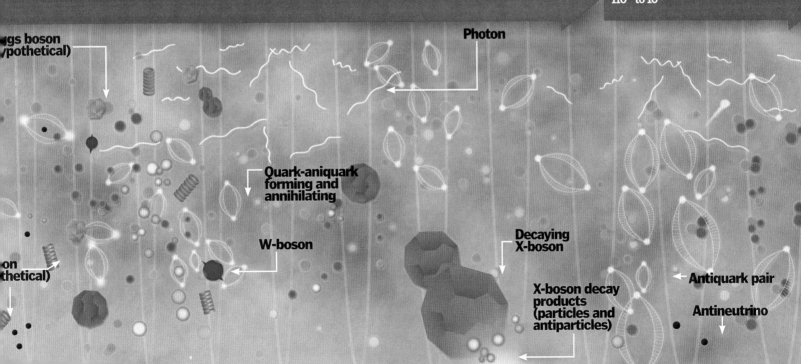

...gs boson (...ypothetical)

Photon

Quark-aniquark forming and annihilating

W-boson

...on (...thetical)

Decaying X-boson

X-boson decay products (particles and antiparticles)

Antiquark pair

Antineutrino

The origins of matter

Everything in the universe – the galaxies, the stars, the planets, even your big toe – is made of matter. In the beginning (roughly 13.7 billion years ago), matter and radiation were bound together in a superheated, super-dense fog. As the universe cooled and expanded, the first elemental particles emerged: quarks and anti-quarks. As things cooled further, the strong force separated, pulling together clumps of quarks into protons and neutrons, building the first atomic nuclei. Half a million years later, conditions were finally cool enough for nuclei to pull in free electrons, forming the first stable atoms. Small fluctuations in the density of matter distribution led to clusters and clouds of matter that coalesced, over hundreds of millions of years, into the stars and galaxies we explore today.

Dark forces

So what is the universe made of? Well, there is more to the universe than meets the eye. Cosmologists have proven that the visible or 'luminous' portions of the cosmos – the stars, galaxies, quasars and planets – are only a small fraction of the total mass and composition of the universe. Using super-accurate measurements of cosmic microwave background radiation fluctuations, scientists estimate that only 4.6 per cent of the universe is composed of atoms (baryonic matter), 23 per cent is dark matter (invisible and undetectable, but with a gravitational effect on baryonic matter), and 72 per cent is dark energy, a bizarre form of matter that works in opposition to gravity. Many cosmologists believe that dark energy is responsible for the accelerating expansion of the universe, which should be contracting under its own gravitational pull.

Hadron era

When the expanding universe cooled to 1,013K (ten quadrillion degrees Celsius), quarks became stable enough to bond together through the strong force. When three quarks clump together in the right formation, they form hadrons, a type of particle that includes protons and neutrons. Miraculously, every single proton and neutron in the known universe was created during this millisecond of time.

Lepton era

During this comparatively 'long' era, the rapidly expanding universe cools to 109K, allowing for the formation of a new kind of particle called a lepton. Leptons, like quarks, are the near mass-less building blocks of matter. Electrons are a 'flavour' of lepton, as are neutrinos.

Nucleosynthesis era

For 17 glorious minutes, the universe reached the ideal temperature to support nuclear fusion, the process by which protons and neutrons bond together to form atomic nuclei. Only the lightest elements have time to form – 75 per cent hydrogen, 25 per cent helium – before fusion winds down.

10^{-6} to 1 second

1 second to 3 minutes

3 minutes to 20 minutes

Electron

Newly formed hadron

Pion, a type of meson

Photon

Positron (antielectron)

Electron

Electron

Proton

Neutron

Free quark

Helium-3 nucleus

Helium-4 nucleus

Photon

Positron

Neutrino

Pion

HEAD 2 HEAD
Scientists

MOST FAMOUS

1. Albert Einstein
Albert Einstein's revolutionary Theory of General Relativity paved the way for the idea that all matter in the universe was uniformly distributed from a common source.

LESS FAMOUS

2. Edwin Hubble
Edwin Hubble calculated that galaxies moved away from one another at a rate relative to the distance between them, first proving that the universe was expanding.

LEAST FAMOUS

3. Gamow, Alpher & Herman
In the Forties, these three analysed creation of elements from the Big Bang's fallout, discovering that only hydrogen and helium could've been produced in large quantities.

DID YOU KNOW? If there were more matter in the universe, its mass would be too great and it would collapse on itself

Cosmic microwave background radiation
The residual heat from the big bang can give us a clue to the origin of the universe

As the universe expands, it also cools. The inconceivable heat released during the Big Bang has been slowly dissipating as the universe continues its 14 billion-year expansion. Using sensitive satellite equipment, cosmologists can measure the residual heat from the Big Bang, which exists as cosmic microwave background radiation (CMBR). CMBR is everywhere in the known universe and its temperature is nearly constant (a nippy 2.725K over absolute zero), further proof that the radiation emanated from a single, ancient source.

Minute differences in microwave background radiation levels (+/- 0.0002K) reveal fluctuations in the density of matter in the primitive universe

Opaque era
These are the 'dark ages' of the universe, when light and matter were intertwined in a dense cosmic fog. Photons of light collided constantly with free protons (hydrogen ions), neutrons, electrons and helium nuclei, trapping the light in a thick plasma of particles. It is impossible for cosmologists to 'see' beyond this era, since there is no visible light.

Balance of elements
When the temperature dropped to 10,000K, electrons slowed down enough to be pulled into orbit around atomic nuclei, forming the first stable, neutral atoms of hydrogen, helium and other trace elements. As atoms started to form, photons were freed from the cosmic fog, creating a transparent universe. All cosmic background radiation originated with this 'last scattering' of photons.

Matter era
During the Opaque era, matter and light were stuck together as plasma. Photons of light applied radiation pressure on matter, preventing it from bonding together to form atoms and larger particles. When light and matter 'decoupled', the radiation pressure was released as light, freeing matter to clump and collect in the first clouds of interstellar gas. From there, the first stars were born around 400 million years after the Big Bang.

20 minutes to 377,000 years

500,000 to the present

Photon

Helium atom (two protons and two electrons)

Free photon

Proton

Hydrogen atom (single proton and single electron)

Electron

The 'God' particle
We take for granted the idea that if something is made of protons, neutrons and electrons, then it inherently has mass. But cosmologists now believe that no particle has mass simply by merit of its existence. Instead, mass is bestowed on particles as they pass through a Higgs field, a theoretical quantum field named after British physicist Peter Higgs. Imagine the Higgs field as a bowl of honey and quantum particles as a string of pearls. As you drag the pearls through the honey, they are imbued with mass. Every quantum field has a fundamental particle, and the particle associated with Higgs field is the Higgs boson. One of the goals of the Large Hadron Collider at CERN is to prove the existence of the elusive Higgs boson once and for all.

A star is born

There may be as many as 10 billion trillion stars in the 100 billion galaxies throughout the universe, but "only" about 100 billion in our galaxy, the Milky Way. Most stars comprise plasma, helium and hydrogen. They form when giant molecular clouds (GMCs), also known as star nurseries, experience a gravitational collapse. This increase in pressure and temperature forces fragments into a body known as a protostar. Over the course of its life, a typical star goes through continuous nuclear fusion in its core. The energy released by this fusion makes the star glow.

Stars are classified according to the Hertzsprung-Russell Diagram, which lists their colour, temperature, mass, radius, luminosity and spectra (which elements they absorb). There are three main types of star: those above, below and on the main sequence. Within these types, there are seven different classifications. We're most familiar with the main sequence star that we call the Sun, a type G yellow-white star with a radius of 700,000 kilometres and a temperature of 6,000 kelvin. However, some stars above the main sequence are more than a thousand times larger than the Sun, while those below the main sequence can have a radius of just a few kilometres. ⚙

LOW-MASS STARS

Red dwarf

The cool star
Red dwarfs are small and relatively cool stars, which while being large in number tend to have a mass of less than one-half that of our Sun. The heat generated by a red dwarf occurs at a slow rate through the nuclear fusion of hydrogen into helium within its core, before being transported via convection to its surface. In addition, due to their low mass red dwarfs tend to have elongated life spans, exceeding that of stars like our Sun by billions of years.

Giant molecular cloud

Proto-stars

SUN-LIKE STARS

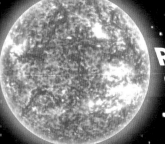
Red giant

A star explodes
If a star has enough mass to become a supergiant, it will supernova instead of becoming a white dwarf. As nuclear fusion ends in the core of a supergiant, the loss of energy can trigger a sudden gravitational collapse. Dust and gas from the star's outer layers hurtle through space at up to 30,000 kilometres per second

Almost a star
A protostar is a ball-shaped mass in the early stages of becoming a star. It's irregularly shaped and contains dust as well as gas, formed during the collapse of a giant molecular cloud. The protostar stage in a star's life cycle can last for a hundred thousand years as it continues to heat and become denser

Star or planet?
A brown dwarf is sometimes not even considered a star at all, but instead a sub-stellar body. They are incredibly small in relation to other types of stars, and never attained a high enough temperature, mass or enough pressure at its core for nuclear fusion to actually occur. It is below the main sequence on the Hertzsprung-Russell Diagram. Brown dwarfs have a radius about the size of Jupiter, and are sometimes difficult to distinguish from gaseous planets because of their size and make-up (helium and hydrogen)

Brown dwarf

HIGH-MASS STARS

The rarest star
Supergiants are among the rarest types of stars, and can be as large as our entire solar system. Supergiants can also be tens of thousands of times brighter than the Sun and have radii of up to a thousand times that of the Sun. Supergiants are above the main sequence on the Hertzsprung-Russell Diagram, occurring when the hydrogen of main sequence stars like the Sun has been depleted

NEAREST

1. Proxima Centauri
Other than our Sun, the closest star to Earth is Proxima Centauri. It is about four light-years from the Sun.

LARGEST

2. VY Canis Majoris
The largest known star, VY Canis Majoris, has a radius of between 1,800 and 2,100 times that of the Sun.

OLDEST

3. HE0107-5240
HE0107-5240, a giant star in the Milky Way, may be nearly as old as our universe at about 13.2 billion years old. It could've once been part of a binary star system.

DID YOU KNOW? A star may have a life cycle of millions to trillions of years. The larger the star is, the shorter its life cycle

Compared to other stars, the Sun is in the middle of the pack when it comes to size and temperature

Only gas pressure counter-balances gravity

Star starts to collapse as hydrogen is used up

Star continues to collapse as no helium burning occurs

Small, dim star gradually fades

Black dwarf

Catch a dying star
White dwarfs are considered the final phase in a star's life cycle unless it attained enough mass to supernova (and more than 95 percent of stars don't). The cores of white dwarfs typically comprise carbon and oxygen, left over after the gas is used up during nuclear fusion and occurring after a main sequence star has gone through its giant phase. A white dwarf is small, with a volume comparable to that of Earth's, but incredibly dense, with a mass about that of the Sun's. With no energy left, a white dwarf is dim and cool in comparison to larger types of stars

The stellar remnant
Black dwarfs are the hypothetical next stage of star degeneration after the white dwarf stage, when they become sufficiently cool to no longer emit any heat or light. Because the time required for a white dwarf to reach this state is postulated to be longer than the current age of the universe, none are expected to exist yet. If one were to exist it would be, by its own definition, difficult to locate and image due to the lack of emitted radiation

White dwarf

Black dwarf

Beyond the supernova
A hypernova is a supernova taken to an even larger degree. Supergiant stars with masses that are more than 100 times that of the Sun are thought to have these massive explosions. If a supergiant were close to Earth and exploded into a hypernova, the resulting radiation could lead to a mass extinction

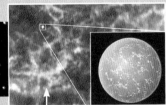

Neutron star

The neutron dance
Neutron stars are a potential next stage in the life cycle of a star. If the mass that remains after a supernova is up to three times that of the Sun, it becomes a neutron star. This means that the star only consists of neutrons, particles that don't carry an electrical charge

The absence of light
Stellar black holes are thought to be the end of the life cycle for supergiant stars with masses more than three times that of our Sun. After supernova, some of these stars leave remnants so heavy that they continue to remain gravitationally unstable

Super giant

Super-novae

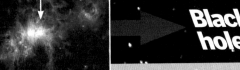

Hypernovae

Black hole

Zombie stars

Plus six other celestial wonders explained

Flare stars are usually red dwarfs, which are cooler and smaller than our Sun

1 Flare stars

If you're looking for a star that's unpredictable, then the flare star is it. With their dramatic bursts of brightness, flare stars often come in the form of dim red dwarfs, which are small and relatively cool stars compared to our Sun. They're not too dissimilar to our very own star, though – the material that erupts from their surfaces is similar to how solar flares storm from the Sun's surface – and these phenomena are all down to magnetic reconnection in the stars' atmospheres.

Magnetic reconnection is when magnetic fields are rearranged, causing high temperatures and particles to race away at high speeds. From Earth, flare stars usually appear quite faint to us despite turning up the brightness. In fact, in order to be able to see one, you would need to use your own space telescope.

In April 2014, NASA's Swift satellite observed a record-breaking sequence of eruptions from a nearby red dwarf star at a distance of roughly 60 light years. The blasts were so bright that they were measured to be as much as 10,000 times more powerful than the biggest solar flare ever recorded.

Flare stars play host to unpredictable bursts in brightness

Blue stragglers can be identified as bright blue stars at the centre of star clusters

2 Blue stragglers

The blue stragglers are a bit of a contradiction. These stars, which burn hot and shine blue, would appear to be quite young, yet they reside in open or globular star clusters – gatherings of ancient stars that are usually around the same age because they all formed and "grew up" together.

They're called blue stragglers because in terms of their evolution, they appear to be lagging behind their neighbours. Just how they come to exist is still a bit of a mystery and two possible ways are shown below. According to astronomers, the most obvious explanation is that these young stars must have been made from the merger of two older, low-mass stars within the dense confines of the cluster, making a more massive star that is rejuvenated and appears much younger.

The collision model

1 Collision course
Two low-mass stars head toward each other for a head-on collision.

2 Stellar tango
As the two stars enter into each other's gravitational influence, they begin rotating around each other before spinning into one another.

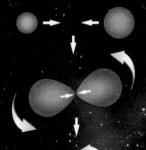

Ejected debris

3 A reborn star
The new merged star appears from the debris of the collision and shines hot and blue.

4 Swollen star
The evolution of the star is not over yet. The extra heating causes the star to swell and expand, turning red as its rotation slows.

5 Contraction
As the interior of the star settles down, it contracts again, turning a blue hue once more.

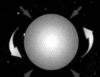

The slow coalescence model

1 Close companions
Sometimes stars come in close pairs – so close that they are actually touching and begin to transfer material.

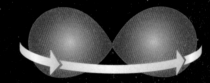

2 Vampire star
The larger star's stronger gravity wins out, and begins cannibalising the smaller partner. As it does so, the larger star spins up.

3 Fast spinner
The larger star grows more massive, hotter and bluer, and spins at least 75 times faster than our familiar Sun.

3 Zombie stars

We know the Type Ia supernova as the explosive death of a white dwarf star, completely blown to smithereens. There can be survivors in such a catastrophe, however. These beat the odds in what is known as a Type Iax supernova eruption. Occasionally, the supernova explosion is unusually weak (relatively speaking), allowing a portion of the original white dwarf star to survive. In 2014, astronomers studying archived Hubble images identified one such battered and bruised supernova survivor. These white dwarf remnants appear to come back to life as they explode, earning them the nickname of zombie stars.

If a supernova explosion is relatively weak, bits of a white dwarf star can survive

Crusty star
A strange quark star would form inside a neutron star, so it is expected to have a thick crust of neutrons surrounding it.

Stable star
A particularly massive quark star could have enough gravitational energy to start using strange matter as fuel, remaining stable for about 10 million years.

4 Quark stars

This type of star is one of the most exotic of all – so exotic that we're yet to even find one. Quarks are fundamental particles – they make up the protons and neutrons we find in the nuclei of atoms. So why would we find an entire star made not of atoms, nor protons and neutrons, but just quarks? When massive stars explode, their cores are compressed down to the point that their atoms are crushed so that protons merge with electrons to form a neutron star. The theory behind quark stars is, if the pressure is great, it can even squeeze the neutrons apart into their component quarks.

- Up Quarks
- Down Quarks
- Strange Quarks

Explosive stars
A handful of supernovas have been seen to have exploded brighter than any others, and some scientists think they signal the birth of quark stars.

Small stars
Quark stars would be very small, less than 10km (6.2mi) across.

Free Quarks

Strange quarks
Another type is the 'strange' quark, and some theories speculate that some quark stars could be made entirely of strange quarks.

Up and down
The most common types of quark are described as 'up' and 'down' and make up protons and neutrons.

5 Hybrid stars

Akin to a Russian doll, a hybrid star is actually quite bizarre – especially since they exist as one star encased inside the shell of another – simply because the larger star has gobbled up the smaller one.

It was physicist Kip Thorne and astronomer Anna Zytkow who proposed that such a star existed back in the Seventies, but it wasn't until 40 years of searching that a hybrid star – also known as a Thorne-Zytkow object – was uncovered. To look at, a hybrid star seems like your standard red supergiant, similar to Betelgeuse in the constellation of Orion. But it's the chemical fingerprints they leave, measured by analysing the red supergiant's starlight, that give a neutron star away.

Inside a hybrid
Thorne-Zytkow objects are bizarre hybrids, so we get two stars for the price of one

The red giant
The outside of the star is the red giant, which is the puffed-up transformation of a Sun-like star near the end of its life.

Different elements
The difference in temperature of the two stars might result to rather unusual stellar chemistry, with different isotopes of elements being created.

Hot meets cool
The neutron star is very hot, over 1bn°C (1.8bn°F), while the red giant is just a few thousand degrees hot.

Neutron star
At the core of the star is the neutron star. In this diagram its size has been exaggerated, as neutron stars are only 10-20km (6.2-12.4mi) across, but incredibly dense.

Tobias Roetsch

Tobias Roetsch

Betelgeuse

Betelgeuse
Betelgeuse is a star that will one day go supernova. Heavy elements are created within such stars.

The Sun
9 billion years younger than HD 140283, the Sun has an abundance of heavy elements 250 times greater than the Methuselah Star.

The Methuselah star
The oldest star currently known to us at 13.7 billion years old, HD 140283 has a very low amount of heavy elements.

Capella

Aldebaran

Pleiades

Sirius ☉

Sun

HD 140283

Rigel

6 Oldest star

The universe is 13.8 billion years old, and there's one star that is almost the same age. The star HD 140283, nicknamed the Methuselah star, is estimated to be at least 13.7 billion years old. This star, which is 190 light years away from Earth, sports a very low abundance of heavy elements. These elements are forged inside stars and build up over many stellar generations. To have such a low heavy-element abundance, the Methuselah Star must have formed right after the very first generation of stars.

Old-timer
This is the view of the sky as seen from HD 140283, which is the oldest known star in the Milky Way galaxy

The Pleiades
At the other end of the age scale is the Pleiades star cluster, containing around a thousand stars just 100 million years old.

Whirling dervish
How Vega loses its spherical shape because it's too quick

Debris disc
Vega is a relatively young star, which is why it still has its debris disc and younger stars tend to spin faster.

Dizzying rotation
Fast rotators like Vega and Regulus spin at hundreds of thousand of kilometres per hour.

7 Egg-shaped star

You haven't really met a strange-looking star until you've come across an egg-shaped one. Regulus, which you can see from Earth in the constellation of Leo, is one such stellar abnormality that we know of.

Stars like to spin, with some moving faster than others. Our Sun is able to hit speeds of 7,242 kilometres (4,500 miles) per hour. However, the giant star Regulus, which is at least three times bigger than the Sun, clocks a velocity of almost 1.13 million kilometres (700,000 miles) per hour despite its sheer size. Another speedy spinner is Vega, the bright star in the constellation of Lyra, which spins at a rate of 986,400 kilometres (613,000 miles) per hour. Being fast movers means these stars lose their spherical shape as centrifugal forces cause their equators to bulge outward and the stars appear

A quick spin
Vega takes just 12.5 hours to complete one revolution. In comparison, our Sun

Temperature
Vega's bulge means the surface temperature varies across the star, with the hottest temperatures

Mysterious magnetic stars

Meet a star with a magnetic field that's quadrillions of times more powerful than Earth's

There are plenty of exotic objects in the universe and many might agree that the magnetar fits neatly into this category. Magnetars are exactly what their name infers – they are stars with a monstrous magnetic field, quadrillions of times stronger than any magnet humans can build. It's said the magnetar is so powerful that if you placed one at a distance halfway to the Moon, it would have no trouble stripping information from all the credit cards in the world. But what makes them so powerful?

Magnetars are rapidly spinning neutron stars, made from the collapse of a massive star during a supernova explosion. However, the full details of how they are made is still a mystery that continues to baffle astronomers to this day. It's said that if you were to scoop a teaspoon full of material from this object's surface, it would weigh in at 1 billion tons. What's more, a magnetar can also shift its bulk at alarming speeds, completing one pirouette in no more than ten seconds. It's also capable of spitting out very strong bursts of X-rays and gamma rays – the most penetrative of radiation – which is truly characteristic of the magnetar.

These bizarre objects don't live for very long in astronomical terms. It's believed they start to feel their age and wind down after about 10,000 years and, as a result, astronomers estimate there are at least 30 million inactive magnetars in the Milky Way galaxy compared to a very much alive and confirmed 23. ✿

Dynamo power!
It's thought an extremely turbulent, yet dense, fluid provides the magnetar with its incredibly powerful magnetic field

An explosive formation
Magnetars are made when, in a supernova, a star collapses to make a neutron star with its magnetic field increasing dramatically in strength

A dying breed
To date, just over 20 active magnetars have been found. Estimates suggest there are likely to be over 30 million 'dead' magnetars in the Milky Way alone

Anatomy of the magnetar
The astronomical make-up the universe's strongest magnets

Lethal magnetic field
It's said that a magnetar's magnetic field is so powerful that even at a distance of 1,000km (620mi) it would still be bad news for life, distorting molecules

Heavyweight champion
They might only have a diameter of 16km (10mi), but magnetars are much heavier than our Sun

Living a short life
The powerful magnetic fields these rapidly spinning stars exude are very short-lived. After about 10,000 years the magnetar becomes increasingly powerless

How were magnetars discovered?

In March 1979, after dropping satellites onto the surface of Venus, two Soviet spacecraft were sent drifting though the Solar System when they were all of a sudden blasted by an immense burst of gamma radiation, causing the readings on both probes to skyrocket from 100 counts per second on to over 200,000 counts per second. The numbers jumped in almost an instant, or mere fractions of a second.

Amazed and somewhat bemused by the finding, scientists followed up on the mysterious blast that saturated the likes of NASA's Helios 2 probe, the Pioneer Orbiter around Venus and, mere seconds later, many satellites orbiting our own planet. The radiation seemed to seep in everywhere, which made it easier for astronomers to work out where it was coming from. Narrowing the direction down, they figured out the radiation was coming from a magnetar made by a star that had gone supernova around 3000 BCE.

They can spin fast or slow

We know magnetars spin incredibly fast, but what's more interesting is that they're also capable of putting on the brakes, so to speak, and slowing themselves down. It's an interesting observation but it's also one that can't be easily explained by our existing theories of physics, making the magnetar even more mysterious.

That's not to say that astronomers haven't had some intelligent guesses as to what could be causing the behaviour they refer to as the "anti-glitch issue." They speculate there are pockets of fluid inside the star that's rotating faster and faster until it's sloshing around much faster than the stellar crust on the surface. Of course, this theory has not been proven yet, but scientists are beginning to wonder if these disturbances cause a magnetar's crust to crack, leading to their decline.

Hubble has shown us more of the universe than we ever expected

Dark history

The Hubble Space Telescope has successfully mapped a cross-section of dark matter in the universe to a distance of 6.5 billion light years. Astronomers measured the shape of galaxies in images of this cross-section – the huge amount of dark matter acts as a gravitational lens, warping the light from the galaxies. The degree of lensing shows how much dark matter is present. The results showed that dark matter has become clumpier with time, as gravity pulls it and ordinary matter into a giant web across the universe.

STRANGE BUT TRUE
THAT'S DARK, MAN

What is VIRGOHI21?
A The astrological star sign of dark matter
B A dark galaxy made almost totally of dark matter
C The study of dark matter in the constellation Virgo

Answer:
VIRGOHI21 is a galaxy made almost entirely out of dark matter, discovered by astronomers at Cardiff University in 2005. VIRGOHI21 contains a thousand times more dark matter than baryonic matter, has no stars and is a tenth of the size of the Milky Way.

DID YOU KNOW? New research from 2014 suggests that dark matter might be hiding in microscopic black holes

THE MYSTERY OF DARK MATTER

Hunting for the invisible mass that makes up 85 per cent of matter in the universe

Out there in the universe, something is going on that we're not able to fully explain. Over three billion light years away from Earth, two great clusters of galaxies are colliding. The stars in both are relatively unaffected in the melee, but clouds of hot, X-ray emitting gas are crashing into one another, stitching the two galaxy clusters into one new one: meet the Bullet Cluster, one of the most energetic events in the cosmos. Yet amid the epic confrontation of the clusters, something mysterious lurks, something for which the only name we have is 'dark matter'.

Within the Bullet Cluster we can see the galaxies. We can see the gas, which actually makes up most of the mass that emits light,

more than even the galaxies. But there is a completely invisible component – dark matter – yet its presence is perhaps the most crucial.

Dark matter's name implies that this mysterious substance is dark, but it is more than that – it is invisible, refusing to emit or absorb any forms of light or radiation that could reveal its existence. It passes straight through ordinary matter. We cannot smell, taste, touch or see it. What we do know is that it accounts for 27 per cent of all the mass and energy within the universe (normal matter is only five per cent and dark energy, the mysterious force accelerating the expansion of the universe, makes up the remaining 68 per cent) and it's likely to be made of some form of undiscovered subatomic particle.

"Little is known about it and all that the numerous searches for dark matter particles have done is rule out various hypotheses, but there have never been any 'positive' results", says astrophysicist Maxim Markevitch, who has carefully studied the Bullet Cluster for the effects of dark matter using NASA's Chandra X-ray Observatory.

However, there is one way in which it grabs our attention, which is through the force of gravity. One of the effects of this is clearly played out in the Bullet Cluster. It is this that allows astronomers to work out where the dark matter in the Bullet Cluster is located, even though we cannot even see it. Albert Einstein's General Theory of Relativity described how mass can bend space. Some people like to use the analogy of a cannonball on a sheet of rubber - the cannonball causes the sheet to sag. If you imagine the ball is an object like a galaxy or a star and the rubber sheet as space, you can see how mass bends space. However, light prefers to take straight paths through the universe, so what happens when it arrives at a region of space that has been warped in this manner? The light will follow the path of curved space, bending its trajectory. In this way a massive object in space can act like a lens, bending and magnifying light. This effect was predicted by Einstein nearly 100 years ago and we call these gravitational lenses.

Because galaxy clusters are so huge, they create formidable gravitational lenses. They can magnify the light of even more distant galaxies, but it is not a clear image, rather distorted arcs or smudges of light and occasionally a complete ring. We can see gravitational lensing by the Bullet Cluster, magnifying the light of distant galaxies. But when scientists analysed the gravitational lens, they found something stunning – the lensing effect was too strong to be accounted for by the mass of only the galaxies and the gas. There must be some other type of mass there, hidden. This is dark matter. From the pattern of the lensing, it is possible to work out where the dark matter in the cluster is, which has lead to another remarkable discovery. As the clusters collided, the galaxies and the gas have begun to merge, but the dark matter surrounding each cluster has slid silently through, not interacting with anything at all.

The Bullet Cluster was not the first time we saw the effects of dark matter. That discovery goes all the way back to 1933 when famous astronomer Fritz Zwicky at the California Institute of Technology (Caltech) noticed that galaxies orbiting around the edge of galaxy clusters were moving faster than they should.

Why should they be moving at a particular speed? In the 17th century, Johannes Kepler devised his laws of orbital motion, the third one being that "the square of the orbital period of a planet is directly proportional to the cube of the semi-major axis of its orbit." In other words, the farther from the Sun, and therefore the centre of mass of the Solar System, the slower a planet orbits. This should also be the case for galaxies orbiting galaxy clusters, but Zwicky found that galaxies on the edges of clusters were orbiting just as fast as those closer in. This implied there must be some unseen mass in the cluster helping things along with its gravity. He called this dark matter, but his idea was generally ignored. It was only in the 1970s when astronomer Vera Rubin of the Carnegie Institution for Science noticed the

Cosmic lenses
The huge amounts of dark matter in clusters create powerful gravitational telescopes

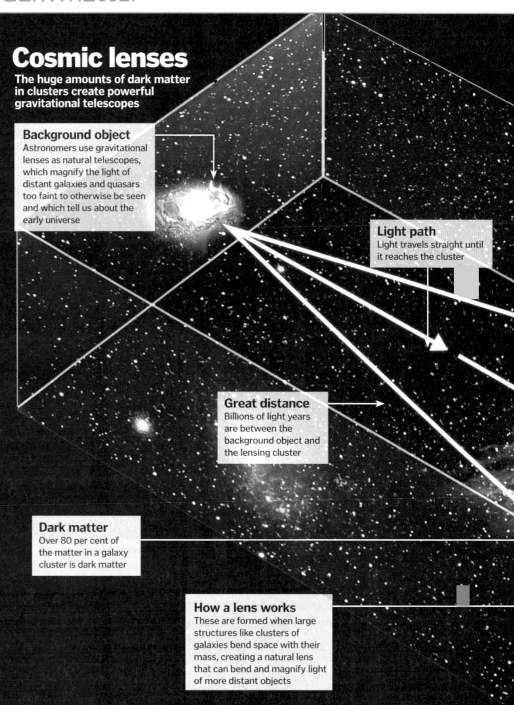

Background object
Astronomers use gravitational lenses as natural telescopes, which magnify the light of distant galaxies and quasars too faint to otherwise be seen and which tell us about the early universe

Light path
Light travels straight until it reaches the cluster

Great distance
Billions of light years are between the background object and the lensing cluster

Dark matter
Over 80 per cent of the matter in a galaxy cluster is dark matter

How a lens works
These are formed when large structures like clusters of galaxies bend space with their mass, creating a natural lens that can bend and magnify light of more distant objects

The ingredients of the universe

68%
DARK ENERGY

27%
DARK MATTER

5%
ORDINARY MATTER

KEY DATES
A BRIEF HISTORY OF DARK MATTER

1930s
Fritz Zwicky postulates the existence of dark matter to explain the motion of galaxies in clusters.

1970s
Astronomer Vera Rubin finds evidence for the existence of dark matter by studying the motion of stars in galaxies.

2003
NASA's Wilkinson Microwave Anisotropy Probe reveals 24 percent of the universe is dark matter.

2006
Studies of the Bullet Cluster reveal the first evidence for how dark matter causes a gravitational lens.

2013
ESA's Planck mission refines the amount of dark matter as 26.8 per cent of the universe.

DID YOU KNOW? Dark matter exists in our Milky Way galaxy, forming a giant halo inside which our galaxy is embedded

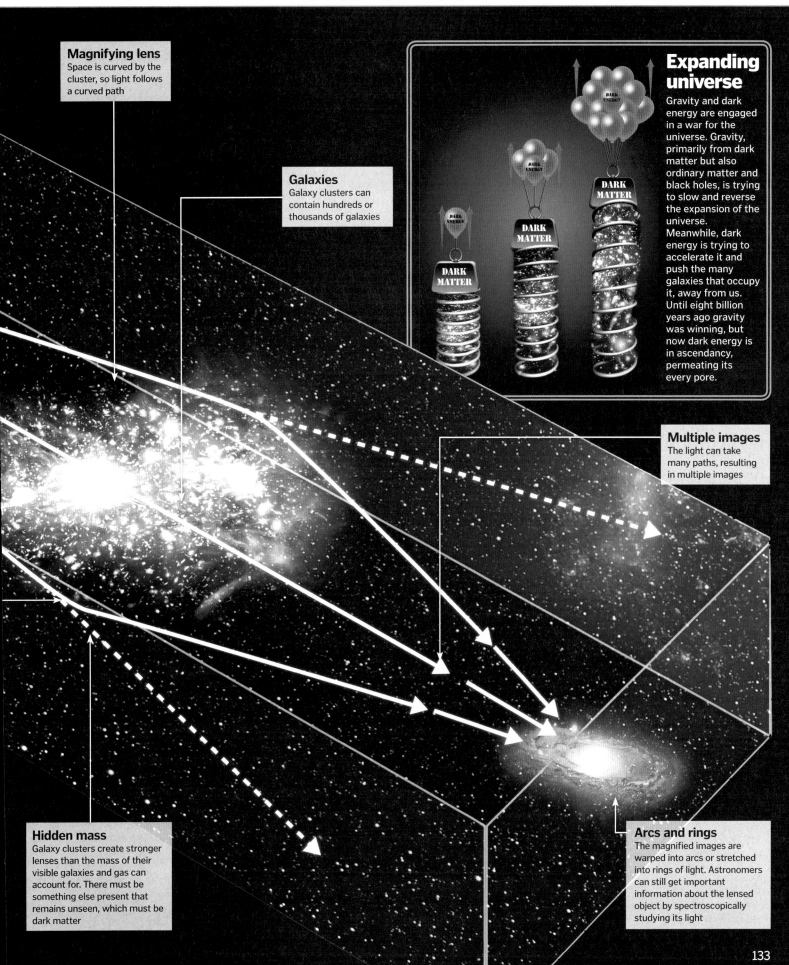

Magnifying lens
Space is curved by the cluster, so light follows a curved path

Galaxies
Galaxy clusters can contain hundreds or thousands of galaxies

Expanding universe
Gravity and dark energy are engaged in a war for the universe. Gravity, primarily from dark matter but also ordinary matter and black holes, is trying to slow and reverse the expansion of the universe. Meanwhile, dark energy is trying to accelerate it and push the many galaxies that occupy it, away from us. Until eight billion years ago gravity was winning, but now dark energy is in ascendancy, permeating its every pore.

Multiple images
The light can take many paths, resulting in multiple images

Hidden mass
Galaxy clusters create stronger lenses than the mass of their visible galaxies and gas can account for. There must be something else present that remains unseen, which must be dark matter

Arcs and rings
The magnified images are warped into arcs or stretched into rings of light. Astronomers can still get important information about the lensed object by spectroscopically studying its light

133

The Alpha Magnetic Spectrometer

Scientists are attempting to detect evidence for dark matter in an experiment called the Alpha Magnetic Spectrometer (AMS) on board the International Space Station. It is designed to detect charged particles called positrons, a type of antimatter, which are thought to be emitted at certain energies when two dark matter particles collide. In 2013, scientists studying the data from AMS revealed it had detected more than 400,000 positrons at those energies, strongly hinting they were from dark matter, although there was not enough information to be certain.

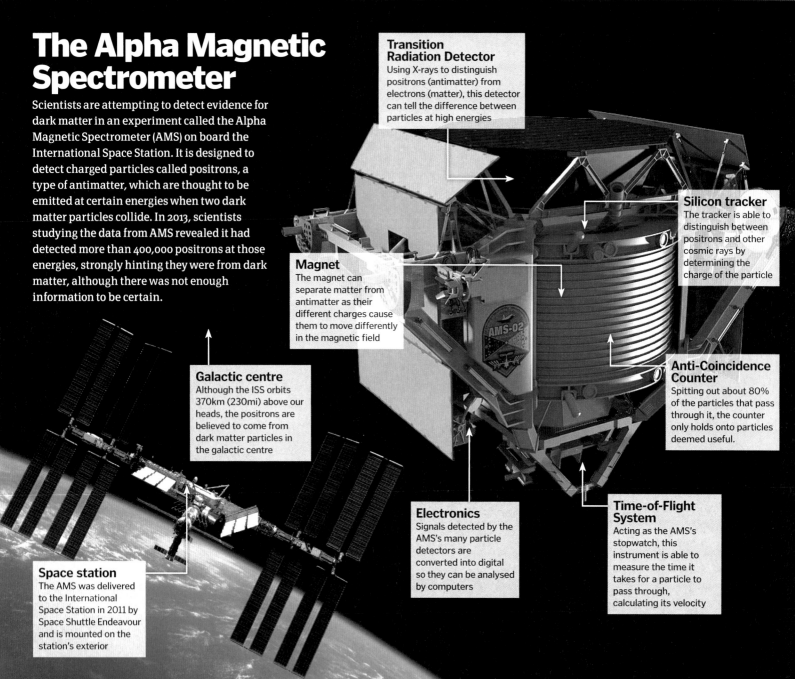

Transition Radiation Detector
Using X-rays to distinguish positrons (antimatter) from electrons (matter), this detector can tell the difference between particles at high energies

Silicon tracker
The tracker is able to distinguish between positrons and other cosmic rays by determining the charge of the particle

Magnet
The magnet can separate matter from antimatter as their different charges cause them to move differently in the magnetic field

Galactic centre
Although the ISS orbits 370km (230mi) above our heads, the positrons are believed to come from dark matter particles in the galactic centre

Anti-Coincidence Counter
Spitting out about 80% of the particles that pass through it, the counter only holds onto particles deemed useful.

Electronics
Signals detected by the AMS's many particle detectors are converted into digital so they can be analysed by computers

Time-of-Flight System
Acting as the AMS's stopwatch, this instrument is able to measure the time it takes for a particle to pass through, calculating its velocity

Space station
The AMS was delivered to the International Space Station in 2011 by Space Shuttle Endeavour and is mounted on the station's exterior

same problem with the orbits of stars and gas near the edges of galaxies. This time the problem was noticed and today dark matter is one of the biggest puzzles of cosmology. Dark matter now forms an integral part of our models of how galaxies grow – we envisage galaxies in halos of dark matter, which is spread across the universe in a great cosmic web, pulling matter toward it and making galaxies and clusters expand.

The Bullet Cluster might hold the best evidence for dark matter, but astronomers and particle physicists seeking to shed light

on this substance are building new experiments to try to catch dark matter so that we can finally find out what it is. Although evidence from space suggests that dark matter does not interact with ordinary matter on large scales, physicists suspect that on the scale of individual particles, dark matter sometimes does interact. There must be trillions of these particles passing through us at any given moment, but the interactions are so rare that scientists may have to wait years in order to observe one. Physicists describe these particles as WIMPs,

an abbreviation that stands for Weakly Interacting Massive Particles.

In order to trap a dark matter particle in the act, most experiments take place far underground, away from any cosmic ray radiation on the surface that could potentially interfere with and contaminate the results. Experiments such as the Cryogenic Dark Matter Search, located in a mine in Minnesota in the United States, have freezing cold detectors, cooled to fractions of a degree above absolute zero, in order to help them search for the heat produced when a

Dark matter is for WIMPs

The Large Underground Xenon (LUX) experiment is buried deep beneath South Dakota, now home to the Sanford Underground Laboratory. It consists of a large tank filled with 370 kilograms (816 pounds) of liquid xenon and works on the assumption that dark matter is made of Weakly Interacting Massive Particles, or WIMPs. Occasionally a WIMP should interact with a xenon atom, emitting electrons and ultraviolet light. LUX has been working since 2012 and so far has found no evidence for WIMPs, but this has allowed scientists to constrain their models to narrow the search.

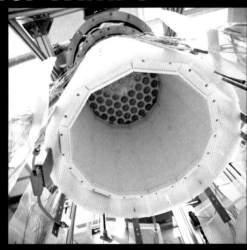

Going underground

The Large Underground Xenon experiment is searching for dark matter in South Dakota

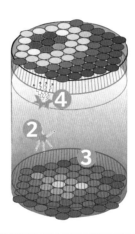

❶ **Liquid xenon**	❷ **Interaction**	❸ **Ultraviolet**	❹ **Electrons**	❺ **Tank**	❻ **Light sensors**	❼ **Cryostat**
Some theories on dark matter suggest it could occasionally interact with atoms such as xenon.	During the interaction, the xenon atoms recoil and an electron and a UV photon are emitted.	At a wavelength of 175nm, the UV photons are detected by sets of photomultiplier tube	The electrons drift to the top of the tank where they are electrically stimulated to emit visible light.	The experiment is shielded inside an 8x6m (26.2x19.7ft) water tank that keeps out external radiation.	Two sets of photomultiplier tubes, 122 in all, are arranged at the top and bottom of the experiment.	The experiment has to be kept cold for xenon to remain liquid, cooling LUX to -120°C (-184°F).

WIMP collides with an atom of a substance such as germanium. Another experiment, the Large Underground Xenon (LUX) dark matter detector, is located 1.6 kilometres (one mile) under the Black Hills of South Dakota, USA. It contains tanks of liquid xenon for WIMPS to interact with, the interaction producing signature radiation that can then be detected.

The hunt for dark matter also takes place in space, however. On rare occasions dark matter particles could collide and annihilate each other, releasing an antimatter particle known as a positron (the anti-particle to the negatively charged electron), but because there is so much dark matter in space, particularly in dense clusters close to the centre of the galaxy, there should in theory be a steady stream of positrons being produced. Now an experiment on the International Space Station, the Alpha Magnetic Spectrometer, may have detected some of these positrons.

Some astronomers think we shouldn't be searching for dark matter at all, as they don't believe it even exists. Concerned that dark matter theory adds more complexity to the universe than is necessary, they argue that the gravitational effects we infer as being down to dark matter suggest that we simply need to tweak the laws of gravity instead. As a result, dark matter now has a theoretical rival called Modified Newtonian Dynamics, or MOND. Will the theory of dark matter be usurped or vindicated? As time goes on, the chances of experiments detecting dark matter will increase, so the answers for which we've been searching may soon come into the light. ✿

Space volcanoes

Volcanoes can be much cooler elsewhere in our Solar System

It's not just Earth that has volcanoes, they can be found on several other celestial bodies too. The volcanoes on other terrestrial planets like Venus and Mars, and moons such as Jupiter's Io, are very similar to those on Earth, spewing out hot molten rock from below. However, those found on icy moons such as Enceladus and Titan, which orbit Saturn, eject something much colder. They are called cryovolcanoes, or ice volcanoes, and work in a very different way to their hotter cousins. ✹

Hot versus cold

How these two types of space volcano differ

Lava eruption
The magma escapes through vents in the surface and soon cools and solidifies into lava.

Molten rock
Building pressure forces the molten rock, or magma, upwards towards the surface.

Heated core
The planet or moon's core is usually heated by radioactive decay and the residual heat from its formation. However, in Io's case, the moon's heat is generated by tidal friction.

Cryomagma
The cryomagma solidifies after eruption in the cooler temperatures, and some even escapes the moon's orbit due to low gravity.

Icy eruption
A plume of cryomagma; ice particles and water vapour mixed with methane and ammonia, spews out from the moon's surface.

Melted ice
The heated core melts the ice above it, and as pressure builds, it is forced up between ice sheets on the surface.

Tidal friction
Gravity from a nearby planet generates tidal friction that heats the moon's core of silicate rock.

What is a meteor shower?

Discover how falling comet debris becomes shooting stars

A meteor shower occurs when lots of meteoroids enter the Earth's atmosphere one after the other. Meteoroids are bits of dust and rock from comets that are released when their orbit brings them close to the Sun. The Sun's heat boils off some of the comet's icy surface and the resulting debris then trails it in orbit.

Meteoroids that enter the Earth's atmosphere are known as meteors, and can regularly be seen travelling across the sky alone. However, several times each year, the Earth's orbit crosses with the orbit of a comet causing it to collide with a bunch of meteoroids all at once.

Meteors travel through the Earth's atmosphere at very high speeds - up to 72 kilometres (45 miles) per second. Friction of the atmosphere causes the meteor to heat up so the cloud of gas around it glows, and it's this that we see shooting through the sky. As they are usually very small, most meteors burn up in the atmosphere before they reach the Earth's surface, but those that do occasionally hit the ground are known as meteorites. ✹

Meteor showers are named after the constellations they appear to be falling from, such as the Orionids from Orion

Light years

The distance light travels in a year

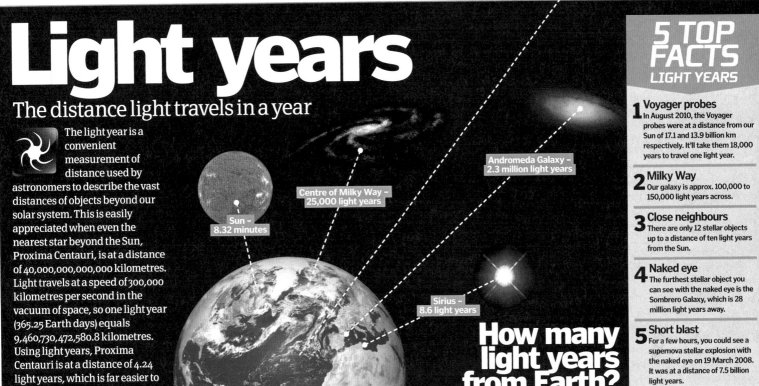

The light year is a convenient measurement of distance used by astronomers to describe the vast distances of objects beyond our solar system. This is easily appreciated when even the nearest star beyond the Sun, Proxima Centauri, is at a distance of 40,000,000,000,000 kilometres. Light travels at a speed of 300,000 kilometres per second in the vacuum of space, so one light year (365.25 Earth days) equals 9,460,730,472,580.8 kilometres. Using light years, Proxima Centauri is at a distance of 4.24 light years, which is far easier to write and comprehend. ✿

x4 images © NASA I Earth © iStock

Andromeda Galaxy –
2.3 million light years

Centre of Milky Way –
25,000 light years

Sun –
8.32 minutes

Sirius –
8.6 light years

How many light years from Earth?

Searching for hidden planets

How bending light can reveal hidden worlds

It's been over 80 years since Einstein first published his general theory of relativity and he's still making headlines. Astronomers are now using a central tenet of Einstein's revolutionary theory – that massive objects like stars and galaxies can bend the fabric of space-time – to create celestial magnifying glasses called gravitational lenses.

Here's how it works. Using Einstein's theory, scientists proved that light travelling toward Earth from a distant star bends slightly as it passes by the Sun. The bending effect is almost imperceptible because the Sun doesn't contain tremendous amounts of mass.

But imagine if an entire galaxy sat between the Earth and a far-off star. The mass of the galaxy cluster would act like a thick lens, bending and warping the light as it passed. To someone on Earth, the effect would be multiple images of the star, or in some cases, a glowing halo called an 'Einstein ring'.

To discover one of farthest 'extrasolar' planets – a planet 15,000 light years from our solar system – astronomers have used a version of a gravitational lens. In this case, astronomers used a nearby star as a 'lensing star' to bend the light of a distant source star. They chose the lensing star because of its size and its likelihood to have orbiting planets.

What they observed was remarkable. When the source star aligned behind the lensing star, the astronomers observed a double image of the source star. Then they witnessed two sudden spikes in the brightness of the double images. The spikes, they deduced, were caused by the gravitational pull of an unseen planet orbiting the lensing star. Powerful gravitational lenses also act as magnifying glasses, detecting faint light from distant sources. ✿

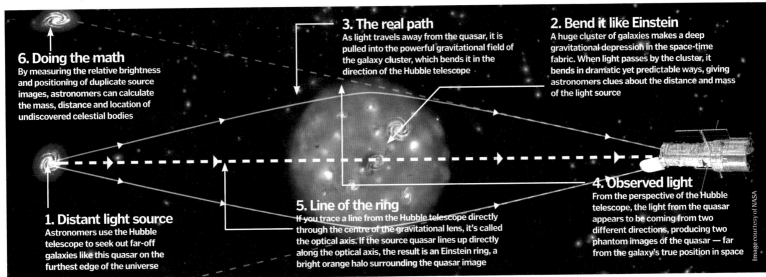

6. Doing the math
By measuring the relative brightness and positioning of duplicate source images, astronomers can calculate the mass, distance and location of undiscovered celestial bodies

3. The real path
As light travels away from the quasar, it is pulled into the powerful gravitational field of the galaxy cluster, which bends it in the direction of the Hubble telescope

2. Bend it like Einstein
A huge cluster of galaxies makes a deep gravitational depression in the space-time fabric. When light passes by the cluster, it bends in dramatic yet predictable ways, giving astronomers clues about the distance and mass of the light source

1. Distant light source
Astronomers use the Hubble telescope to seek out far-off galaxies like this quasar on the furthest edge of the universe

5. Line of the ring
If you trace a line from the Hubble telescope directly through the centre of the gravitational lens, it's called the optical axis. If the source quasar lines up directly along the optical axis, the result is an Einstein ring, a bright orange halo surrounding the quasar image

4. Observed light
From the perspective of the Hubble telescope, the light from the quasar appears to be coming from two different directions, producing two phantom images of the quasar — far from the galaxy's true position in space

Image courtesy of NASA

The search for a new Earth

Discover how new advances in technology are revealing hundreds of extrasolar planets across our galaxy

Hunting ground
Most of the new planets found have been within about 300 light years from our Sun

Since Galileo pointed a telescope at the heavens 400 years ago, the discovery of exoplanets beyond our own solar system is a goal astronomers have long cherished. Allied to this is the greater hope of finding Earth-like planets capable of supporting life. If it is proved we are

alone in this universe, or share it with other life forms, the answer will have huge implications for humanity.

Earth-based techniques introduced in the Nineties, using interferometry and coronagraphy, finally proved that other star systems do have giant extrasolar planetary bodies orbiting them. The race to

discover life-supporting Earth-sized planets, that are light years away, needs far greater precision and accuracy. To meet this challenge observatories throughout the world are constantly upgrading their technology, but the biggest hopes are pinned on telescopes launched into outer space.

DISCOVERED FIRST
1. 51 Pegasi b
This extrasolar planet was detected in 1995 and named Bellerophon. It is a hot Jupiter-type planet, 50.1 light years away from us, in the Pegasus constellation.

BIGGEST
2. WASP-17 b
Discovered by the UK's super WASP (Wide Area Search for Planets), in August 2009. This exoplanet is a gas giant twice the size of Jupiter.

TRIPLE SYSTEM
3. HD 188753 Ab
This hot Jupiter was the first to be discovered in a system with three suns. It is 149 light years away and was discovered by the Keck observatory back in 2005.

DID YOU KNOW? *The search for exoplanets requires measurements that are fractions of an arcsecond*

How are we looking?

Extrasolar planets are small, distant and hidden in the glare of their parent stars, unable to be seen directly by telescope. Astronomers use four main methods to infer their existence…

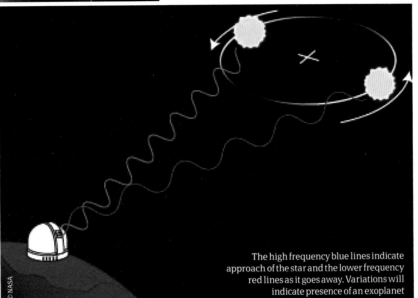

The high frequency blue lines indicate approach of the star and the lower frequency red lines as it goes away. Variations will indicate presence of an exoplanet

Doppler shift

This is based on analysing the spectrum of the light from a star. The spectrum of a star is as individual to it as a fingerprint. When light is refracted through a prism, it creates a spectrum of violet, indigo, blue, green, yellow, orange and red light. A rainbow naturally produces this effect. The invisible electromagnetic radiation at either end of the spectrum, like x-rays and infrared, can also be analysed by astronomers.

As a star moves towards us its light waves shift towards the higher-frequency blue end of the spectrum, and when it moves away they go to the lower frequency red end of the spectrum. This phenomenon is known as Doppler shift.

If a star has a nearby large planet, the two will orbit around a common centre of mass. The star will move faster around this centre of mass the bigger and closer the planet. This radial velocity can be measured, as the spectrum of the star will show correspondingly bigger colour shifts.

Transit method

As a planet passes (transits) in front of its parent star, it will cause the apparent brightness of the star to be reduced. During the transit, the spectrum of the light from the planet's atmosphere can be detected and analysed. Furthermore, when the Sun transits the planet the photometric intensity of the star can be compared with the data gathered during the planet's transit, enabling astronomers to calculate the temperature of the planet.

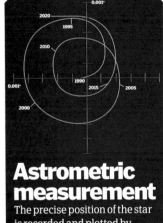

Astrometric measurement

The precise position of the star is recorded and plotted by telescope to detect the slight wobble of a star caused by radial velocity, implying the effects of a nearby planet. Astrometry is the earliest method of searching for exoplanets that dates back to the use of hand-plotted stars in the 18th Century.

Where are we looking?

The search for exoplanets is presently restricted to our own Milky Way spiral galaxy, which has a diameter of about 100,000 light years. This is mainly due to the various limitations on the technology and techniques used to seek them out.

Using astrometric and Doppler shift methods, the area of search is a range of from 100 to 300 light years. This can be extended by the transit method to 6,000 light years and using chronometry, as proposed for the TPF-C spacecraft, to 12,000 light years. Gravitational lensing can find extrasolar planets 25,000 light years away. As these techniques are refined, the search range is constantly being extended.

One theory is that the galaxy itself has a Goldilocks Zone, so that star systems in the spiral arms or too close to the centre of the galaxy would be too inhospitable for life-supporting planets. If this is true then Earth-like life-supporting exoplanets will be rarer to find.

Gravitational microlensing

This technique uses the lensing effect produced when one star is in alignment with another star. The gravitational field of the star nearest the observer magnifies the light from the star behind it, and if the foreground star has a planet, it will cause detectable variations in this lensing effect. Huge numbers of stars have to be monitored to discover these alignments that last only a few days or weeks.

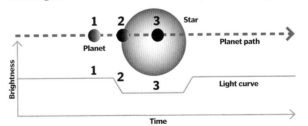

Observer · Planet · Lens star · Source star

Milky Way and Sun © NASA

Zone conditions

The Goldilocks Zone explains why the Earth's position is perfect for us to survive

The term 'Goldilocks Zone' comes from the 'Goldilocks and the Three Bears' story. Goldilocks tested bowls of porridge to find out which one was not too hot or too cold. Earth is inside the Goldilocks Zone that is just right for habitation. If Earth was closer to the Sun, like Mercury and Venus, conditions are too hot for us. If we were further away, like Mars and beyond, conditions are too cold and arid.

Our Sun is a G-dwarf type star, for larger stars like A-dwarfs the habitable zone is further away, and for cooler stars like M-dwarfs the habitable zone is closer. Life is also dependent on the rotation, axial tilt and orbit of Earth that gives us our regular procession of days, seasons and years. If these factors were too extreme or irregular, the variations in temperature and effects on our climate and ecosystem would not be suitable for us.

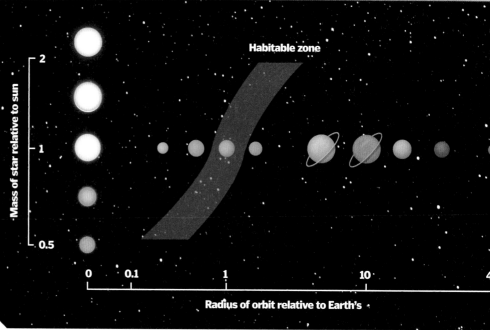

Habitable zone

Mass of star relative to sun

Radius of orbit relative to Earth's

What has been found?

Up to July 2014, over 1800 extrasolar planets have been discovered. Only one Earth-sized planet has been found (orbiting the Alpha Centauri solar system); the majority are hot Jupiters or gas giants. Hot Jupiters have a mass between 110 to 430 times that of Earth. They are created beyond their parent star before forming a close orbit around it. Other types include super Earths, which have a mass between that of Earth and Jupiter. So far hundreds of super Earth

candidates have been detected. A good example is COROT-7 b, which was discovered in 2009 by the European COROT (Convection Rotation and planetary Transits) spacecraft. It resides 500 light years away in the Unicorn constellation, and orbits a Sun-like G-class star. Unfortunately, it orbits very close to its parent star and its surface could be as hot as 2,600°C. In addition, it orbits its star at the rate of 466,030mph; making Earth's 67,000mph look sluggish.

COROT found its 23rd confirmed exoplanet in 2011. Named COROT-23b, it has a steady but rapid orbit around its parent star of just 3.6 days. It is positioned in the Serpens constellation and, at 2.8 Jupiter masses, is likely to be yet another hot gas giant.

In March 2010, HAT-P-14b was discovered 670 light years away in the Hercules constellation, and 235 light years away in the Andromeda constellation HAT-P-16b was reported too. These are also hot Jupiter exoplanets but there is the possibility of a smaller exoplanet existing near HAT-P-14b.

NASA's Kepler space telescope analysed 150,000 stars to detect any exoplanets using the transit method when it started operating in May 2009. This early data revealed five exoplanets, named Kepler 4b, 5b, 6b, 7b and 8b that were confirmed by ground-based observatories. All of them are in the Cygnus constellation and are hot Jupiter-type exoplanets. It has since obtained data from thousands more stars that revealed hundreds of potential candidate planets, and in February 2014, NASA announced the discovery of 715 newly verified extrasolar planets around 305 stars by the Kepler Space Telescope.

An artist's impression of the COROT spacecraft

©NASA

HEAD2 HEAD
EXOPLANET-FINDING TELESCOPES

BIGGEST TWIN

1. W. M. Keck Observatory
The Keck's twin 10-metre primary mirrors weigh 300 tons each. It is located on the top of an extinct volcano on Hawai'i Island.

NEW CONTENDER

2. Large Binocular Telescope (LBT)
Located on Mount Graham, Arizona, USA, it has twin 8.4-metre (27.6-foot) primary mirrors.

A FUTURE GIANT

3. European Extremely Large Telescope (E-ELT)
This will have a 42-metre mirror and is planned to search for Earth-like exoplanets in the Goldilocks Zone in 2022.

DID YOU KNOW? COROT-7 b orbits its star at a speed of 466,030mph

Future planet-finding missions

Space agencies have proposed the following spacecraft missions to study extrasolar planets

NASA's Terrestrial Planet Finder (TPF) Project

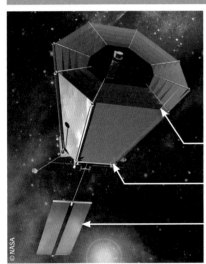

TPF Coronagraph

Solar coronagraphs were originally used with telescopes to block out the disc of the Sun to study its corona – this is hot plasma emitted by stellar bodies that travels millions of miles beyond its surface. Applied to the search for extrasolar planets the problem of blocking out the direct light of a star poses a much bigger problem. By isolating and studying the stellar corona, any planet within this area should be detected by the TPF-C spacecraft's telescope combined with coronagraph detection equipment.

Sunshade
The conical v-grooved sunshade fans out to insulate the telescope from the changing position of the Sun

Primary mirror
Located at the base of the sunshade, the mirror is set at an angle to deflect its light to the top of the secondary mirror

Secondary mirror tower
The smaller secondary mirror is mounted on top of this tower. The light from this and the primary mirror is reflected down the tower to the coronagraph assembly

TPF Interferometer

This TPF-I mission would employ a formation of five spacecraft. Four would each be equipped with a four-metre infrared telescope, and one spacecraft would receive the data from them and combine it. The interaction of the light waves from the telescopes produces interference that can be used to eliminate the glare of a star by a factor of 1 million. This so-called nulling technique allows the detection of any infrared emissions from planets near its parent star. The term interferometer is explained by the fact that it can also be used to measure the distance and angles of celestial objects.

Stray light baffles
Beams of light from the collector spacecraft telescopes travel along these 35-metre-long baffles to the combiner spacecraft

Collector spacecraft
Each has a four-metre diameter telescope mirror shielded and cooled by a five-layer sunshade

Combiner spacecraft
It receives the light from the collector craft and analyses it in a 'nulling beam combiner'

SIM Lite

The SIM Lite spacecraft will take five and a half years to reach an orbit around the Sun at a distance of 82 million km from the Earth. Here it will search the Goldilocks Zones of 60 stars for Earth-sized planets at a distance of up to 33 light years away. To achieve this it employs sensitive interferometer equipment that can detect a star's wobble to an accuracy of 20 millionths of an arcsecond. These are incredibly small measurements; an arcsecond is 1/60th of an arcminute, which in turn is 1/60th of a degree. A star-tracking telescope is also carried by the craft to carry out astrometric calculations to compare and use with the inferometric data.

Collecting apertures
The twin mirrors of a six-metre baseline 'science' telescope have 50cm apertures at either end of the craft, and a 'guide' telescope with a 4.2 metre baseline has twin 30cm apertures

Inside spacecraft
The images from the science and guide telescopes inside the spacecraft are sent to central beam combiners and analysed by inferometric equipment

Communications antenna
Once a week the craft will transmit the data it has collected back to Earth

Interview
Wesley Traub
Chief scientist, NASA Navigator Program

We caught up with Wesley Traub, the chief scientist for NASA's Exoplanet Exploration Program, and the project scientist for the Terrestrial Planet Finder Coronagraph (TPF-C)

Q: What type of outer space missions are needed in order to find exoplanets?
Wesley Traub: An astrometric mission is needed to discover planets around our nearest neighbour stars. This mission could determine the orbital parameters of each planet and accurately measure its mass.

This is important because we need a list of planets that are close enough to Earth that we can measure their properties; nearest-neighbour planets are bright enough for us to measure, but more distant ones are not.

Q: Will you be able to find evidence of Earth-type and even life on these planets?
WT: A visible spectroscopy mission is needed to look for biomarkers in the visible wavelength range. For an Earth-like planet these biomarkers include oxygen, ozone, water, an atmosphere at least as thick as the Earth's (via the blue colour of a blue sky, like ours), and possibly the enhanced reflection of red light from vegetation (grass, trees and plants, all of which look green to us but also reflect red light that we cannot see).

For a planet like the early Earth, you could see methane and carbon dioxide, in addition to the blue-sky effect. An infrared spectroscopy mission is needed to look for different biomarkers like carbon dioxide, ozone, and water. This mission could also measure the temperature of the planet, and its size. We need to look for these biomarkers in both wavelength ranges because together they give us a more complete picture than either one alone. For example, we can measure oxygen only in the visible spectrum, and temperature only in the infrared.

Q: What is the most important objective for these missions?
WT: I think the most important thing would be to answer the question of whether there's life on other planets. I guess at heart I believe there are planets with life on them. I don't know about intelligent life. The usual argument is that there are billions of stars out there, and today we think the chances of planets being around each one of them are pretty high, which we didn't used to think. And we think that life formed very quickly, as soon as it was possible on Earth. But out of the billions of stars in our galaxy, we only have a chance of looking at about 200 stars that are nearby. The chances of intelligent life being there on one of those, right now, are pretty small.

Q: Will TPF-I, TPF-C or SIM Lite go ahead?
WT: None of these missions have started development yet. Once the current suite of missions in development is completed, then an exoplanet mission may begin development. The earliest a mission of this type can be flown is towards the end of this decade.

Where on an Earth?

Exoplanet study has only been conducted over the past 15 years, and has already revealed completely different planetary bodies from those in our own solar system. Due to the limitations of our current technology, we have so far only found giant exoplanets. In future, we might discover rogue planets that do not orbit a parent star and exoplanets that are dominated by oceans, fields of ice, or boiling hot volcanic crusts like COROT-7b. None of these are likely to sustain life, as we know it, so the Holy Grail of this work is to find life-supporting Earth-type planets.

Different types of galaxies explained

They might be grouped like a galactic tuning fork, but galaxy types don't always sing from the same hymn sheet

There are several different galaxy classification systems, but the most widely used is the Hubble Sequence, devised by the great Edwin Hubble in 1926 and later expanded upon by Allan Sandage among others. It's more commonly known as the Hubble tuning fork due to the shape the system represents in diagrammatic form.

Hubble's system was designed to demonstrate the various classifications of three main classes of galaxy broken down into elliptical, spiral and lenticular shapes. The latter is essentially an intermediate of the other two types. The tuning fork was erroneously thought that each galaxy type represented snapshots of the entire life span of galaxies, but it has since been demonstrated that this is not the case.

The most recent version of Hubble's tuning fork comes courtesy of the Spitzer Space Telescope's infrared galaxy survey made up of 75 colour images of different galaxies and includes a new sub-section of irregular galaxy types. You can find a full resolution image of this remarkable accomplishment at http://sings.stsci.edu/Publications/sings_poster.html. Thanks to the internet, anyone can try their hand at galaxy classification and further the science – simply go to www.galaxyzoo.org and join in alongside 150,000 other volunteers.

Edwin Hubble's classification scheme

Ellipticals

E0   E3   E5   E7   S0

Spirals

Sa   Sb   Sc

SBa   SBb   SBc

Edwin Hubble
Pioneer to the stars

No person in history has had a greater impact in determining the extent of our universe than Edwin Hubble. From proving that other galaxies existed to giving evidence that galaxies move apart from one another, Hubble's work defined our place in the cosmos. Shown above posing with the 48-inch telescope on Palomar Mountain, the Orbiting Space Telescope was named in memory of his great work.

Today a great controversy rages on about the rate of the universe's expansion, parameterised by a quantity known as Hubble's constant.

Types of galaxies

Galaxies can be categorised into these types...

Elliptical galaxies
On the far left of the Hubble Sequence lies the elliptical galaxy type. They show no defined features like the intricate dust lanes seen in classic spiral galaxy types, besides a bright core. Ellipticals are represented by the letter E, followed by a number that represents the ellipticity of its shape

Spiral types
Appearing flatter on the sky than an elliptical galaxy, spiral galaxies feature two or more spiral 'arms' that wrap around the galaxy core and are made up of vast lanes of stars. The upper half is populated with the standard spiral type, while the lower half contains 'bar' spirals. The twist of the spiral begins at the end of an extended bar

Lenticular galaxies
Where the handle of the tuning fork and the two spiral arms meet lie the lenticular galaxies. These galaxies feature aspects of both spiral and elliptical galaxies and didn't actually feature on Hubble's original sequence. They have a bright central bulge like an elliptical galaxy, but are surrounded by a structure not unlike a disc

NASA's Hubble Space Telescope took this image of the Antennae galaxies, which began colliding a few hundred million years ago

Galaxy collisions

What happens when two galaxies collide?

When two galaxies cross paths, the chance of any stars colliding is almost zero. In fact, if the Milky Way collided with the nearby Andromeda galaxy, we would barely notice a thing on Earth. Instead, the multitude of dust and gas in each galaxy interacts and creates the characteristic spectacle. As the material inside the stars interacts gravitationally, newly formed gas clouds give birth to stars. Friction between the gases can cause numerous shock waves, which would also become instrumental in the formation of new stars.

Colliding galaxies usually take millions or even billions of years to merge. As they collide, tidal gravitational forces will rip the smaller of the two galaxies apart, scattering dust and stars. The inner core of the collision will heat up and radiate strongly, creating one of the brightest infrared objects in space. In this instance the larger galaxy will swallow the smaller one, but on some occasions the galaxies may pass through each other and emerge almost unharmed. ✿

Joining forces
What happens when two galaxies collide?

1. First contact
The first signs of a galaxy collision will be a bridge of matter between the two, caused by gravitational forces

2. Tidal tails
Long streams of gas and dust known as tidal tails spiral out of the collision as the material is thrown out

3. Ripped apart
Gravitational forces pull the matter in all directions, creating shock waves throughout the cloud of gas

4. A star is born
The core of the collision is subjected to intense frictional and gravitational forces, resulting in the formation of massive stars

© images x4 ESA / NASA

143

SUPERNOVAS

With more energy than a billion suns, a size greater than our solar system and the potential to destroy entire planets millions of miles away, some stars certainly know how to go out with a bang. Here we take a look at supernovas, some of the most powerful explosions in the universe

When we delve into certain realms of astronomy, the scale of events and objects are often impossibly large to imagine. If we think of planets like Earth and Mars we can at least get some sort of grasp as to their size, as we can consider them relative to other bodies. As we get to bigger objects, like Jupiter and the Sun, our understanding gets somewhat muddled, but we can still comprehend how enormous they are by using Earth as a starting point (for example, the Sun is over 100 times the size of Earth). It's when we get to the larger celestial occurrences, like supergiant stars and black holes,

however, that things really start to become unfathomable. In this article we'll be taking a look at one of these mammoth celestial events – supernovas – and we'll try to get our heads around just how large, powerful and crucial they are.

Supernovas have fascinated astronomers for millennia, appearing out of nowhere in the night sky and outshining other stars with consummate ease. The first recorded supernova, known today as SN 185, was spotted by Chinese astronomers in 185 AD and was apparently visible for almost a year. While this is the first recorded sighting, there have doubtless been many supernovas in preceding

years that confounded Earth dwellers who were unable to explain the sudden appearance of a bright new star in the sky.

One of the most notable supernova events likely occurred about 340,000 years ago when a star known as Geminga went supernova. Although it was unrecorded, astronomers have been able to discern the manner of its demise from the remnant neutron star it left behind. Geminga is the closest known supernova to have exploded near Earth, as little as 290 light years away. Its proximity to Earth meant that it might have lit up the night sky for many months, casting its own shadows and

CLOSEST

1. Betelgeuse
Expected to explode within a million years, this star, which is 18 times the mass of the Sun, is just 640 light years from Earth.

SOONEST

2. Eta Carinae
This giant star – which is 100 times the mass of our Sun and over 8,000 light years away – could go supernova in just 10,000 years time.

BIGGEST

3. SN 2006gy
In 2006 this giant supernova from a star 150 times the mass of our Sun was discovered 238 million light years away.

DID YOU KNOW? *Supernova is derived from the Latin term nova, meaning new, to denote the next phase in a star's life*

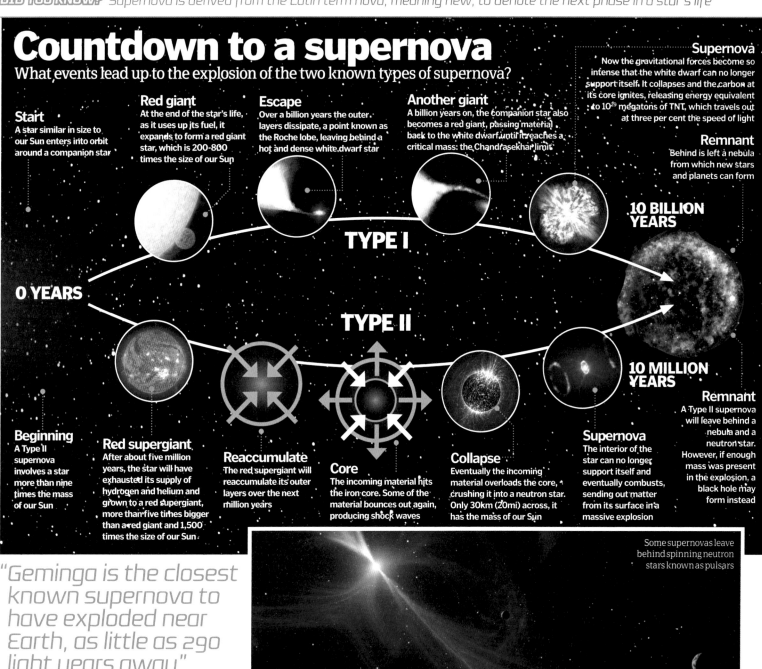

Countdown to a supernova
What events lead up to the explosion of the two known types of supernova?

Start
A star similar in size to our Sun enters into orbit around a companion star

Red giant
At the end of the star's life, as it uses up its fuel, it expands to form a red giant star, which is 200-800 times the size of our Sun

Escape
Over a billion years the outer layers dissipate, a point known as the Roche lobe, leaving behind a hot and dense white dwarf star

Another giant
A billion years on, the companion star also becomes a red giant, passing material back to the white dwarf until it reaches a critical mass: the Chandrasekhar limit

Supernova
Now the gravitational forces become so intense that the white dwarf can no longer support itself. It collapses and the carbon at its core ignites, releasing energy equivalent to 10^{25} megatons of TNT, which travels out at three per cent the speed of light

Remnant
Behind is left a nebula from which new stars and planets can form

TYPE I

0 YEARS

10 BILLION YEARS

TYPE II

10 MILLION YEARS

Beginning
A Type II supernova involves a star more than nine times the mass of our Sun

Red supergiant
After about five million years, the star will have exhausted its supply of hydrogen and helium and grown to a red supergiant, more than five times bigger than a red giant and 1,500 times the size of our Sun

Reaccumulate
The red supergiant will reaccumulate its outer layers over the next million years

Core
The incoming material hits the iron core. Some of the material bounces out again, producing shock waves

Collapse
Eventually the incoming material overloads the core, crushing it into a neutron star. Only 30km (20mi) across, it has the mass of our Sun

Supernova
The interior of the star can no longer support itself and eventually combusts, sending out matter from its surface in a massive explosion

Remnant
A Type II supernova will leave behind a nebula and a neutron star. However, if enough mass was present in the explosion, a black hole may form instead

Images © ESO/L Calcada/JPL-Caltech/ESA/HST

Some supernovas leave behind spinning neutron stars known as pulsars

© NASA/JPL-Caltech

> "Geminga is the closest known supernova to have exploded near Earth, as little as 290 light years away"

rivalling the Moon for brightness, turning night into day. So bright and large was this supernova that the ancients would have seen the light of it stretching from horizon to horizon. Left behind after this supernova was a neutron star rapidly rotating at about four times a second, the nearest neutron star to Earth and the third largest source of gamma rays to us in our observations of the cosmos. Other notable stellar explosions include Supernova 1987A, a star located in the Large Magellanic Cloud that went supernova in 1987. This originated from a supergiant star known as Sanduleak -69°202. It almost outshone the North Star (Polaris) as a result of its brightness, which was comparable to 250 million times that of the Sun.

It is a testament to the scale of these explosions that even ancient civilisations with limited to no astronomical equipment were able to observe them. Supernovas are bright not only visually but in all forms of electromagnetic radiation. They throw out x-rays, cosmic rays, radio waves and, on occasion, may be responsible for causing giant gamma-ray bursts, the largest known explosions in the universe. It is by measuring these forms of electromagnetic radiation that astronomers are able to glean such a clear picture of the formation and demise of supernovas. In fact, it is estimated that 99 per cent of the energy that a supernova exerts is in various forms of electromagnetic radiation other than visible light, making the study of this invisible (to the naked eye at least) radiation incredibly important, and something to which many observatories worldwide are tuned. Another type of stellar explosion you may have heard of is a nova. This is similar in its formation to a supernova, but there is one key difference post explosion: a supernova obliterates the original star, whereas a nova leaves behind an intact star somewhat similar to the original progenitor of the explosion.

Our understanding of the universe so far suggests that pretty much everything runs in cycles. For

Only a Type II supernova can become a black hole

Could a superno

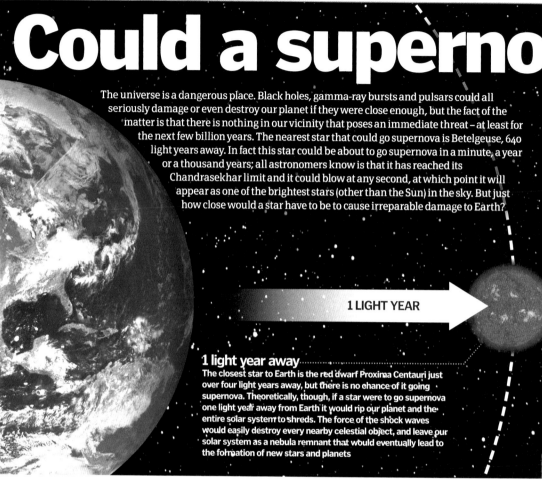

The universe is a dangerous place. Black holes, gamma-ray bursts and pulsars could all seriously damage or even destroy our planet if they were close enough, but the fact of the matter is that there is nothing in our vicinity that poses an immediate threat – at least for the next few billion years. The nearest star that could go supernova is Betelgeuse, 640 light years away. In fact this star could be about to go supernova in a minute, a year or a thousand years; all astronomers know is that it has reached its Chandrasekhar limit and it could blow at any second, at which point it will appear as one of the brightest stars (other than the Sun) in the sky. But just how close would a star have to be to cause irreparable damage to Earth?

1 LIGHT YEAR

1 light year away
The closest star to Earth is the red dwarf Proxima Centauri just over four light years away, but there is no chance of it going supernova. Theoretically, though, if a star were to go supernova one light year away from Earth it would rip our planet and the entire solar system to shreds. The force of the shock waves would easily destroy every nearby celestial object, and leave our solar system as a nebula remnant that would eventually lead to the formation of new stars and planets

example, a star is born from a cloud of dust and gas, it undergoes nuclear fusion for billions of years, and then destroys itself in a fantastic explosion, creating the very same dust and gas that will lead to the formation of another star. It is thanks to this cyclic nature of the universe that we are able to observe events that would otherwise be extremely rare or nonexistent. If stars were not constantly reforming, there would be none left from the birth of the universe 13.7 billion years ago.

As destructive as they may be, supernovas are integral to the structure and formation of the universe. It is thought that the solar system itself formed from a giant nebula left behind from a supernova while, as mentioned earlier, supernovas are very important in the life cycle of stars and lead to the creation of new stars as the old ones die out. This is because a star contains many of the elements necessary for planetary and stellar formation including large amounts of helium, hydrogen, oxygen and iron, all key components in the structure of celestial bodies. On top of these, many other elements are thought to form during the actual explosion itself.

There's no doubt that supernovas are one of the most destructive forces of the universe, but at the same time they're one of the most essential to the life cycle of solar systems. As we develop more powerful telescopes over the coming years we will be able to observe and study supernovas in more detail, and possibly discover some that do not fall into our current classification of Type I or Type II. The study of supernovas alone can unlock countless secrets of the universe, and as we further our understanding of these colossal stellar explosions we'll be able to learn more about the cosmos as a whole.

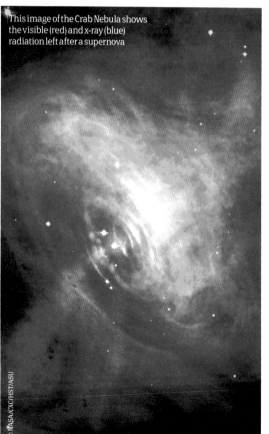

This image of the Crab Nebula shows the visible (red) and x-ray (blue) radiation left after a supernova

All that remains...

What is left behind once a star goes supernova?

Inside a massive star, before it goes supernova, the nuclei of light elements like hydrogen and helium combine to form the basic constituents of other celestial bodies and even life (such as carbon and oxygen). Stars release these vital elements when they go supernova, providing the material for new stellar and planetary formation.

To date there are roughly 300 known supernova remnants in the universe. Depending on the type and mass of a supernova (see the diagram on the previous page), the remnants left behind can be one of several things. In the vast majority of cases some form of nebula will be left behind. Inside this nebula will often be a spinning neutron star. The rate of spin of this neutron star, also known as a pulsar, depends on the original mass of the exploded star, with some pulsars rotating upwards of a thousand times per minute!

These highly dense stars contain the mass of the Sun packed into an area no bigger than the city of London. If the supernova remnant exceeds four solar masses (the mass of our Sun), due to an extremely heavy initial star or by more material accumulating around the remnant from nearby objects, then the remnant will collapse to form a black hole instead of continuing to expand.

Superstar

One of the most famous supernova remnants in reasonably close proximity to Earth is the Crab Nebula, the remains of a star that went supernova in 1054, about 6,000 light years away. A spinning neutron star known as the Crab Pulsar is located at its centre.

destroy Earth?

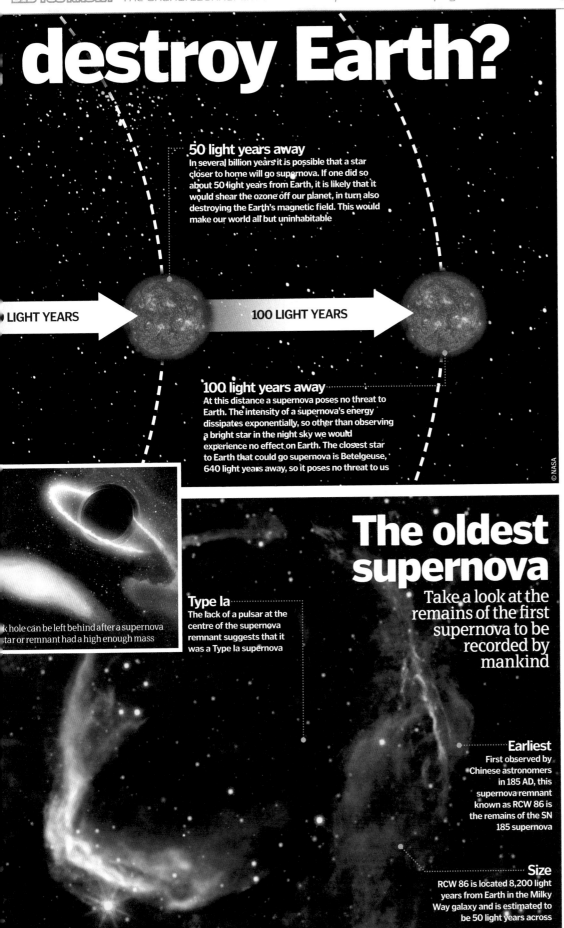

50 light years away

In several billion years it is possible that a star closer to home will go supernova. If one did so about 50 light years from Earth, it is likely that it would shear the ozone off our planet, in turn also destroying the Earth's magnetic field. This would make our world all but uninhabitable

LIGHT YEARS

100 LIGHT YEARS

100 light years away

At this distance a supernova poses no threat to Earth. The intensity of a supernova's energy dissipates exponentially, so other than observing a bright star in the night sky we would experience no effect on Earth. The closest star to Earth that could go supernova is Betelgeuse, 640 light years away, so it poses no threat to us

© NASA

k hole can be left behind after a supernova
tar or remnant had a high enough mass

The oldest supernova

Take a look at the remains of the first supernova to be recorded by mankind

Type Ia

The lack of a pulsar at the centre of the supernova remnant suggests that it was a Type Ia supernova

Earliest

First observed by Chinese astronomers in 185 AD, this supernova remnant known as RCW 86 is the remains of the SN 185 supernova

Size

RCW 86 is located 8,200 light years from Earth in the Milky Way galaxy and is estimated to be 50 light years across

SIZE OF A SUPERNOVA

How much energy does a supernova release?

1,000,000,000,000,000,000,000 yottajoules (10^{44} joules)
Energy released from a supernova

1,000 zettajoules (1 yottajoule)
Total energy from the Sun that reaches Earth in a year

1,000 exajoules (1 zettajoule)
Energy of the entire Earth's petrol reserves

1,000 petajoules (1 exajoule)
Estimated energy in the 2011 Japanese earthquake and tsunami

1,000 terajoules (1 petajoule)
Energy in 1 megaton of TNT

1,000 gigajoules (1 terajoule)
Approximate energy in a small nuclear bomb

1,000 megajoules (1 gigajoule)
Average energy in a lightning bolt

1,000 kilojoules (1 megajoule)
Approximate daily male energy intake

1,000 joules (1 kilojoule)
Explosion of less than 1g (0.03oz) of TNT

1 joule of energy
Flash of a camera

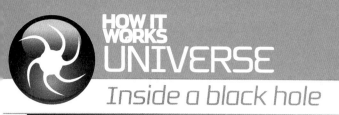
Inside a black hole

Almost incomprehensible in size, black holes are hauntingly beautiful phenomena where the laws of space and time are rewritten. We take a look at the Sagittarius A* black hole at the centre of our galaxy

A black hole is a region of space containing, at its centre, matter compressed into a point of infinite density called a singularity (an area where spacetime curvature becomes infinite), which itself is surrounded by a sphere of space where the gravitational pull is so total that not even light can escape its pull – hence its name. The black hole is the result of the deformation and warping of spacetime (a mathematical model where space and time are combined into a single continuum) caused by the total collapse of individual stars or by the coalescence of binary neutron stars.

This collapse occurs at the culmination of a star's life span when, under the pressure of gravity, it is compressed perpetually – unable to resist due to the non-existence of nuclear fusion in its core – until it reaches critical mass. At this point, providing the star is over 1.4 to three solar masses (our Sun equals one solar mass) – a necessity for black hole formation instead of a white dwarf – the star will go into core-collapse supernova, expelling much of its remaining outer layers at one tenth the speed of light and leaving behind either a neutron star or, if the solar mass is high enough, a black hole.

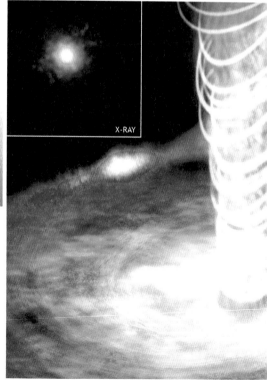

X-RAY

LARGE

1. Stellar-mass black hole
Stellar-mass black holes have masses up to 15-20 solar masses. These mainly form from stars going into core-collapse supernova.

LARGER

2. Intermediate-mass black hole
These type of black holes contain thousands of solar masses. These variants mainly form from collisions of smaller black holes.

LARGEST

3. Supermassive black hole
The biggest black holes by far, supermassive variants can contain hundreds of thousands to billions of solar masses.

DID YOU KNOW? Sagittarius A* is a massive 26,000 light years from Earth

The Milky Way
The position of Sagittarius A* in our galaxy

Sagittarius A* lies at the heart of out galaxy the Milky Way. Unfortunately, from Earth Sagittarius A* is blocked from optical sight and presently scientists can only observe it through the actions of its surrounding stars.

Sagittarius A*

Introducing the Milky Way's very own supermassive black hole

At the heart of almost every galaxy lies a black hole, even our own the Milky Way, which centres on a region of space called Sagittarius A* – at the middle of which lies a supermassive black hole. Black holes like these, however, do not form directly but from the coalescence of multiple smaller stellar-mass and intermediate mass black holes, which then form a supermassive black hole such as Sagittarius A*. Supermassive black holes also often form from the slow accretion of matter from neighbouring stars, the mass collapse of large stellar gas clouds into a relativistic star (a rotating neutron star), or directly from external pressure caused by the Big Bang.

While unimaginable due to its very nature (it absorbs all light), its distance from Earth and the fact that the Sagittarius A* region is removed by 25 magnitudes of extinction from Earth (blocked from optical sight), our own supermassive black hole can only be observed by scientists through the actions of neighbouring cosmic phenomena. Indicating the presence of its existence most notably is the movement of star S2, which has been monitored by scientists following a slow elliptical orbit with a period of 15.2 years and a closest distance of less than 17 light hours from its orbit centre. From the slow motion of S2, scientists have extrapolated that the object which it is orbiting around has a solar mass of 4.1 million, which when taken with its relatively small diameter, strongly affirms that it is a black hole since no other known object can have such a large mass at such a small volume.

Sagittarius A* is a relatively small supermassive black hole when compared with others of its ilk, such as the black hole at the centre of the OJ 287 galaxy, which has a mass of 18 billion solar masses.

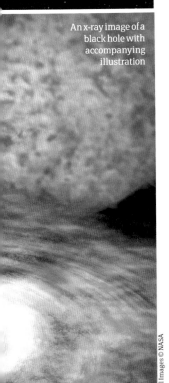

An x-ray image of a black hole with accompanying illustration

Composite image of a black hole

Centre
At the heart of the black hole its huge extragalactic jet bursts forth

Ergosphere
The surrounding ergosphere and stellar clouds from which the black hole accretes mass

Event horizon
The event horizon of the black hole, a one-way border in spacetime from which nothing can escape

X-ray

Radio

Optical

Inside our black hole

What are its properties and structure?

To understand our Sagittarius A* black hole it is important to understand how black holes in general work. After any black hole stabilises post formation, it has only three possible independent physical properties: charge, mass and angular momentum. Now, when an object is accreted (swallowed) by a black hole its own mass, charge and momentum is equalised with the black hole's own, distributing the matter evenly along its event horizon (a one-way spacetime boundary), which then oscillates like a stretchy membrane. The course that this pattern follows, however, depends on the individual black hole's properties and type.

The simplest black holes have mass but neither charge nor angular momentum, accreting mass to a point-singularity centre, however most types of black hole formed from the core-collapse supernova of a star are thought to retain the nearly neutral charge it once possessed. Other, and theorised by scientists to be far more common, types of black holes – due to the spinning nature of stars – are rotating variants. These form from the collapse of stars or stellar gas with a total non-zero angular momentum and can be both charged and uncharged. These black holes, unlike the totally round, static variants, bulge near their equator under the phenomenal velocity of their spin (the quicker the rotation the more deformed the black hole will be) and instead of accreting matter to a point-singularity do so to a smeared disc singularity. Eventually all black holes, however dependent on their charge or rotation, revert to a non-rotating, uncharged variant.

Unfortunately, from the measurements taken from the stars surrounding our Sagittarius A* black hole, scientists have been left unsure about its physical properties. However, recent research from the University of California, Berkeley, suggests that A* rotates once every 11 minutes or at 30 per cent the speed of light. This information, when combined with the known close proximity of the surrounding stars (a spinning black hole drags space with it, allowing atoms to orbit closer to one that is static), would seem to suggest that not only is the gravitational pull of Sagittarius A* mitigated to a degree by its rotation but also that these measurements are accurate.

Microlensing magnification region
An illustration depicting swirling clouds of stellar gas pouring into a black hole

Formation of extragalactic jets from black hole accretion disk

Extragalactic jet
Relativistic jets, extremely powerful streams of plasma, carry energy away from the heart of the accretion disk

EXTRAGALACTIC JET

Black hole
The singularity at the centre of the black hole. All mass that reaches this point is crushed to infinite density

Accretion disk
The black hole's accretion disk is formed from diffuse material orbiting around its centre

As mass is accreted by a black hole it is heated up under the pressure of gravity

How spacetime is distorted

Away from a black hole, particles can move freely in any direction, only being restricted by the speed of light

EVENT HORIZON

BLACK HOLE

TIME
SPACE

As particles approach the event horizon of the black hole, spacetime starts to deform, restricting the freedom of the paths in which particles can follow

TIME
SPACE

5 TOP FACTS
BLACK HOLES

Do the worm
1 Certain theories postulate that rotating black holes could be avoided by entities and actually used as a wormhole shortcut through space and time.

Weakling
2 Despite their colossal size and perpetual accretion of matter, black holes can only suck in matter from a very small surrounding region as gravity is incredibly weak.

Primordial
3 In the current epoch of the universe only the collapse of stars carry the requisite density to form a black hole, however shortly after the big bang densities were greater.

Micro-management
4 Theoretically it is possible for micro-black holes to form through the high-speed collision of sub-atomic particles, although this is unlikely to ever happen.

Spaghetti
5 Any object that passes an event horizon will be stretched into long thin strands under the strong gravitational field of the black hole.

DID YOU KNOW? *The coinage of the phrase 'black hole' didn't occur until 1967*

Let's do the time warp

The theoretical consequences of time and space distortion

The event horizon (a boundary in spacetime through which matter and light can only pass through inwardly) of a black hole is one of its central characteristics, and one that brings a host of issues for any object that passes through it. As predicted by general relativity (our geometric theory on gravitation) due to the colossal mass of the black hole – which by these rules is infinite at the heart of the black hole – spacetime is deformed, as mass has a direct bearing on it. Indeed, when the event horizon is passed, the mass's

distortion becomes so great that particle paths are bent inwardly towards the singularity (centre) of the black hole, unable to alter their course. At this point both time and space begin to be warped.

The consequences of this, while theoretical, are mind blowing. For example, general theory states that if a hypothetical astronaut were about to cross the event horizon of a black hole, then apart from being stretched physically (spaghettification), they'd also be stretched in time. So, while the astronaut would pass

the event horizon at a finite point in his own time, to a hypothetical distant observer, he'd appear to slow down, taking an infinite time to reach it. Further, if the astronaut were wearing a watch, it would tick more slowly as he approached the event horizon than a watch worn by the observer, an effect known as gravitational time dilation. Finally, when the astronaut reached the singularity, he'd be crushed to infinite density and over an infinite time (to the observer) before having his mass added to that of the black hole.

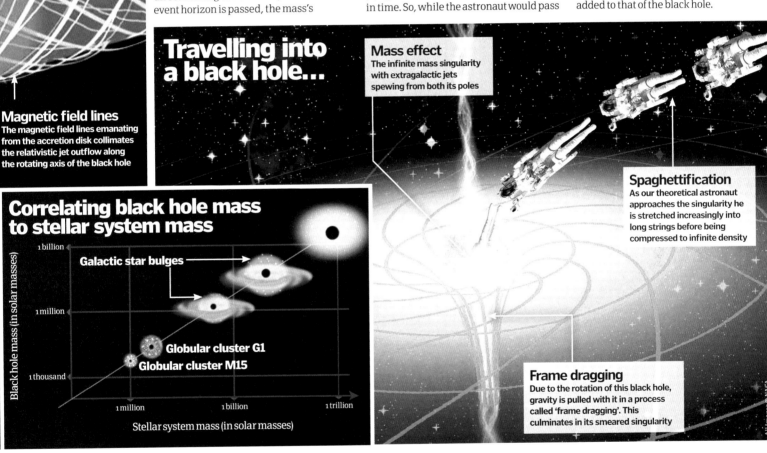

Travelling into a black hole...

Mass effect
The infinite mass singularity with extragalactic jets spewing from both its poles

Magnetic field lines
The magnetic field lines emanating from the accretion disk collimates the relativistic jet outflow along the rotating axis of the black hole

Spaghettification
As our theoretical astronaut approaches the singularity he is stretched increasingly into long strings before being compressed to infinite density

Correlating black hole mass to stellar system mass

Black hole mass (in solar masses)
- 1 billion
- 1 million
- 1 thousand

Galactic star bulges

Globular cluster G1
Globular cluster M15

Stellar system mass (in solar masses)
- 1 million
- 1 billion
- 1 trillion

Frame dragging
Due to the rotation of this black hole, gravity is pulled with it in a process called 'frame dragging'. This culminates in its smeared singularity

All Images © NASA

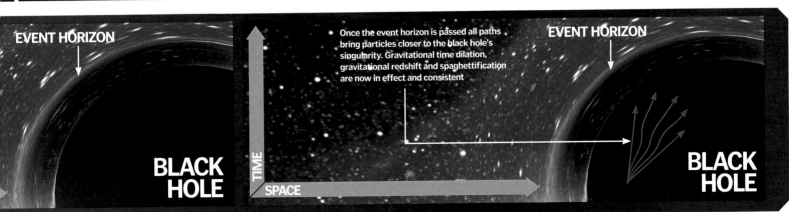

EVENT HORIZON

EVENT HORIZON

Once the event horizon is passed all paths bring particles closer to the black hole's singularity. Gravitational time dilation, gravitational redshift and spaghettification are now in effect and consistent

TIME

SPACE

BLACK HOLE

BLACK HOLE

Searching for alien messages

1. Vast potential
The Milky Way galaxy contains 500 million stars, which have exoplanets in the habitable zone that are capable of supporting intelligent life forms

2. Signal
If aliens create technology like ours they might strive to contact other alien civilisations, using radio signals in the electromagnetic spectrum

3. Distance
Star systems with known exoplanets are from 20 to 75,000 light years away. Any message will already be as old as the time it takes to get here

4. Reception
Radio telescopes have to filter out interference from man-made and natural radio emissions, and target areas of the galaxy and wavelengths that are most likely to be sending out signals

5. Message
What kind of message can we expect? Will we be able to decode it if it contains complex information? Should we answer it?

The search for extraterrestrial life

Our galaxy could be the home to millions of different alien life forms, but how do we find them?

5 TOP FACTS
FALSE ALARMS

Martian canals
1 At the beginning of the 20th Century, American astronomer Percival Lowell popularised the idea that long dark lines on Mars were canals built by intellectual Martians.

Signals from Mars
2 Nikola Tesla received signals that repeated the numbers 1, 2, 3 and 4. He claimed they came from Mars, but research suggests they were radio emanations from Jupiter.

CTA 102
3 Gennady Sholomitskii believed a powerful variable radio emission represented a signal from a super civilisation. It was later identified as a quasar, designated CTA 102.

Little green men
4 Jocelyn Bell and Antony Hewish discovered a 1.3373-sec signal via radio telescope. They named it 'little green men' (LGM-1), but it was the first pulsar (CP1919).

GCRTJ1745-3009
5 The Very Large Array telescope at Socorro, New Mexico recorded five highly energetic low-frequency radio emissions in 2002. They might be caused by a pulsar or neutron star.

DID YOU KNOW? *Carl Friedrich Gauss suggested cutting a giant Pythagoras triangle in the Siberian forest to signal to ETs*

Virtually every part of our planet is teeming with life, and it would be extraordinary that life – even on the lowest microbial level – does not exist on planets beyond our solar system. On a statistical level, our Milky Way spiral galaxy has a diameter of 100,000 light years and contains between 200 and 400 billion stars, a quarter of which have planets orbiting them. Of them, there could be 500 million planets that move in the habitable zone that can sustain life like our own.

If an alien civilisation were to reach our level of technological ability, it seems only logical that they would beam out messages in search of other life forms. The main restriction is that energy, matter, or information cannot travel faster than the speed of light – which is 300,000 kilometres (186,411 miles) per second. A far-flung alien message might take some 75,000 light years to reach Earth. Indeed, at best the nearest habitable zone planet, called Gliese 581g, is around 20 light years away.

When Enrico Fermi looked at the odds of intelligent life evolving to our level of technology, he was surprised that we had not been contacted already. The Fermi paradox is that despite the probability of extraterrestrial life, we have no evidence of its presence. There are several answers to the Fermi paradox; it might simply be that we are alone and that our creation was a very rare series of events that has not been duplicated elsewhere. Intelligent life forms might have a tendency to die out through natural disaster or warfare, or they could have transcended our technology and use more sophisticated forms of communication that are currently beyond our means of detection.

Radio telescopes have mainly been used to listen for any regular 'alien' signals in a narrow radio bandwidth. Another possibility is that aliens might signal to us in the optical wavelengths using powerful laser beams. In 2006 the Planetary Society began searching for an extraterrestrial laser signal using a 1.8-metre (72-inch) reflecting telescope. Although it processes as much data in one second as all books in print, it has only detected a few pulses of light as it searches the northern hemisphere, and all of them have been ruled out as extra terrestrial signals.

Astrobiologists consider the possibilities of detecting alien microbial life through their biosignature. Extremophile Earth microorganisms have been found to survive and reproduce, which at least offers some hope to finding this type of microbial life elsewhere in the solar system. Astrobiologists are also working on mass spectrometers and high-energy

Habitable zones...
...and where we are looking

1. Venus
Outside the inner boundary of the HZ – too hot (460°C) to sustain life

2. Earth
Earth orbits in the centre of the habitable zone that surrounds the Sun

3. Mars
Mars is on the outer boundary of the HZ; further exploration will determine if it is or was in the HZ

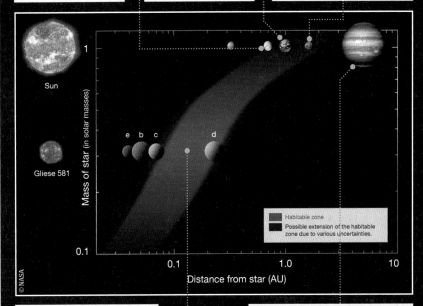

5. Extrasolar planets
Extrasolar planets, like Gliese 581d and g, are in an HZ that is closer to its smaller parent star

4. Jupiter
Although Jupiter and Saturn are outside the HZ, some of their moons might have primitive organisms living on them

The habitable zone (HZ) is a belt of space around a star that is either too hot or too cold for life to exist on any planet orbiting in this zone. The habitable zone is often called the Goldilocks zone after the children's story, referring to finding conditions for life that are "just right". The HZ varies according to the size, mass, luminosity and life-cycle of the parent star. Stars with a low mass and luminosity will have an HZ closer to them than a larger, brighter star. Unstable or short-lived stars are less likely to nurture life.

Primitive life might live outside the HZ, but it is very likely to be microbial or extremely different to 'life' as we know it. It is also postulated that life only occurs in star systems in the galactic habitable zone (GHZ), that are close enough to the galactic centre to form Earth-like planets but far enough away from fatal levels of radioactivity. The GHZ of our galaxy is about 6,000 light years wide and 25,000 light years from the centre.

SETI research concentrates its efforts on the newly discovered extrasolar planets in their respective habitable zone, and radio telescopes concentrate on listening to transmissions between 1,420 MHz (21cm) emissions from neutral hydrogen and 1,666 MHz (18cm) emissions from hydroxyl. This quiet range of the electromagnetic spectrum, nicknamed the water hole, is a logical place for water-based life to send signals as hydrogen and hydroxyl form water.

Extrasolar planets are being discovered with increasing regularity

The Drake equation

American astronomer Frank Drake formulated the Drake equation in 1961, to estimate the number of possible intelligent extraterrestrial civilisations that might exist in our Milky Way galaxy

N
The number of alien civilisations capable of transmitting signals into space, based on estimates in the rest of the equation

ne
The number of planets that might potentially support living organisms

fi
The fraction of planets that develop can intelligent life

L
The length of time alien civilisations might exist and send out communications

$$N = R^* \, f_p \, n_e \, f_l \, f_i \, f_c \, L$$

R*
This estimates the yearly rate of star formations in the Milky Way galaxy

fp
The fraction of star formations that support planetary systems

fl
The proportion of planets that actually develop and nurture living organisms

fc
The number of alien civilisations that can create a technology to broadcast signals into space

Is there anybody out there?

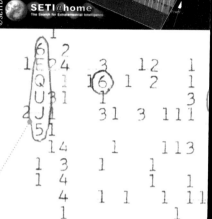

The Berkeley Open Infrastructure for Network Computing version of SETI@home harnesses your computer's unused power to analyse signal patterns

x-rays to detect life that does not consist of RNA, DNA or proteins.

Meteorites have been closely examined to see if they contain evidence of alien life forms. The Allan Hills 84001 (ALH84001) meteorite, which is thought to have come from Mars 13,000 years ago, was declared by David McKay to contain minute traces of fossilised bacteria. This hit the headlines in 1996, but terrestrial contamination and non-biological processes have been given as alternative explanations. Microfossils in carbonaceous meteorites were also discovered by astrobiologist Richard B Hoover in March 2011.

SETI (Search for Extraterrestrial Intelligence) research has also had several false alarms, the most famous being the so-called 'Wow' signal received in 1977 by the Big Ear radio telescope at the Ohio State University. Dr Jerry Ehman was so impressed by the 72-second long signal originating from the constellation Sagittarius, he wrote "Wow!" next to the alphanumeric code 6EQUJ5 on the printout.

It has never been detected again and might have been created by a terrestrial signal.

Until recently, we were not sure that star systems hosted Earth-like planets. Since October 1995 when a Hot Jupiter extrasolar planet was found in the Pegasus constellation, 50 light years away, hundreds of extrasolar planets have been discovered. NASA's Kepler spacecraft was launched in 2009 to search for Earth-sized planets in the habitable zone of star systems up to 3,000 light years away, which are on the same galactic plane as Earth. So far, it's discovered 54 planets orbiting in the habitable zone of its parent planet. Now these planets have been identified, work is being carried out to find oxygen and other chemical signatures that might indicate that they actually harbour life on them.

When, or if, we find primitive life or contact intelligent ET life depends on whether there is life to find. Throughout our search, we need to take into account exotic or advanced ET life forms that might be unrecognisable to us.

For more information about SETI@home, visit the website http://setiathome.berkeley.edu

The wow factor
The note Dr Jerry Ehman scribbled to indicate his amazement of the 72-sec long signal via radio telescope

What is SETI?

SETI (Search for Extraterrestrial Intelligence) is conducted by several organisations to detect extraterrestrial life. SETI@home is unique because instead of using a huge supercomputer purpose-built to analyse the data collected by a specific radio telescope, it uses internet-connected computers to create a virtual supercomputer.

SETI@home software works as a screensaver, which borrows your computer when you're not using it. It collects the data in small chunks from the internet, analyses it and then sends the results back to SETI@home. The digital data is taken piggyback from the Arecibo telescope. The network is linked to 456,922 active computers worldwide and is run

by the Space Sciences Laboratory at the University of California. Despite the equivalent of 2 million years of computing time, it has yet to come across an unambiguous ET signal. A weak signal was observed from SHGb02+14a between the Pisces and Aries constellations at the 1420MHz frequency. There is no star system observable at this location and could have been produced by a technical glitch.

The SETI Institute is a non-profit organisation that covers virtually every aspect of SETI research. In the Nineties, it ran Project Phoenix using the Parkes radio telescope in Australia and a radio telescope in West Virginia, to study 800 stars within a 200 light year range of Earth. No ET signals were found.

The Arecibo message

The Arecibo radio telescope in Puerto Rico sent the first message to be deliberately beamed into space on 16 November 1974. The 1,679 binary-digit message was sent over a three-minute long period on the 2,380MHz radio frequency. Data such as DNA was aimed at the Messier 13 star cluster in the Hercules constellation, and will take 25,000 years to reach it.

The Golden Record

The Voyager 1 and 2 spacecraft were launched in 1977 to explore the outer planets of the solar system and beyond. Both deep space probes are expected to be in interstellar space by 2014. Like a message in a bottle, they carry a 30cm (12in) diameter gold-plated copper disc. The disc contains greetings from Earth in 55 different languages and a range of Earth-related pictures, sounds and music chosen by a committee headed by the late astronomer Carl Sagan.

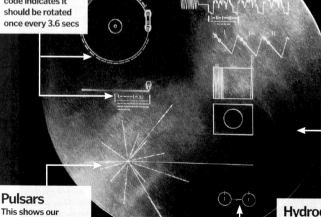

Instructions
The plan and side view shows how to play the disc. Binary code indicates it should be rotated once every 3.6 secs

Decoding pictures
These four diagrams indicate how pictures can be decoded by using the signal from the disc

Clock
The record is coated with a pure source of Uranium -238, which steadily decays into its daughter isotopes

Pulsars
This shows our solar system in relation to 14 pulsars. The period of their pulsations is given in binary code

Hydrogen atom
These circles represent the hydrogen atom in its two lowest states, acting as a time reference for the data

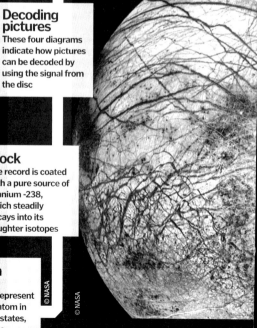

DID YOU KNOW?

Pale blue dot
The Earth is a mere 0.12 pixel-sized speck as viewed by the Voyager 1 spacecraft at a distance of 6.1 billion kilometres (3.7 billion miles). Astronomer Carl Sagan called this a "pale blue dot" that is "the only home we've ever known."

2x © NASA

DID YOU KNOW? Some SETI researchers believe we should look for alien space probes in our galactic neighbourhood

Life on Mars

Mars was regarded as the home of human-like life until the Sixties, when the Mariner space probes showed it was a cratered planet with an atmosphere consisting of carbon dioxide (CO_2). The 1972 Mariner 9 mission did, however, show evidence of running water on the surface of the planet in the past.

In 1976, the Viking 1 and 2 spacecraft landed on Mars to put soil samples in a nutrient labelled with radioactive carbon-14. If any organism were present, it would digest the nutrient and give off recognisable gasses. However, results gave no clear sign of life.

Since their arrival on the Red Planet in 2004, the two Mars Exploration rover craft Spirit and Opportunity have all but confirmed that liquid water did flow on the surface of Mars several hundred million years ago. This indicates that life could have existed on Mars and might still be hidden beneath its surface.

NASA's Mars Science Laboratory, which consists of the Curiosity rover, will analyse samples of Martian soil in great detail to find out for certain whether microbial life is present or can live in this environment when it lands in mid-2012 as planned.

MastCam
Mounted at human eye level, it provides hi-res colour, stereo images and video of the area. It can also analyse light from other parts of the electromagnetic spectrum

ChemCam
Uses a laser to zap rocks at a range of 1-9m (3.3-30 ft). An on-board spectrograph can analyse the composition of the rock from the spark created by the laser

Robotic hand
The arm uses a Mars hand lens imager (MHLI) to examine rocks and an alpha particle x-ray spectrometer (APXS) to determine their chemical composition

SAM
Sample analysis at Mars instrument (SAM) features a mass spectrometer, gas chromatograph and tuneable laser spectrometer to analyse soil and the atmosphere, to determine oxygen, nitrogen and hydrogen

ChemMin
The robotic hand can deposit soil samples into the Chemistry and Mineralogy instrument (ChemMin) on board the rover. It beams x-rays through the sample to identify the soil structure

© NASA

Life in the solar system

Several surprising places might harbour life beyond Mars. Hopes that the brew of methane, ammonia, hydrogen and water stirred by lightning in Jupiter's atmosphere would create life have been considered and dismissed. Now, as a result of two Voyager probes passing Jupiter in 1979, Europa, one of Jupiter's moons, is discovered to have an icy surface with a liquid water ocean underneath it. If heat is being vented at the bottom of the ocean, it could well promote the existence of microbial life.

Two moons of Saturn are also regarded as having oceans of water beneath their surface. NASA's Cassini spacecraft found that the 505km (313mi) diameter Enceladus has potential for life, due to water indicated by geysers of ice particles that jet from its surface. The 5,150km (3,200mi) diameter Titan has a smoggy atmosphere and ethane/methane lakes that may contain primitive organisms and indicate similar conditions to those on Earth millions of years ago. NASA is planning to send a Titan Mare Explorer (TiME) in 2015.

Titan, whose Earth-like conditions could harbour primitive life
© NASA

INTERVIEW
Philip Plait

Dr Philip Plait is an astronomer, author and blogger who covers all things universe-related in the Bad Astronomy blog

Q: Have you personally taken part in any search for alien life projects?
Philip Plait: No, but some years ago, when I was working on Hubble, I tried to get pictures of extrasolar planets – which, unfortunately, didn't work out. However, I've written numerous times on astrobiology topics, and it was the subject of an episode of a TV show I filmed.

Q: What are our chances of finding aliens?
PP: I know Seth Shostak of SETI has said that if aliens are out there and broadcasting using radio, we'll detect them in the next 25 years or so. There are a lot of assumptions in there, but it's an interesting calculation. I can't say for sure when it will happen, of course, but I'd sure like to be around if and when it does. One way or the other, though, I doubt it'll be via spaceships. It's far more likely that it'll be through some sort of light-speed communication method, like radio.

Q: Where do you think we should be looking?
PP: Everywhere! It might make sense to look at stars like the Sun to start with, since we know they can have planets and live long lives, enough time for intelligent life to develop. But one thing we know about nature is that it's more clever than we are, so I wouldn't limit the search at all.

Q: Do you think there's intelligent life out there, or is it likely to be microbial?
PP: Given what we know now – there are billions of Sun-like stars out there, and a good fraction of them have planets – I suspect there's lots of life in the Milky Way. But out of the 4.5 billion years the Earth's been around, it had basically gloop living on it for more than half that time. So I think if we ever travel to other planets, that's what we'll find mostly. But open this up to the "whole universe", and I'm thinking the answer leans towards yes, there are other civilisations out there. The number of stars is in the quintillions. That's a pretty good number to start with.

Q: What is the current status of ET searching?
PP: SETI's Allen Telescope Array is currently mothballed due to lack of funds, and that's not good. The technology is advancing rapidly, which is why Seth gave that 25-year timeframe. I'm hoping that they'll get the ATA running again soon.

Q: What current or future mission most excites you about the search for ET?
PP: Right now, Kepler is the best thing going: it may very well detect planets the mass and size of Earth orbiting their stars at the right distance to have liquid water on their surface. That's not finding life, but it would be a major step in that direction. I don't think any astronomer would bet against it, but knowing there's another possible Earth out there would be motivating.

Q: Do you think aliens may have visited/communicated with us in the past?
PP: In recent history, I doubt it – the evidence simply isn't there. But time is very long and deep; any civilisation may well have come here a long time ago...

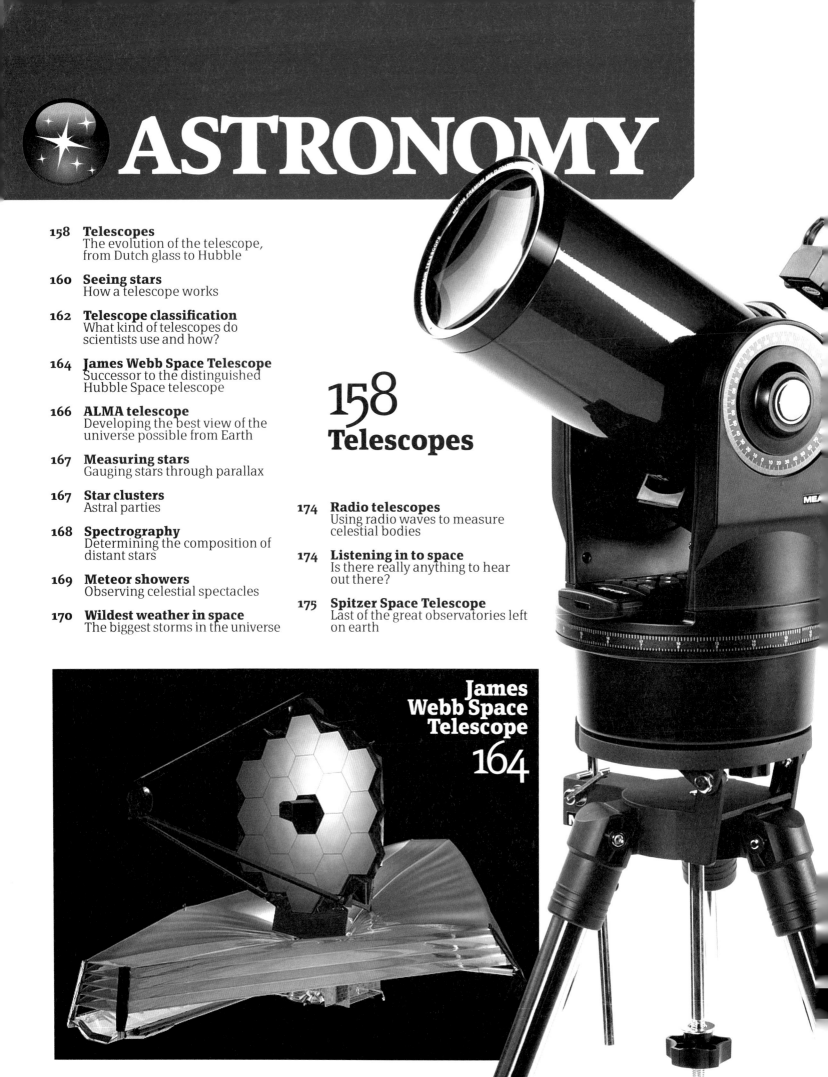

ASTRONOMY

158 Telescopes

James Webb Space Telescope 164

**166
ALMA
telescope**

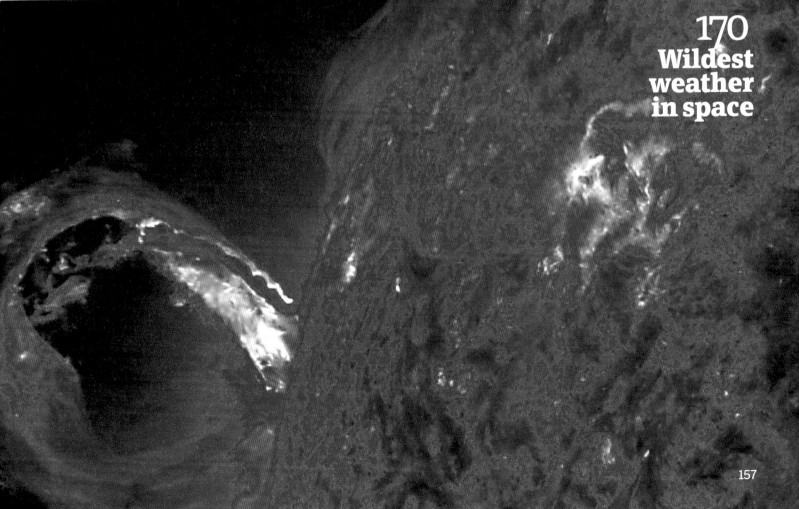

**170
Wildest
weather
in space**

Telescopes

The telescope was the first step in really opening up the universe for scrutiny...

Telescopes are all designed to do the same thing: collect and magnify light so that we can examine it. Practically speaking, we most often use them to observe the cosmos. There are three main types of scope: refractive, reflective and compound. Hans Lippershey is credited with inventing the first working telescope in 1608, which was a refracting type using lenses. Lippershey's invention was known as a Dutch perspective glass and probably consisted of a convex lens at the end and a concave lens as an eyepiece. Numerous other astronomers worked to improve upon this initial design, including Galileo Galilei and Johannes Kepler; Galileo's version of the refracting telescope was the first to be called a 'telescope', with Greek poet Giovanni Demisiani coining the name.

All refracting telescopes had one flaw, however: the lenses created chromatic aberration, resulting in a blurry image. To combat this, astronomers made telescopes with longer and longer tubes, among other designs, but these were hard to manoeuvre.

In 1668, Isaac Newton created the first reflecting telescope, which used mirrors to focus the light and avoided chromatic aberration. After Newton, Laurent Cassegrain improved on the reflecting telescope by adding a secondary mirror to reflect light through an opening in the primary mirror. The refracting telescope still held pull though

because it was simply better at observing deep-sky objects as well as distant terrestrial objects. Since the lens was the issue, British inventor Chester Moor Hall came up with the achromatic lens in 1773.

The Herschelian telescope (made by William Herschel), a reflector built in 1778, did away with the secondary mirror by tilting the primary mirror slightly. Astronomers tried making more reflective mirrors to better optimise light. Advancements such as coating mirrors with silver and, later on, aluminium, allowed for reflective telescopes with ever-larger diameters to be built.

In 1930, German optician Bernhard Schmidt sought to create a hybrid telescope that took the best features of both refractive and reflective. The first compound, or catadioptric, telescope, had a primary mirror in the back of the telescope and a lens at the front. Later, a secondary mirror was added to create the Schmidt-Cassegrain model, and many variations followed. The compound telescope is the most popular design today.

Through the 20th century telescopes began to be developed for other types of electromagnetic wavelengths, such as radio, gamma ray, X-ray and ultraviolet.

© ESO

The ESO's Very Large Telescope (VLT) actually comprises four main telescopes called Antu, Yepun, Melipal and Kueyen

Telescope timeline

We reveal how this visual amplification device has evolved century by century

1608
Dutch perspective glass
He may not have been the first to build one, but German-born spectacle maker Hans Lippershey is credited with designing the first telescope, a refracting one with 3x magnification; it was called the Dutch perspective glass.

1610
Galilean telescope
Galileo Galilei perfected Lippershey's design, creating a telescope with a 33x magnification. He used it to make some significant discoveries, like the phases of Venus and some of Jupiter's moons.

1600s

1668
Newtonian telescope
The first reflecting telescope was honed by Isaac Newton, who created it to help prove his theory that white light actually consists of a spectrum of colours. His telescope used a concave primary mirror and a flat, diagonal secondary mirror.

1672
Cassegrain telescope
Priest Laurent Cassegrain came up with a new design for reflecting telescopes, using a concave primary mirror and a convex secondary mirror. This enabled light to bounce through a hole in the primary mirror onto an eyepiece.

Maks-Cass telescope up close

The Meade ETX 125 combines quality and portability to make it one of the most popular Maksutov-Cassegrain telescopes around

Lens
The Maksutov-Cassegrain is mainly a reflecting telescope, but has a lens through which light passes before it reaches the mirror to help counteract any aberrations. This corrector lens is a negative meniscus, which has a concave surface on one side and a convex surface on the other

Tube
Maks-Cass scopes have a short tube length relative to the distance that the light actually travels. That's because the mirror setup 'folds' light. Light reflects off the primary mirror at the back of the telescope, which is concave, back to the front. The secondary mirror, which is smaller and convex, reflects the light back through a tiny hole in the primary mirror

Computer controls
Many telescopes can be computer-controlled, which further simplifies locating celestial bodies. You plug in the controller, and you can use it to slew (move) the telescope in any direction. You can also put in your location, and the device will move and locate objects in the sky for quick and easy stargazing

Viewfinder
It can be difficult to locate an object in a telescope, so most come with a viewfinder – a small, wide-field scope that has crosshairs and helps you to centre the telescope on a specific object. This model includes a dew shield

Eyepiece
Light ultimately reaches the back of the telescope, where the eyepiece is located. This telescope uses a Plössl, or symmetrical, eyepiece, which comprises two lenses: one concave and one convex. It makes for a large apparent field of view (the circle of light seen by your eyes)

Setting circles
The declination (on the side) and right ascension (on the bottom) setting circles are used to locate stars and other celestial bodies based on equatorial co-ordinates often found in sky maps. Many telescopes have digital setting circles, which provide the viewer with a database of objects and make it simple to point your telescope in the right direction

1840
First lunar photo
John William Draper was the first to capture the Moon in 1840. Using the daguerreotype process and a 13cm (5in) reflecting telescope, Draper took a 20-minute long exposure and helped found the field of astrophotography.

1967
First automated telescope
Arthur Code and other researchers used one of the first minicomputers to control a 20cm (8in) telescope. It measured a fixed sequence of stars using a punched paper tape.

1993
Keck telescopes
The Keck telescopes are two 10m (33ft)-diameter reflecting telescopes that saw first light in May 1993. They are located at the WM Keck Observatory on Mauna Kea in Hawaii. Each large mirror is actually composed of smaller segments, which are adjusted and controlled via computers.

> 1800s   > 1900s   > 2000s>

1917
Hooker 100-inch telescope
With a 2.5m (8.2ft) reflecting mirror, Hooker's telescope in Los Angeles, CA, was the largest in the world until 1948. Interestingly, in 1924 Edwin Hubble used it to observe galaxies outside the Milky Way, ultimately concluding that our universe is expanding.

1990
Hubble Space Telescope
NASA's Discovery shuttle placed the Hubble Space Telescope into low Earth orbit in April 1990. It is a reflecting telescope that contains five different scientific instruments for space observations, including spectrographs and photometers.

2005
Large Binocular Telescope
Located in Arizona, the Large Binocular Telescope is one of the most advanced optical telescopes in the world. Built in 2005, it has two 8.4m (28ft) aperture mirrors. The first image observed was of the spiral galaxy NGC 2770, 88 million light years away.